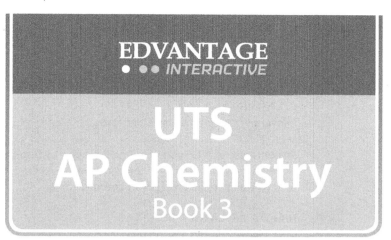

EDVANTAGE
● ●● INTERACTIVE

UTS
AP Chemistry
Book 3

Development Team

Authors

Cheri Smith
Yale Secondary
School District 34 Abbotsford

Gary Davidson
School District 22 Vernon

Megan Ryan
Walnut Grove Secondary
School District 35 Langley

Chris Toth
St. Thomas More Collegiate
Burnaby, British Columbia

Program Consultant

Lionel Sandner
Edvantage Interactive

Customization by
Jennifer Pitt-Lainsbury
UTS, Toronto

EDVANTAGE
● ●● INTERACTIVE

COPIES OF THIS BOOK MAY BE
OBTAINED BY CONTACTING:

Edvantage Interactive

E-MAIL:
info@edvantageinteractive.com

TOLL-FREE FAX:
866.275.0564

TOLL-FREE CALL:
866.422.7310

UTS AP Chemistry – Book 3
Copyright © 2016, Edvantage Interactive

ISBN 978-1-77249-461-7
University of Toronto Schools – 2016 Version

Care has been taken to trace ownership of copyright material contained in this text.
The publishers will gladly accept any information that will enable them to rectify
any reference or credit in subsequent printings.

Vice-President of Marketing: *Don Franklin*
Director of Publishing: *Yvonne Van Ruskenveld*
Design and Production: *Donna Lindenberg*
Proofreading: *Eva van Emden*
Editorial Assistance: *Rhys Sandner*
Index: *Noeline Bridge*
Photos: *p. 33, K. Jung; p. 34, Bureau international des poids et mesures (BIPM)*

*The AP Big Ideas at the beginning of each chapter are quoted from AP Chemistry: Course and
Exam Description, revised edition, effective Fall 2013, published by the College Board, New
York, NY. Advanced Placement, AP and College Board are registered trademarks of the
College Board.*

QR Code — What Is This?

The image to the right is called a QR code. It's similar to bar
codes on various products and contains information that
can be useful to you. Each QR code in this book provides you
with online support to help you learn the course material. For
example, find a question with a QR code beside it. If you scan
that code, you'll see the answer to the question explained in a
video created by an author of this book.

You can scan a QR code using an Internet-enabled mobile device. The program to
scan QR codes is free and available at your phone's app store. Scanning the QR code
above will give you a short overview of how to use the codes in the book to help
you study.

Note: We recommend that you scan QR codes only when your phone is connected
to a WiFi network. Depending on your mobile data plan, charges may apply if you
access the information over the cellular network. If you are not sure how to do this,
please contact your phone provider or us at
info@edvantageinteractive.com

Contents

Book 1

Book 2

Book 3 - Chemical Equilibrium

Book 4

5
Chemical Systems and Equilibrium

Big Ideas

☐ Chemical systems are dynamic and respond to changing conditions in predictable ways.

☐ Applications of chemical systems at equilibrium have significant implications for nature and industry.

Overall Expectations

By the end of this course, students will

☐ E1. analyse chemical equilibrium processes, and assess their impact on biological, biochemical, and technological systems;

☐ E2. investigate the qualitative and quantitative nature of chemical systems at equilibrium, and solve related problems;

☐ E3. demonstrate an understanding of the concept of dynamic equilibrium and the variables that cause shifts in the equilibrium of chemical systems.

Learning Goals	Success Criteria
Relating Science to Technology, Society and the Environment	*Relating Science to Technology, Society and the Environment*
☐ Analyse the optimal conditions for a specific chemical process related to the principles of equilibrium that takes place in nature or is used in industry	☐ I can identify a specific chemical process (the production of sulfuric acid, electrolyte balance in the human body, sedimentation in water systems or other) and explain how the principles of equilibrium operate in that process ☐ I can provide a research-based explanation of how to optimize and manipulate the equilibrium to maximize desired outputs ☐ I can assess the social, environmental and scientific benefits and drawbacks of these technologies
☐ Assess the impact of chemical equilibrium processes on various biological, biochemical, and technological systems	☐ I can identify how reaction equilibria can be manipulated to provide medical, environmental and industrial advantages (e.g. removal of heavy metals, optimization of pharmaceuticals in buffered systems, lowering the solubility of toxic heavy metals) ☐ I understand how changes in a chemical environment effect solubility, product and reactant concentrations, gas pressure and heat absorbed or evolved in industrial, medical and environmental contexts.
Developing Skills of Investigation and Communication	*Developing Skills of Investigation and Communication*
☐ Use appropriate terminology related to chemical systems	☐ I can properly describe the terms homogeneous, closed system, reversible reaction, equilibrium constant, equilibrium concentration, molar solubility, and buffers

☐	Use Le Chatelier's Principle or the reaction quotient to predict the reactant and product outcomes of a chemical system	☐	I can explain how to change the volume, temperature and amount of product or reactant in a chemical system qualitatively using Le Chatelier's Principle
		☐	I can explain how to change the amount of aqueous or gaseous product or reactant in a chemical system quantitatively using the reaction quotient
		☐	I can predict the response of a system to the addition or removal of chemical species, changes in temperature, changes in volume and dilution of a reaction system with water or another solvent
		☐	I can predict the direction in which a reaction will proceed based by comparing Q and K
		☐	I can predict the effects of a stress on experimentally measurable changes in a chemical system such as pH, temperature, colour of a solution and pressure of a gas
		☐	(AP only) I can explain how to change the thermal energy output or requirements of a chemical system using the Gibb's Helmoltz equation.
☐	Conduct an inquiry to determine the value of an equilibrium constant for a chemical reaction	☐	I understand how to measure changing concentrations of reactants or products
		☐	I can design an experiment which allows the collection of data related to changing concentrations or reactants or products or reaction rate given changing initial concentrations of reactants.
☐	Solve problems related to equilibrium	☐	I can calculate K_{eq}, K_{sp}, K_a, K_b, K_w, K_c, K_p, pH and pOH given equilibrium reactant and product concentrations
		☐	I can calculate reactant and product concentrations at equilibrium given equilibrium constants and initial reactant and product concentrations.
		☐	I understand the qualitative implications of the common ion effect
		☐	I can calculate the equilibrium reactant and product concentrations of a system to which a common ion is introduced
		☐	I can use the relationship between pH, pOH
		☐	I can calculate the percent ionization of a weak acid or weak base given two of reactant concentration, product concentration and/or equilibrium constant.
☐	Use titration data to solve acid-base equilibria	☐	For weak acid, strong base or weak base, strong acid neutralizations, I can determine the buffer region and the half equivalence point of the reaction
		☐	For a weak acid, strong base titration, I can determine the pK_a of an acid from the pH at the half-equivalence point if both the concentration of the titrant and the analyte are known (and the parallel determination for pK_b of a weak base)
		☐	I understand why the pH changes at the beginning of any titration are very small and why the pH near the equivalence point are relatively large from both a quantitative and qualitative (particle diagrams) perspective

		☐	I can determine the equivalence point of a strong acid, strong base reaction.
		☐	I can determine the equivalence point of a weak acid, strong base or strong acid, weak base reaction.
		☐	I can determine the pH and the pOH of an acid base reaction at any point during a titration
		☐	I understand that the reaction of an acid and base is a neutralization reaction that goes to completion
		☐	I understand that equilibria in acid/base systems are the result of the dissociation of acidic or basic salt products of neutralization reactions
		☐	I understand how the titration curves, calculations and chemical system for a strong acid/strong base neutralization differs from a weak acid/strong base or a strong acid/weak base neutralization
		☐	(AP) I understand that polyprotic acids have titration curves with multiple rises, indicating the number of labile protons
☐	Understand how pH can be controlled with buffers (AP)	☐	I understand the relationship between the pH of a buffer, its pK_a and the concentration ratio of the acid base forms of the buffer.
		☐	I can calculate the pH of a buffer using the relationships between pH, pK_a and the concentration ratio of the acid base forms of the buffer.
		☐	I can explain a buffer's capacity both quantitatively and qualitatively using the relationships between pH, pK_a and the concentration ratio of the acid base forms of the buffer.
		☐	I understand that a 10-fold change in magnitude of the acid/base ratio of a buffer causes a change of 1 in the pH of the buffer
		☐	I understand what makes a good choice of reagents for a buffer
		☐	For a target buffer pH, I can design a viable buffer system by selecting appropriate concentrations and options for the acid and base components
		☐	I understand why weak acids and their conjugate bases make good buffer systems
		☐	I can identify buffer systems
		☐	I can determine the reactions that occur as acids or bases are added to buffer systems
☐	Advanced understanding of solution systems and equilibrium (AP)	☐	I have memorized the solubility rules
		☐	I understand that the magnitude of the free energy change for the dissolution of a substance involves the relationship between the lattice energy, the energy of hydration and the entropic effects on the system
		☐	I can provide qualitative reasoning to support a hypothesis of the magnitude of the free energy of dissolution of a system
		☐	I understand why a salt is less soluble in the presence of a common ion and I can articulate my understanding using Le Chatelier's Principle
		☐	I understand that the solubility of a salt will be pH sensitive when one of the ions is an acid or base

☐	The equilibrium constant is related to temperature and the difference in Gibbs Free Energy between reactants and products (AP)	☐	I understand that the equilibrium constant is related to free energy by $K = e^{-\Delta G^\circ/RT}$
		☐	I can calculate K given the Gibbs Free Energy of a reaction and vice versa
		☐	I can estimate the relationship between an equilibrium constant and free energy qualitatively by relating enthalpy and entropy changes to the magnitude of K and state whether K is close to 1 or I s significantly higher or lower than 1
		☐	I can use the value of K to determine whether a reaction is endergonic ($\Delta G^\circ > 0$) or exergonic ($\Delta G^\circ < 0$)
	Understanding Basic Concepts		*Understanding Basic Concepts*
☐	Explain the concept of dynamic equilibrium	☐	I can use examples of physical and chemical equilibrium systems to explain the concept of dynamic equilibrium
☐	Explain the concept of chemical equilibrium	☐	I can use the relationship between the concentrations of reactants and products in a chemical system to explain the concept of chemical equilibrium
☐	Explain Le Chatelier's Principle	☐	I can use Le Chatelier's Principle to explain the changes in an chemical reaction which is initially at equilibrium
☐	Identify common equilibrium constants	☐	I can differentiate between, apply the correct label to and write the equilibrium expressions for K_{eq}, K_{sp}, K_a, K_b, K_w, K_c and K_p
		☐	I can calculate and understand the meaning of pK_a, pK_b and pK_w
☐	Use the ionization constant of water K_w	☐	I can calculate pH, pOH, $[H_3O^+]$ and $[OH^-]$ using K_w
☐	Explain the Bronsted-Lowry theory of acids and bases	☐	I can identify acid/base conjugate pairs
		☐	I can determine the conjugate of an acidic or basic chemical species
		☐	I can calculate the equilibrium constant of a conjugate acid/base given the equilibrium constant of its conjugate acid/base pair using K_w
		☐	I can articulate the Bronsted-Lowry theory of acids and bases
		☐	I can demonstrate, with particulate diagrams and by writing chemical reactions, how Bronsted Lowry acids increase the hydronium ion concentration in solution and how Bronsted Lowry bases increase the hydroxide ion concentration in solution
		☐	I can use the relationship $pK_a + pK_b = 14$ at 25°C to reason qualitatively about the relative strength of acid/base conjugate pairs
☐	Compare the properties of strong and weak acids and bases	☐	I can name the six strong acids
		☐	I can explain why strong acids and bases dissociate completely in water, whereas weak acids and bases dissociate very little and create a chemical system in dynamic equilibrium
		☐	I can compare the chemical properties of strong acids and bases to weak acids and bases qualitatively
		☐	I can predict whether a salt is acidic, basic or neutral in solution based on an analysis of the cations and anions present
☐	Describe the chemical characteristics of buffer solutions	☐	I understand why weak acids and their conjugate bases make good buffer systems
		☐	I can identify buffer systems
		☐	I understand that it takes more base to neutralize a weak acid solution as compared to a strong acid solution at the same pH because of the un-ionized acid molecules in the weak acid solution

5 Chemical Equilibrium

This chapter focuses on the following AP Big Idea from the College Board:

- Big Idea 6: Any bond or intermolecular attraction that can be formed can be broken. These two processes are in a dynamic competition, sensitive to initial conditions and external perturbations.

By the end of this chapter, you should be able to do the following:

- Explain the concept of chemical equilibrium with reference to reacting systems
- Predict, with reference to entropy and enthalpy, whether reacting systems will reach equilibrium
- Apply Le Châtelier's principle to the shifting of equilibrium
- Apply the concept of equilibrium to a commercial or industrial process
- Draw conclusions from the equilibrium constant expression
- Perform calculations to evaluate the changes in the value of K_{eq} and in concentrations of substances within an equilibrium system

By the end of this chapter, you should know the meaning of these **key terms**:

- chemical equilibrium
- closed system
- dynamic equilibrium
- enthalpy
- entropy
- equilibrium concentration
- equilibrium constant expression
- equilibrium shift
- Haber process
- heterogeneous reaction
- homogeneous reaction
- ICE table
- K_{eq}
- Le Châtelier's principle
- macroscopic properties
- open system
- PE diagram

When the number of shoppers travelling between the two floors on the escalators is equal, the crowd has reached equilibrium.

5.1 Introduction to Dynamic Equilibrium

Warm Up

Every weekday from 7 a.m. to 9 a.m. a large volume of traffic flows into Toronto as people who live in the surrounding communities drive to work.

1. Are there any cars leaving Toronto between 7 a.m. and 9 a.m.?

   _____

2. Explain how the number of cars in Toronto remains relatively constant between 10 a.m. to 2 p.m. when cars are still entering the city.

   _____

3. The number of cars in Toronto decreases between 3 p.m. and 7 p.m. Describe the traffic flow during this period.

   _____

Defining Chemical Equilibrium

Many chemical reactions are reversible. For example a decomposition reaction is the reverse of a synthesis reaction. This reversibility of chemical reactions facilitates an important phenomenon known as chemical equilibrium.

> **Chemical equilibrium** exists when the forward rate of a chemical reaction equals its reverse rate.

Chemical equilibria are said to be *dynamic*, which means they are active. In chemical equilibria, the forward and reverse reactions continue to occur. This contrasts with a *static* equilibrium of forces, such as the equal and opposite forces acting on a weight hanging motionless on the end of a string. In a chemical equilibrium, each reactant is being "put back" by the reverse reaction at the same rate that it is being "used up" by the forward reaction and vice versa for each product. Note that the rate at which one chemical is being consumed and produced is not necessarily the same as the rate at which another chemical is being consumed and produced. The consumption and production ratios are provided by the coefficients in the balanced chemical equation. The example below describes the synthesis and decomposition of water. The equation shows that hydrogen is consumed and produced at twice the rate in moles per second that oxygen is.

$$2\,H_2(g) + O_2(g) \rightleftharpoons 2\,H_2O(g)$$

Sample Problem 5.1.1 — Determining Equivalent Reaction Rates at Equilibrium

NO_2 is being consumed at a rate of 0.031 mol/s in the equilibrium below. How many moles of N_2O_4 are being consumed each second?

$$2\,NO_2(g) \rightleftharpoons N_2O_4(g)$$

What to Think About	How to Do It
1. Recall that, at equilibrium, the rate of any chemical's consumption equals the rate of its production. Therefore, NO_2 is also being produced at 0.031 mol/s.	$0.031\,\dfrac{\text{mol }NO_2}{s} \times \dfrac{1\text{ mol }N_2O_4}{2\text{ mol }NO_2} = \dfrac{0.016\text{ mol }N_2O_4}{s}$
2. Look at the coefficients.	The coefficients in the balanced equation indicate that 1 mol of N_2O_4 is consumed for each 2 mol of NO_2 produced.

Practice Problems 5.1.1 — Determining Equivalent Reaction Rates at Equilibrium

SO_2 and O_2 are placed in a sealed flask where they react to produce SO_3. When equilibrium is achieved, SO_3 is being produced at a rate of 0.0082 mol/s.

$$2\,SO_2(g) + O_2(g) \rightleftharpoons 2\,SO_3(g)$$

1. How many moles of SO_3 are being consumed each second?

2. How many moles of O_2 are being produced each second?

3. How many grams of O_2 are being consumed each second?

Recognizing Chemical Equilibrium

How do chemists recognize a chemical equilibrium? There are three criteria for a system to be at chemical equilibrium. It must:

1. have constant **macroscopic** properties. Macroscopic properties are those that are large enough to be measured or observed with the unaided eye.
2. be closed.
3. shift when conditions change.

1. Constancy of Macroscopic Properties

A system at equilibrium has constant macroscopic properties such as color, pH, temperature, and pressure because the amount of each reactant and product remains constant. Each chemical is being produced (put back) at the same rate that it is being consumed (removed). There is no macroscopic activity in a system at equilibrium because the continuing forward and reverse reactions are not observable because we cannot see atoms or molecules. Minor unobservable fluctuations in rates and concentrations are presumed to occur in equilibria since reaction rates are dependent on random collisions between reactant species. Another notable characteristic of equilibria is that they are self-perpetuating because the forward and the reverse reactions continuously supply each other with reactants.

2. Closed System

A system is **closed** if no chemicals are entering or leaving the defined system. If a system's properties are constant but the system is open then it is a **steady state** rather than an equilibrium (Figure 2.1.1). In a steady state, components enter and leave the system at the same rate rather than going back and forth within an equilibrium system. A steady state exists when the water level behind Cleveland dam stays constant because water is flowing into Capilano Lake, the lake behind the dam, at the same rate that it is flowing through the dam.

Figure 5.1.1 *Equilibrium occurs only in a closed system. In an open system, steady state can be reached, but not equilibrium.*

A reaction occurring in aqueous solution may only achieve equilibrium if all the reactant particles, product particles, and solvent water molecules remain in the solution. If an equilibrium system is temporarily disrupted by opening it and removing chemicals, the remaining chemicals will re-establish equilibrium if the system is closed again. Chemicals could be removed in a disruption, for example, if a chemical in the aqueous equilibrium is precipitated out or evaporates.

For a system to be at equilibrium, it must be closed and at a constant temperature (constancy of macroscopic properties). The intent of these conditions is to hold the amount of matter and energy constant within the system. For a system to be at a constant temperature it must be at thermal equilibrium with its surroundings, meaning that kinetic energy must be entering and leaving the system at the same rate.

3. A Shift due to Changed Conditions

The world is full of closed systems at constant temperatures in which nothing appears to be happening. In the vast majority of these, there really is nothing happening. They are just chemical mixtures. Equilibrium exists in only a small percentage of those systems that meet the first two criteria. Just as a child might poke a snake to see if it's alive, chemists "poke" chemical systems by changing their conditions. A change in temperature usually forces an equilibrium to reveal itself by causing a change or a *shift* in the amounts of reactants and products. When the solution's original temperature is restored, so are the original amounts. The equilibrium shifts back. Various shifts in response to changes of conditions will be discussed in sections 5.2 and 5.3. If the reaction is photoactivated, it will respond to a change in lighting conditions rather than a change in temperature.

Quick Check

1. Why are chemical equilibria referred to as dynamic? _____

2. List three criteria that must be satisfied for chemical equilibrium to exist.

   _____   _____

   _____

3. What is a closed chemical system? _____

4. What is a macroscopic property? _____

How Equilibrium Is Established

Recall that, as a reaction proceeds, reactant concentrations fall. Hence, the forward rate of the reaction (r_f) decreases. In a closed system, the product concentrations rise at the same time as the reactant concentrations are falling. Hence, the reverse rate of the reaction (r_r) increases. This continues until $r_r = r_f$ and equilibrium is established (Figure 5.1.2).

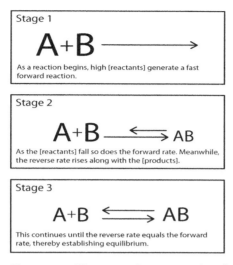

Figure 5.1.2 *Diagrammatic representation of chemical equilibrium being established*

Figure 5.1.3 shows equilibrium being achieved at about $t = 7$ s when the reactant and product concentrations become constant. It is important to note that the concentrations of reactants are not equal to the concentration of products at equilibrium. Only the forward and reverse reaction *rates* are equal.

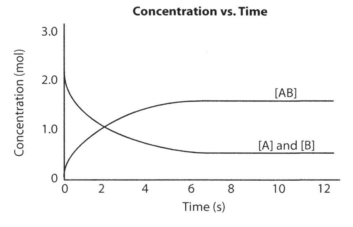

Figure 5.1.3 *This graph shows what happens with reactant and product concentrations as a function of time as equilibrium is established.*

Quick Check

Is each question below true or false? Place T or F in the places provided.

1. The reactant concentrations always equal the product concentrations at equilibrium. _____

2. When approaching equilibrium, [reactants] decreases while the [products] increases. _____

3. The [reactants] hold steady at equilibrium. _____

4. Before achieving equilibrium, the forward rate (r_f) is less than the reverse rate (r_r). _____

5.1 Review Questions

1. Identify each of the following as being either an *equilibrium* or a *steady state*:
   (a) As bees go back and forth from their hive to a flowerbed, the number of bees inside the hive and at the flowerbed remains constant.

   (b) Despite people checking in and out of a motel each day, the number of guests registered at the motel each night remains constant.

   (c) During a basketball game, team members are frequently being substituted in and out of the game. There are always five players on the floor and seven players on the bench.

   (d) Two new students enrol in your chemistry class each day because they hear from their friends how interesting the class is. Unfortunately two students also withdraw each day.

   (e) Shoppers at the Hotel California Mall can never leave (but it's a lovely place). Shoppers travel back and forth on escalators between the mall's two levels though the number of shoppers on each level never changes.

2. An equilibrium exists when a reaction's forward rate equals its reverse rate. Answer the questions below for the following equilibrium:

$$2\,NO(g) + Cl_2(g) \rightleftharpoons 2\,NOCl(g)$$

   (a) Do the moles of NO consumed per second equal the moles of NO produced per second?

   (b) Do the moles of NO consumed per second equal the moles of NOCl consumed per second?

   (c) Do the moles of NOCl produced per second equal the moles of Cl_2 consumed per second?

   (d) Do the grams of NO consumed per second equal the grams of NO produced per second?

   (e) Do the grams of NO consumed per second equal the grams of NOCl consumed per second?

3. $H_2(g)$ is being consumed at a rate of 0.012 mol/s in the following equilibrium:

$$N_2(g) + 3 H_2(g) \rightleftharpoons 2 NH_3(g)$$

(a) How many moles of N_2 are being produced and consumed each second?

(b) How many grams of NH_3 are being produced and consumed each second?

4. Melting and evaporating are physical changes, not chemical changes, but changes of physical state can also form dynamic equilibria.

(a) An ice cube floats in a water bath held at 0°C. The size of the ice cube remains constant because the ice is melting at the same rate as the water is freezing. Describe and explain what you would observe if the temperature of the water bath was increased slightly.

(b) The water level in a flask drops as water evaporates from it. The flask is then closed using a rubber stopper. The water level continues to drop for a while but eventually holds steady. Explain why the water level is no longer falling. (Has the evaporation stopped?)

5. A chemist observes a closed system at a constant temperature in which no macroscopic changes are occurring. To determine whether or not the system is at equilibrium, the chemist increases its temperature and notes a change in the properties of the system. Can you be sure that this system is at equilibrium? Explain your answer.

6. Nobel laureate (prize winner) Ilya Prigogine coined the term *dissipative structures* for systems such as candle flames that are in steady state. The chemical reaction for burning one type of wax is:

$$C_{25}H_{52}(g) + 38\ O_2(g)\ \rightarrow\ 25\ CO_2(g) + 26\ H_2O(g)$$

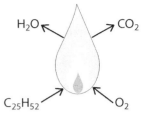

A continuous reaction occurs in a flame. The amount of each reactant and product in the flame remains relatively constant as reactants are continuously drawn in to replace those consumed and the products continuously dissipate into the surrounding air.

(a) How is this situation like an equilibrium?

(b) How is this situation different from an equilibrium?

Fascinate your friends by blowing out a candle flame and then re-igniting the evaporating paraffin gas by placing a lit match a couple centimeters above the wick. Try it!

7. Clock reactions are often used to demonstrate the effect of concentration and temperature on reaction rates. The distinctive aspect of clock reactions is a long delay followed by a sudden appearance of product. This peculiar behavior frequently results from a cyclic mechanism. Consider the mechanism of the iodine clock reaction below:

Step 1 $3\ HSO_3^- + IO_3^- \rightarrow I^- + 3\ H^+ + 3\ SO_4^{2-}$
Step 2 $10\ I^- + 12\ H^+ + 2\ IO_3^- \rightarrow 6\ I_2 + 6\ H_2O$
Step 3 $I_2 + H_2O + HSO_3^- \rightarrow 2\ I^- + 3\ H^+ + SO_4^{2-}$

Why is the two-step iodine cycle at the end of this mechanism not an equilibrium even when the two steps are proceeding at the same rate?

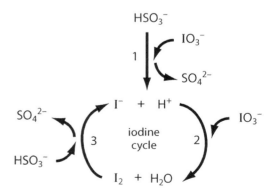

8. When considering equilibria, chemists sometimes forget that the forward and reverse reactions may occur through a series of steps. Consider the following reaction mechanism approaching equilibrium:

Step 1: $2 NO + H_2 \rightarrow N_2 + H_2O_2$
Step 2: $H_2O_2 + H_2 \rightarrow 2 H_2O$
Overall: $2 NO + 2 H_2 \rightarrow N_2 + 2 H_2O$

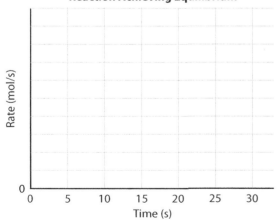

If a reaction is at equilibrium, every step in its mechanism must be at equilibrium. When the above reaction establishes equilibrium, how do you know that:

(a) step 1 must be at equilibrium?

(b) step 2 must be at equilibrium?

9. A chemical reaction achieves equilibrium 20 s after it is initiated. Plot and label the forward reaction rate and the reverse reaction rate as a function of time from $t = 0$ s (initiation) until $t = 30$ s. (Caution: This is **not** the same kind of plot as in Figure 5.1.3. Here you are plotting the rate as a function of time whereas in Figure 5.1.3, we plotted the concentration of reactants and products as a function of time.)

Rate (forward and reverse) vs. Time for a Reaction Achieving Equilibrium

Rate (mol/s) vs. Time (s)

0   5   10   15   20   25   30
Time (s)

10. Nitrogen dioxide gas is placed in a sealed flask.

$$2\,NO_2(g) \rightarrow N_2O_4(g)$$

orange　　　colorless

(a) What would you see as the reaction approaches equilibrium?

(b) Describe the change in the concentrations of reactants and products as the reaction approaches equilibrium.

(c) Describe the change in the forward and reverse rates as the reaction approaches equilibrium.

11. A system at equilibrium has all of its reactants suddenly removed. Describe how the system would restore equilibrium in terms of its forward and reverse reaction rates and its reactant and product concentrations.

5.2 The Equilibrium Constant

Warm Up

A **constant** is a specific piece of information that does not change value, possibly within a set of described parameters. You have already used many constants in your science and mathematics classes. Some constants simply relate one system of measurement to another. For example, there are 2.54 cm in an inch.

1. Pi (π) is a mathematical constant that relates the circumference of a circle to its radius. What is the approximate value of pi?

    _____

2. The speed of light (c) in a vacuum is a physical constant with a value of 3.00×10^8 m/s. What famous formula of Albert Einstein's uses the speed of light to relate energy to mass?

    _____

3. State the name, symbol, and value of a chemical constant that provides the number of items in a mole of anything.

    _____

4. Why is it important to scientists to have accurate constants?

    _____

Deriving the Equilibrium Expression

Figure 5.2.1 provides the forward and reverse rate equations for the following reaction at equilibrium:

$$H_2(g) + I_2(g) \rightleftharpoons 2\,HI(g)$$

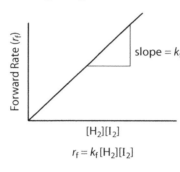
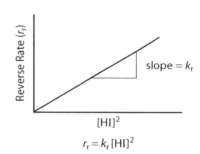

$$r_f = k_f[H_2][I_2] \qquad\qquad r_r = k_r[HI]^2$$

Figure 5.2.1 *Forward and reverse reaction rates for the equation above*

At equilibrium: $r_f = r_r$

Therefore: $k_f[H_2][I_2] = k_r[HI]^2$

Rearranging to isolate the constants we get:

$$\frac{k_f}{k_r} = \frac{[HI]^2}{[H_2][I_2]}$$

A constant divided by another constant equals a third constant. In this case $k_f \div k_r$ provides a constant that chemists call the equilibrium constant, K_{eq}.

Therefore: $K_{eq} = \dfrac{[HI]^2}{[H_2][I_2]}$

Regardless of the initial concentrations of reactants and possibly products, when equilibrium is achieved and the equilibrium concentrations are substituted into this expression, the calculated value will always be the same at any given temperature. Since the rate constants k_f and k_r are temperature dependent, so too is the equilibrium constant, K_{eq}, that can be derived from them. This relationship is the mathematical "hook" we needed to quantify our understanding and descriptions of equilibrium. It provides chemists and chemical engineers with the ability to predict the concentrations that will be present when equilibrium is achieved.

The **equilibrium expression** refers to *the formula* for the equilibrium constant in terms of the equilibrium concentrations of reactants and products. The **equilibrium constant** refers to *the numerical value* provided by the equilibrium expression. The units of equilibrium constants vary too much from equation to equation to be useful and are therefore not required for this course.

The *equilibrium law* states that for the general equation:

$$p\,A + q\,B \rightleftharpoons r\,C + s\,D$$

$$K_{eq} = \frac{[C]^r[D]^s}{[A]^p[B]^q}$$

where p, q, r, and s are the coefficients in the balanced chemical equation.

The equilibrium law is valid for both single-step equilibria and multiple-step equilibria. In other words, the equilibrium expression and constant are independent of the reaction mechanism. Consider the following reaction mechanism:

Step 1 $NO_2 + F_2 \rightleftharpoons NO_2F + \cancel{F}$

Step 2 $\cancel{F} + NO_2 \rightleftharpoons NO_2F$

Net reaction $2\,NO_2 + F_2 \rightleftharpoons 2\,NO_2F$

If the reaction is at equilibrium, then step 1 must be at equilibrium to maintain the reactants at a constant concentration. Step 2 must be at equilibrium to maintain the products at a constant concentration. The equilibrium expression for the overall reaction can be derived from the equilibrium expressions for each individual step:

$$K_{eq1} = \frac{[NO_2F][F]}{[NO_2][F_2]} \qquad K_{eq2} = \frac{[NO_2F]}{[F][NO_2]}$$

$$K_{eq1} \times K_{eq2} = \frac{[NO_2F][\cancel{F}]}{[NO_2][F_2]} \times \frac{[NO_2F]}{[\cancel{F}][NO_2]} = \frac{[NO_2F]^2}{[NO_2]^2[F_2]} = K_{eq}$$

The most common and reliable means of determining a reaction's equilibrium constant is to simply substitute equilibrium concentrations into the equilibrium expression.

Sample Problem 5.2.1 — Determining K_{eq} from the Equilibrium Concentrations

For the following equation, 0.19 mol NO_2 and 0.64 mol N_2O_4 are found at equilibrium in a 250 mL flask at 92°C.

$$2\,NO_2(g) \rightleftharpoons N_2O_4(g)$$

What is the equilibrium constant for this reaction at 92°C?

What to Think About	**How to Do It**
1. Write the equilibrium expression for the reaction. As indicated by the notation [ ], K_{eq} values are determined using molar concentrations so it is important to consider the units provided for the reacting species (moles or M) and the container size if the concentrations need to be calculated.	$K_{eq} = \dfrac{[N_2O_4]}{[NO_2]^2}$
2. Substitute the equilibrium concentrations into the expression.	$K_{eq} = \dfrac{(0.64\ mol/0.25\ L)}{(0.19\ mol/0.25\ L)^2} = 4.4$

Practice Problems 5.2.1 — Determining K_{eq} from the Equilibrium Concentrations

1. The following gases are at equilibrium in a flask at 423°C: 4.56×10^{-3} M H_2, 7.4×10^{-4} M I_2, and 1.35×10^{-2} M HI. What is the equilibrium constant for the reaction at this temperature?

    $2\,HI(g) \rightleftharpoons H_2(g) + I_2(g)$

2. A quantity of 3.88×10^{-3} M NO_2 is at equilibrium with 1.73×10^{-4} M N_2O_4 at 60°C.

    $2\,NO_2(g) \rightleftharpoons N_2O_4(g)$

    (a) What is the equilibrium constant for the reaction at 60°C?

    (b) State whether this reaction is endothermic or exothermic by comparing the equilibrium constant for this reaction at 60°C to the constant at 92°C provided in the preceding sample problem. Explain your reasoning.

3. As a slight variation on this type of problem, you could be asked to determine an equilibrium concentration from the K_{eq} and the other equilibrium concentrations. For example, 0.14 M NH_3 is at equilibrium with 0.020 M N_2 at 225°C. What is the equilibrium concentration of H_2 in the reacting mixture?

    $N_2(g) + 3\,H_2(g) \rightleftharpoons 2\,NH_3(g)$ $K_{eq} = 1.7 \times 10^2$ at 225°C

What Does a Bigger Equilibrium Constant Mean?

Recall our derivation of K_{eq}. For the equilibrium system, $H_2(g) + I_2(g) \rightleftharpoons 2\,HI(g)$:

$$\frac{k_f}{k_r} = \frac{[HI]^2}{[H_2][I_2]} = K_{eq} \qquad \text{but } \frac{k_r}{k_f}, \text{ which equals } \frac{[H_2][I_2]}{[HI]^2}, \text{ is also a constant.}$$

Presumably, chemists chose the numerical value provided by the first expression, $[HI]^2/[H_2][I_2]$ to be K_{eq} because the product concentration is in its numerator and the reactant concentrations are in its denominator. This means that the size of the equilibrium constant indicates the extent of the reaction's progress towards products.

> The further a given reaction progresses to the right to achieve equilibrium, the greater its equilibrium constant will be.

This appeals to us because it is consistent with the number line, which also has numbers increasing from left to right. Here we are combining the chemical equation metaphor that changing from reactants to products is proceeding to the right with the number line metaphor that proceeding to the right is increasing in numerical value.

Knowing what a bigger equilibrium constant *does not mean* is perhaps just as important as knowing what it *does mean*. Chemists must be careful not to attempt to infer too much from equilibrium constants. The following two points outline important information about interpreting equilibrium constants:

---

1. It is impossible to infer anything about an equilibrium's position solely from its equilibrium constant. An equilibrium's position depends on the initial reactant concentrations as well as the equilibrium constant. A given reaction therefore has a wide range of equilibrium positions that result from the same equilibrium constant. Consider the following equilibrium:

$$CH_3COOH(aq) \rightleftharpoons H^+(aq) + CH_3COO^-(aq) \qquad K_{eq} = 1.8 \times 10^{-5}$$

   If the initial concentration of CH_3COOH is 1.0 M then there will be a 0.42% yield at equilibrium, but if its initial concentration is 1.0×10^{-6} M then there will be a 95% yield at equilibrium. From Le Châtelier's perspective, diluting the system causes a shift to the right to partially restore the osmotic pressure.

2. Even with the same initial reactant concentrations, it is difficult to make meaningful comparisons between the equilibrium constants of different equilibria unless their expressions have identical forms. The following two equilibria have radically different percent yields even when they have the same equilibrium constant (at different temperatures) and the same initial reactant concentrations. The first equilibrium can have a greater K_{eq} than the second one and still have a lower percent yield.

$$Ni(CO)_4(g) \rightleftharpoons Ni(s) + 4\,CO(g) \qquad K_{eq} = 1$$

   When the initial $[Ni(CO)_4] = 1.0$ M there is a 23% yield at equilibrium.

$$2\,NO(g) \rightleftharpoons N_2(g) + O_2(g) \qquad K_{eq} = 1$$

   When the initial $[NO] = 1.0$ M there is an 83% yield at equilibrium.

Does an Equilibrium Constant Change When the Equilibrium System Shifts?

When an equilibrium is stressed by changing concentration(s), the new concentrations will not provide the equilibrium constant when plugged into the equilibrium expression. The equilibrium will shift to restore a set of concentrations that once again provide the equilibrium constant. It is after all, a constant.

On the other hand, the shift caused by a temperature change makes all the product concentrations increase and all the reactant concentrations decrease or vice versa so it must change the equilibrium constant. Equilibrium constants are temperature dependent. A shift to the right in response to a temperature change causes the equilibrium constant to increase. A shift to the left in response to a temperature change causes the equilibrium constant to decrease.

Changing the temperature is the only way to change a chemical equation's equilibrium constant.

When a temperature change causes an equilibrium system to shift to the right, its [products] increase and its [reactants] decrease; therefore its equilibrium position also shifts to the right. Conversely, when a temperature change causes an equilibrium system to shift to the left, its [reactants] increase and its [products] decrease; therefore its equilibrium position also shifts to the left.

Table 5.2.1 *The Effect of Stresses on the Equilibrium System, Position, and Constant*

$2\,SO_2(g) + O_2(g) \rightleftharpoons 2\,SO_3(g)$		$\Delta H = -198$ kJ/mol	
Stress	**Equilibrium System**	**Equilibrium Position**	**Equilibrium Constant**
Add reactant	shifts right	may shift left or right	no change
Decrease volume	shifts right	shifts right	no change
Decrease temperature	shifts right	shifts right	increases

Quick Check

1. Consider the following equilibrium: $Ag^+(aq) + 2 NH_3(aq) \rightleftharpoons Ag(NH_3)_2^+(aq)$

   (a) In what direction will the system shift if some ammonia (NH_3) is added to it? _____

   (b) How will this affect the equilibrium constant? _____

2. Consider the following equilibrium: $PCl_5(g) + 92.5 \text{ kJ} \rightleftharpoons PCl_3(g) + Cl_2(g)$

   A decrease in temperature will cause the equilibrium system to shift _____

   causing its percent yield to _____ and its equilibrium constant to

   _____.

3. Consider the following equilibrium: $C_2H_2(g) + 3 H_2(g) \rightleftharpoons 2 CH_4(g) \qquad K_{eq} = 0.36$

   True or False? We know that reactants are favored in this reaction because $K_{eq} < 1$. _____

No Liquids or Solids in Equilibrium Expressions

Chemicals in liquid or solid states are not included in equilibrium expressions.

For example, the equilibrium formed when common salt dissolves in water is:

$$NaCl(s) \rightleftharpoons Na^+(aq) + Cl^-(aq)$$

Its equilibrium expression is simply: $K_{eq} = [Na^+][Cl^-]$

While the term *concentration* normally refers the amount of one chemical per unit volume of a mixture, it is sometimes used to describe how concentrated particles of pure matter are. For example, [pure $H_2O(l)$] = 55.6 M. However, the *concentration* of a pure solid or liquid is fixed by its density while the concentration of a solute is not. Regardless, this is a heterogeneous reaction, and it is the surface area of the NaCl that affects the reaction rate, not its concentration. So why is the surface area of the salt not part of the equilibrium expression? Increasing the surface area by grinding the salt or by adding more salt increases the rate of dissolving but does not affect the equilibrium concentrations because the rate of recrystallizing increases equally.

Although our example was a physical equilibrium, this principle holds true for heterogeneous chemical equilibria as well. A solid's surface area, although affecting the rate at which equilibrium is achieved, does not affect the equilibrium position. Solids therefore do not appear in equilibrium expressions. Likewise, adding or removing solids from an equilibrium affects the forward and reverse rates equally and therefore does not cause a shift.

The same logic applies to pure liquids involved in heterogeneous reactions but liquids involved as solvents are not included for a different reason. For example:

$$Cr_2O_7^{2-}(aq) + H_2O(l) \rightleftharpoons 2 H^+(aq) + 2 CrO_4^{2-}(aq)$$

$$K_{eq} = \frac{[H^+]^2[CrO_4^{2-}]^2}{[Cr_2O_7^{2-}]}$$

The [$H_2O(l)$] is not included in any equilibrium expression. In the above chemical equation, water is a reactant and a solvent for the reactant and product ions. Since water's concentration is nearly constant, we omit it from equilibrium expressions.

There is one situation where liquids appear in equilibrium expressions. When there is more than one liquid in the chemical equation, the liquids dilute each other so these chemicals are included in the equilibrium expression.

Quick Check

Write the equilibrium expression for the following reactions:

1. $B_2H_6(g) + 3\,O_2(g) \rightleftharpoons B_2O_3(s) + 3\,H_2O(g)$ _____

2. $4\,HCl(g) + O_2(g) \rightleftharpoons 2\,Cl_2(g) + 2\,H_2O(g)$ _____

3. $H_2(g) + Br_2(l) \rightleftharpoons 2\,HBr(g)$ _____

4. $CaCO_3(s) \rightleftharpoons Ca^{2+}(aq) + CO_3^{2-}(aq)$ _____

The Equilibrium Constant and the Form of the Chemical Equation

The form in which a chemical equation is written affects its K_{eq} expression and constant. To avoid possible ambiguity, chemists should provide the chemical equation with the K_{eq} value.

$$H_2(g) + \tfrac{1}{2}\,O_2(g) \rightleftharpoons H_2O(g)$$

At a particular temperature, 2.0 mol H_2, 4.0 mol O_2, and 12.0 mol H_2O are discovered at equilibrium in a 1.0 L flask.

$$K_{eq} = \frac{[H_2O]}{[H_2][O_2]^{1/2}} = \frac{12.0}{(2.0)(4.0)^{1/2}} = 3.0$$

The same reaction has a different equilibrium expression and a different constant when the coefficients in its equation are doubled:

$$2\,H_2(g) + O_2(g) \rightleftharpoons 2\,H_2O(g)$$

$$K_{eq} = \frac{[H_2O]^2}{[H_2]^2[O_2]} = \frac{(12.0)^2}{(2.0)^2(4.0)} = 9.0$$

The exact same equilibrium concentrations, when substituted into the new expression, provide a value that is the square of the original chemical equation's constant. Doubling a chemical equation's coefficients has the effect of squaring its K_{eq}. This is reasonable since the coefficients in the chemical equation appear as powers in the equilibrium expression.

Reversing a chemical equation has the effect of inverting its equilibrium expression and constant. The K_{eq} for any reaction is the reciprocal of the K_{eq} for its reverse reaction. Reversing the original equation we get:

$$H_2O(g) \rightleftharpoons H_2(g) + \tfrac{1}{2}\,O_2(g)$$

$$K_{eq} = \frac{[H_2][O_2]^{1/2}}{[H_2O]} = \frac{(2.0)(4.0)^{1/2}}{12.0} = 0.33$$

Quick Check

$$2\,HI(g) \rightleftharpoons H_2(g) + I_2(g) \qquad K_{eq} = 0.018 \text{ at } 423°C$$

1. What is the K_{eq} at 423°C of $H_2(g) + I_2(g) \rightleftharpoons 2\,HI(g)$? _____

2. What is the K_{eq} at 423°C of $HI(g) \rightleftharpoons \tfrac{1}{2}\,H_2(g) + \tfrac{1}{2}\,I_2(g)$? _____

3. What is the K_{eq} at 423°C of $\tfrac{1}{2}\,H_2(g) + \tfrac{1}{2}\,I_2(g) \rightleftharpoons HI(g)$? _____

The Reaction Quotient

The numerical value derived when *any* set of reactant and product concentrations is plugged into an equilibrium expression is called the **trial K_{eq}** or the **reaction quotient, Q**. This value tells chemists whether a reaction is at equilibrium and, if not, the direction that the reaction will proceed or shift to achieve equilibrium. If the trial K_{eq} is less than the actual K_{eq} then the reaction must proceed to the right to achieve equilibrium. The reaction quotient's numerator must increase and its denominator decrease until the quotient itself has risen to equal the equilibrium constant. If the trial K_{eq} is greater than the actual K_{eq} then the reaction must proceed to the left to achieve equilibrium. The reaction quotient's numerator must decrease and its denominator increase until the quotient itself has dropped to equal the equilibrium constant.

Sample Problem 5.2.2 — Determining the Direction a System Will Proceed to Achieve Equilibrium, Given its Reactant and Product Concentrations

The following gases are introduced into a closed flask: 0.057 M SO_2, 0.057 M O_2, and 0.12 M SO_3. In which direction will the reaction proceed to establish equilibrium?

$$2\,SO_2(g) + O_2(g) \rightleftharpoons 2\,SO_3(g) \qquad K_{eq} = 85$$

What to Think About	How to Do It
1. Write the equilibrium expression for the reaction provided.	Trial $K_{eq} = \dfrac{[SO_3]^2}{[SO_2]^2[O_2]}$
2. Substitute the concentrations into the equilibrium expression and solve for the trial K_{eq}. Compare the trial K_{eq} to the actual K_{eq}.	$= \dfrac{(0.12)^2}{(0.057)^2\,0.057} = 78 < 85$
3. Note that, by shifting to the right, the [SO_3] will rise while the [SO_2] and [O_2] fall, causing the trial K_{eq} to increase toward 85 and the establishment or restoration of equilibrium.	Therefore this reaction must proceed or shift to the right to achieve equilibrium.

Practice Problems 5.2.2 — Determining the Direction a System Will Proceed to Achieve Equilibrium, Given its Reactant and Product Concentrations

1. The industrial synthesis of hydrogen involves the reaction of steam and methane to produce *synthesis gas*, a mixture of hydrogen and carbon monoxide.

   $CH_4(g) + H_2O(g) \rightleftharpoons CO(g) + 3 H_2(g)$ K_{eq} = 4.7 at 1127°C

   A mixture at 1127°C contains 0.045 M H_2O, 0.025 M CH_4, 0.10 M CO, and 0.30 M H_2. In which direction will the reaction proceed to establish equilibrium?

2. The following gases are introduced into a closed 0.50 L flask: 1.5 mol NO_2 and 4.0 mol N_2O_4. In which direction will the reaction proceed to achieve equilibrium?

   $2 NO_2(g) \rightleftharpoons N_2O_4(g)$ K_{eq} = 0.940.

3. In a container, 0.10 M H^+ and 0.10 M SO_4^{2-} exist in equilibrium with 0.83 M HSO_4^-. A buffer is added that increases the concentration of both the bisulphate and sulfate ions by 0.10 M. What happens to the $[HSO_4^-]$ as equilibrium is restored?

   $HSO_4^-(aq) \rightleftharpoons H^+(aq) + SO_4^{2-}(aq)$

Reactants or Products?

It is awkward to call some chemicals "reactants" and others "products" if they are all present when the reaction starts. It is nevertheless convenient to use these terms so chemists write the chemical equation with the chemicals on the left side of the arrow being called the reactants and those on the right side of the arrow being called the products. Which direction the equation is written and therefore which chemicals are called reactants and which chemicals are called products is arbitrary. Of course, once decided, reversing the equation would invert the equilibrium expression and provide a K_{eq} that is the reciprocal of the original one.

An Addendum to Le Châtelier's Principle

Le Châtelier's principle of *partially* alleviating a stress is based on more than one chemical concentration being involved in the equilibrium process. When an equilibrium removes some of an added chemical, other chemicals' concentrations also change along with it. The changing concentrations of these others essentially prevent the stressed chemical from reaching its original equilibrium concentration before equilibrium is re-established. Consider the following hypothetical equilibrium's response to the stress of adding some A.

$$A + B \rightleftharpoons AB$$

If all the added A were removed (by reacting it with B to form AB) then the forward rate would be less than it was at the original equilibrium (due to the decreased [B]) but the reverse rate would be greater than at the original equilibrium (due to the increased [AB]). To re-establish equilibrium the forward rate must be greater than it was at the original equilibrium and therefore all the added A cannot be removed.

Some heterogeneous chemical reactions and physical processes involve only one chemical concentration. When such a system is stressed by changing that concentration, equilibrium is not re-established until the entire stress is removed and the original concentration restored.

Equilibria that have only one chemical concentration in their equilibrium expression *completely* alleviate any stress that changes that concentration.

For example, any stress that changes the concentration of the lone gaseous product in the following equilibria will be completely, rather than partially, alleviated.

- Water evaporating and condensing in a closed vessel
$$H_2O(l) \rightleftharpoons H_2O(g) \qquad K_{eq} = [H_2O(g)]$$

- Calcium carbonate decomposing and synthesizing within a closed vessel
$$CaCO_3(s) \rightleftharpoons CaO(s) + CO_2(g) \qquad K_{eq} = [CO_2]$$

These equilibrium expressions have only one chemical concentration in them. As this implies, this value is constant at a given temperature. When these systems are stressed by removing some of this chemical, the entire loss must be replaced to restore the reaction quotient back to that of the equilibrium constant.

Quick Check

State whether each of the following equilibria would partially or completely alleviate a stress that changes a reactant's or product's concentration.

1. $CoCl_2(s) + 6\,H_2O(g) \rightleftharpoons CoCl_2 \cdot 6\,H_2O(s)$ _____

2. $NH_4Cl(s) \rightleftharpoons NH_3(g) + HCl(g)$ _____

3. $CO_2(g) + NaOH(s) \rightleftharpoons NaHCO_3(s)$ _____

5.2 Activity: What's My Constant?

Question
How can you determine the mathematical relationship that is common to three sets of numbers? Of course, it's a lot easier to discover the relationship when you know that one actually exists!

Background
Do you think that you could have reasoned or recognized that different sets of equilibrium concentrations have a common mathematical relationship? The Norwegian chemists Cato Maximilian Guldberg and Peter Waage proposed the equilibrium law in 1864 after observing many different sets of equilibrium concentrations.

Procedure
Each set of numbers in the table below satisfies the formula $A - B + C = 5$.

Set	A	B	C
1	10	6	1
2	3	1	3
3	− 4	2	11

$A - B + C = 5$
_____

Continued on next page

5.2 Activity: *Continued*

1. Each set of numbers in the table below can also be substituted into a common formula yielding a constant. Determine that formula.

Set	A	B	C
1	18	3	9
2	6	22	2
3	5	10	15

Easy

_____

2. Repeat procedure step 1 for each table below.

Set	A	B	C
1	3	4	20
2	5	37	3
3	14	24	88

Challenging

_____

Set	A	B	C
1	7	13	20
2	0	5	9
3	3	10	33

Really Hard

_____

Results and Discussion

1. Briefly describe the method(s) you used to determine the expression for each collection of data.

2. How successful were you and your colleagues at this task?

3. Why do you not need anyone to mark this activity to know whether or not you were successful?

5.2 Review Questions

1. At a given temperature the forward and reverse rate equations for the following reaction are as shown (the units for the rate constants are left out for simplicity):

$$2 N_2O_5(g) \rightleftharpoons 2 N_2O_4(g) + O_2(g)$$

$r_f = 2.7 \times 10^{-3} [N_2O_5]^2 \qquad\qquad r_r = 4.3 \times 10^{-2} [N_2O_4]^2[O_2]$

Derive the equilibrium constant, K_{eq}, for this reaction at this temperature.

2. A student claims that the coefficients in balanced chemical equations provide the ratio of the chemicals present at equilibrium? For example, consider the following equation.

$$2 NO(g) + Cl_2(g) \rightleftharpoons 2 NOCl(g)$$

The student asserts that the equation tells us that the ratio of the equilibrium concentrations will be 2 NO: 1 Cl_2: 2 NOCl. Is the student correct? If not, what do the coefficients represent?

3. Write the equilibrium expression for each of the following:

   (a) $HNO_2 (aq) \rightleftharpoons H^+(aq) + NO_2^-(aq)$

   (b) $2 SO_3(g) \rightleftharpoons 2 SO_2(g) + O_2(g)$

   (c) $4 NH_3(g) + 5 O_2(g) \rightleftharpoons 4 NO(g) + 6 H_2O(g)$

4. A 2.0 L flask contains 0.38 mol $CH_4(g)$, 0.59 mol $C_2H_2(g)$, and 1.4 mol $H_2(g)$ at equilibrium. Calculate the equilibrium constant, K_{eq}, for the reaction:

   $$2 CH_4(g) \rightleftharpoons C_2H_2(g) + 3 H_2(g)$$

5. A cylinder contains 0.12 M $COBr_2$, 0.060 M CO, and 0.080 M Br_2 at equilibrium. The volume of the cylinder is suddenly doubled.

$COBr_2(g) \rightleftharpoons CO(g) + Br_2(g)$

(a) What is the molar concentration of each gas immediately after the volume of the cylinder is doubled?

(b) Explain, in terms of Le Châtelier's principle, why the system shifts right to restore equilibrium.

(c) The system re-equilibrates by converting 0.010 M $COBr_2$ into CO and Br_2. Verify that the original equilibrium concentrations and the re-established equilibrium concentrations provide the same value when substituted into the reaction's equilibrium expression.

6. A closed flask contains 0.65 mol/L N_2 and 0.85 mol/L H_2 at equilibrium. What is the $[NH_3]$?

$N_2(g) + 3 H_2(g) \rightleftharpoons 2 NH_3(g)$ $K_{eq} = 0.017$

7. A 1.0 L flask is injected simultaneously with 4.0 mol N_2, 3.0 mol H_2, and 8.0 mol NH_3. In what direction will the reaction proceed to achieve equilibrium? Show your mathematical reasoning.

$N_2(g) + 3 H_2(g) \rightleftharpoons 2 NH_3(g)$ $K_{eq} = 1.0$

8. Write the equilibrium expression for each of the following:

(a) $Fe(s) + 2 H^+(aq) \rightleftharpoons H_2(g) + Fe^{2+}(aq)$

(b) $2 I^-(aq) + Cl_2(aq) \rightleftharpoons I_2(s) + 2 Cl^-(aq)$

(c) $CaO(s) + CO_2(g) \rightleftharpoons CaCO_3(s)$

(d) $CO_2(g) \rightleftharpoons CO_2(aq)$ (Include each chemical's phase in the equilibrium expression.)

(e) $2\,Na_2O(s) \rightleftharpoons 4\,Na(l) + O_2(g)$

9. Write the chemical equation and the equilibrium expression for the equilibrium that develops when:
   (a) Gaseous chlorine dissolves in water.

   (b) Gaseous carbon tetrachloride decomposes into solid carbon and chlorine gas.

   (c) Solid magnesium oxide reacts with sulfur dioxide gas and oxygen gas to produce solid magnesium sulfate.

10. $2\,NOCl(g) \rightleftharpoons 2\,NO(g) + Cl_2(g)$ $K_{eq} = 8.0 \times 10^{-2}$ at 462°C
    For each of the following, what is the K_{eq} at 462°C?
    (a) $NOCl(g) \rightleftharpoons NO(g) + \frac{1}{2}\,Cl_2(g)$

    (b) $2\,NO(g) + Cl_2(g) \rightleftharpoons 2\,NOCl(g)$

    (c) $NO(g) + \frac{1}{2}\,Cl_2(g) \rightleftharpoons NOCl(g)$

11. How would each of the following stresses affect the equilibrium constant, K_{eq}, for:

$$2\ CO(g) + O_2(g) \rightleftharpoons 2\ CO_2(g) \qquad \Delta H = -31\ kJ/mol$$

(a) Add some $CO_2(g)$?

(b) Decrease the volume of the reaction vessel (at a constant temperature)?

(c) Increase the temperature?

(d) Add a catalyst?

12. Can you infer that reactants are favored in the reaction below because $K_{eq} < 1$? Explain.

$$C(s) + H_2O(g) \rightleftharpoons CO(g) + H_2(g) \qquad\qquad K_{eq} = 0.16$$

13. Consider the following two equilibria:

(a) $2\ SO_3(g) \rightleftharpoons 2\ SO_2(g) + O_2(g)$ $\qquad\qquad K_{eq} = 0.25$

(b) $PCl_5(g) \rightleftharpoons PCl_3(g) + Cl_2(g)$ $\qquad K_{eq} = 0.50$

Given that their initial reactant concentrations are equal, can you infer from their equilibrium constants that the first equilibrium has a lower percent yield than the second equilibrium? Explain.

14. Consider the following equilibrium:

$$2\ KClO_3(s) \rightleftharpoons 2\ KCl(s) + 3\ O_2(g) \qquad\qquad \Delta H = 56\ kJ/mol$$

Compare the $[O_2]$ when equilibrium is re-established to its concentration before:

(a) some $KClO_3(s)$ is added.

(b) some $O_2(g)$ is removed.

(c) the temperature is decreased.

5.3 Equilibrium Problems

Warm Up

Chemists use a simple table called an **ICE table** to help solve equilibrium problems. ICE is an acronym for **I**nitial concentration, **C**hange in concentration, and **E**quilibrium concentration. All the units are molarity (M). ICE tables are like Sudoku for chemists and are fun to solve!

The following ICE table shows a system that initially had 3.0 M N_2 and an unknown concentration of Cl_2. In the system, 2.0 M of the N_2 was consumed before achieving equilibrium. Complete the ICE table to determine the initial concentration of Cl_2. The steps following the table will assist you if you need help.

$K_{eq} = 0.128$	$N_2(g)$	+	$3 Cl_2(g)$	$\rightleftharpoons$	$2 NCl_3(g)$
I	3.0		?		0
C	– 2.0				
E					

1. Solve for the equilibrium concentration (E) of N_2. 3.0 – 2.0 = ?
2. Solve for the change of concentration (C) of Cl_2 and NCl_3 using the coefficients in the balanced chemical equation.
3. Solve for the equilibrium concentration (E) of NCl_3.
4. Solve for the equilibrium concentration (E) of Cl_2 using K_{eq}.
5. Solve for the initial concentration (I) of Cl_2.

Solving Equilibrium Problems

There are three related values in any chemical system that develops an equilibrium:
- the equilibrium constant
- the initial concentrations
- the equilibrium concentrations

    In equilibrium problems, you will be given two of these values and asked to determine the third. The only two chemical concepts used to solve equilibrium problems are:
- reaction stoichiometry — the mole ratio in which the reactants are consumed and the products are formed
- the equilibrium law — the relationship between the equilibrium constant and any set of equilibrium concentrations

Determining K_{eq} from Initial Concentrations and One Equilibrium Concentration

The coefficients in a balanced chemical equation provide the mole ratios in which the reactants are consumed and the products are formed. Thus, if you know how much the concentration of one chemical changed in reaching equilibrium, you can easily determine how much the others have changed. The C in the ICE table stands for *change* but it can also remind you to pay attention to the *coefficients*.

    It's important as well to pay attention to the units provided and requested in equilibrium problems. In this type of problem, you may be given the number of moles and liters, thus requiring you to calculate the molar concentrations, or you may have the molarity provided directly.

Sample Problem 5.3.1 — Determining K_{eq} from Initial Concentrations and One Equilibrium Concentration

A student placed 7.00 mol NH_3 in a 0.500 L flask. At equilibrium, 6.2 M N_2 was found in the flask. What is the equilibrium constant, K_{eq}, for this reaction?

$$2\,NH_3(g) \rightleftharpoons N_2(g) + 3\,H_2(g)$$

What to Think About

1. Draw an ICE table and fill in the information provided in the question.

$$\frac{7.00 \text{ mol}}{0.500 \text{ L}} = 14.0 \text{ M}$$

2. Use the coefficients in the balanced chemical equation to relate (in the C row) the moles of reactant consumed to the moles of each product formed.
For every 2 mol of NH_3 that are consumed, 1 mol of N_2 and 3 mol of H_2 are produced.

3. Do the math.

4. Calculate K_{eq} using the equilibrium expression and concentrations.
Exercise caution indicating your final answer to the appropriate degree of certainty. ICE tables involve subtraction and addition. In subtraction and addition, the answer must be rounded to the number of decimal places that the least precise piece of data is rounded to.

How to Do It

	$2\,NH_3(g) \rightleftharpoons$	$N_2(g)$ +	$3\,H_2(g)$
I	14.0	0	0
C			
E		6.2	

	$2\,NH_3(g) \rightleftharpoons$	$N_2(g)$ +	$3\,H_2(g)$
I	14.0	0	0
C	−12.4	+ 6.2	+ 18.6
E		6.2	

	$2\,NH_3(g) \rightleftharpoons$	$N_2(g)$ +	$3\,H_2(g)$
I	14.0	0	0
C	−12.4	+ 6.2	+ 18.6
E	1.6	6.2	18.6

$$K_{eq} = \frac{[N_2][H_2]^3}{[NH_3]^2} = \frac{(6.2)(18.6)^3}{(1.6)^2} = 1.6 \times 10^4$$

Practice Problems 5.3.1 — Determining K_{eq} from Initial Concentrations and One Equilibrium Concentration

1. The following gases were placed in a 4.00 L flask: 8.00 mol N_2 and 10.00 mol H_2. After equilibrium was achieved, 1.20 M NH_3 was found in the flask. Complete the ICE table below and determine the equilibrium constant, K_{eq}.

	$N_2(g)$ +	$3\,H_2(g) \rightleftharpoons$	$2\,NH_3(g)$
I			
C			
E			

Continued opposite

Practice Problems 5.3.1 — *Continued*

2. Equal volumes of 1.60 M Ag^+ and 2.60 M $S_2O_3^{2-}$ were mixed. The $[Ag(S_2O_3)_2^{3-}]$ at equilibrium was 0.35 M. Complete the ICE table below and determine K_{eq}. (Reminder: Whenever you mix aqueous solutions, there is a dilution effect. Mixing equal volumes doubles the solution's volume and halves the concentration of both solutes.)

	$Ag^+(aq)$	+	$2 S_2O_3^{2-}(aq)$	$\rightleftharpoons$	$Ag(S_2O_3)_2^{3-}(aq)$
I			
C			
E			

3. A sample of 6.0 g of carbon was placed in a 1.0 L flask containing 1.4 mol O_2. When equilibrium is established, 1.2 g of carbon remains. Determine K_{eq}. (Note: Because carbon is a solid it is crossed out in the ICE table but the moles of carbon consumed must be calculated — outside the ICE table — to determine the equilibrium concentrations of O_2 and CO.)

	$2 C(s)$	+	$O_2(g)$	$\rightleftharpoons$	$2 CO(g)$
I			
C			
E			

Determining Equilibrium Concentrations from K_{eq} and the Initial Concentrations

The equilibrium law provides chemists with the ability to predict the concentrations that will be present when equilibrium is achieved from any initial set of concentrations. This includes determining the concentrations that will be reached when a stressed system restores equilibrium. In re-equilibration problems, the initial concentrations are created by stressing a previous equilibrium. Such calculations will allow you to verify Le Châtelier's principle.

Chemists solve this type of problem algebraically. There are questions in this course that require the quadratic equation or synthetic division to obtain the answer.

Sample Problem 5.3.2(a) — Determining Equilibrium Concentrations from K_{eq} and the Initial Concentrations

The following gases are injected into a 1.00 L flask: 1.20 mol of $H_2(g)$ and 1.20 mol of $F_2(g)$. What will the concentration of HF be when equilibrium is achieved? (Note: There is no dilution effect when gases are mixed because the mixture's volume isn't increased. Injecting another gas into the same flask is possible because there is so much space between gas particles.)

$$H_2(g) + F_2(g) \rightleftharpoons 2\,HF(g) \qquad K_{eq} = 2.50$$

What to Think About	How to Do It
1. Draw an ICE table and fill in the information provided in the question.	$H_2(g) + F_2(g) \rightleftharpoons 2\,HF(g)$ <table><tr><td>I</td><td>1.20</td><td>1.20</td><td>0</td></tr><tr><td>C</td><td></td><td></td><td></td></tr><tr><td>E</td><td></td><td></td><td></td></tr></table>
2. Set up an algebraic solution using the coefficients in the balanced chemical equation to relate the moles of reactants consumed to each other and to the moles of the product formed. For every x moles of H_2 and F_2 that are consumed, $2x$ moles of HF are produced.	$H_2(g) + F_2(g) \rightleftharpoons 2\,HF(g)$ <table><tr><td>I</td><td>1.20</td><td>1.20</td><td>0</td></tr><tr><td>C</td><td>−x</td><td>−x</td><td>+2x</td></tr><tr><td>E</td><td></td><td></td><td></td></tr></table>
3. Complete the ICE table.	$H_2(g) + F_2(g) \rightleftharpoons 2\,HF(g)$ <table><tr><td>I</td><td>1.20</td><td>1.20</td><td>0</td></tr><tr><td>C</td><td>−x</td><td>−x</td><td>+2x</td></tr><tr><td>E</td><td>1.20 − x</td><td>1.20 − x</td><td>2x</td></tr></table>
4. Solve for x using the equilibrium expression and constant: (i) Find the square root of each side. (ii) Multiply each side by $1.20 - x$. (iii) Expand. (iv) Add $1.58x$ to both sides. (v) Divide each side by 3.58.	$K_{eq} = \dfrac{[HF]^2}{[H_2][F_2]} = \dfrac{(2x)^2}{(1.20 - x)^2} = 2.50$ $\dfrac{2x}{1.20 - x} = (2.50)^{1/2} = 1.58$ $2x = 1.58\,(1.20 - x)$ $2x = 1.896 - 1.58x$ $3.58x = 1.896$ $x = 0.530\ M$
5. Don't forget to answer the question! How could you check your answer?	$[HF]_{eq} = 2x = 2(0.530\ M) = 1.06\ M$

Sample Problem 5.3.2(b) — Determining Equilibrium Concentrations from K_{eq} and the Initial Concentrations

A 3.00 L flask contains 6.00 M H_2, 6.00 M Cl_2, and 3.00 M HCl at equilibrium. An additional 15 mol of HCl is injected into the flask. What is [Cl_2] when equilibrium is re-established?

$$H_2(g) + Cl_2(g) \rightleftharpoons 2\,HCl(g)$$

What to Think About

1. Draw an ICE table and fill in the information provided in the question.
   E_f = final (re-established) equilibrium

   Adding $\dfrac{15.0 \text{ mol}}{3.00 \text{ L}}$ increases the [HCl] by 5.00 M.

2. Le Châtelier predicts that the system will shift to the left to remove some of the added HCl.
   For every x moles of H_2 and Cl_2 that are produced in the shift, $2x$ moles of HCl are consumed.

3. Complete the ICE table.

4. Calculate K_{eq} by substituting the original equilibrium concentrations into the equilibrium expression.

5. Solve for x using the equilibrium expression and constant and by taking the square root of each side.

   Note that this value corroborates our qualitative prediction based on Le Châtelier's principle. The system re-establishes equilibrium by removing only 4 M of the added 5 M HCl.

6. Don't forget to answer the question!

7. Check your answer by substituting your value for x back into the equilibrium expression.

How to Do It

	$H_2(g)$ +	$Cl_2(g) \rightleftharpoons$	$2\,HCl(g)$
I	6.00	6.00	8.00
C			
E_f			

	$H_2(g)$ +	$Cl_2(g) \rightleftharpoons$	$2\,HCl(g)$
I	6.00	6.00	8.00
C	$+x$	$+x$	$-2x$
E_f	$6.00 + x$	$6.00 + x$	$8.00 - 2x$

$$K_{eq} = \frac{[HCl]^2}{[H_2][Cl_2]} = \frac{(3.00)^2}{(6.00)^2} = 0.250$$

$$K_{eq} = \frac{[HCl]^2}{[H_2][Cl_2]} = \frac{(8.00 - 2x)^2}{(6.00 + x)^2} = 0.250$$

$$\frac{8.00 - 2x}{6.00 + x} = (0.250)^{\frac{1}{2}} = 0.500$$

$$x = 2.00 \text{ M}$$

[Cl_2] when equilibrium is restored is:
6.00 M + x = 6.00 M + 2.00 M = 8.00 M

$\dfrac{(8.00 - 4.00)^2}{(6.00 + 2.00)^2}$ does indeed equal 0.250.

Practice Problems 5.3.2 — Determining the Equilibrium Concentrations from K_{eq} and the Initial Concentrations

1. In the lab, 4.5 mol of HCl(g) are pumped into a 3.00 L flask and heated to 80°C. How many moles of Cl_2 will be found in the flask after equilibrium is established? K_{eq} at 80°C = 0.36

	2 HCl(g) $\rightleftharpoons$	H_2(g) +	Cl_2(g)
I			
C			
E			

2. As part of an experiment, 4.00 mol H_2, 4.00 mol C_2N_2, and 8.00 mol HCN are injected into a 2.00 L flask where they establish equilibrium. What is the $[C_2N_2]$ when equilibrium is achieved? K_{eq} = 5.00

	H_2(g) +	C_2N_2(g) $\rightleftharpoons$	2 HCN(g)
I			
C			
E			

3. The table below shows the molarity of three gases at equilibrium. The concentration of HCl is then decreased as shown. What is the [HCl] when equilibrium is re-established?

	H_2(g) +	Cl_2(g) $\rightleftharpoons$	2 HCl(g)
E_o	6.00	6.00	12.0
I	6.00	6.00	5.00
C			
E_f			

Determining past conditions from present ones is perhaps even more remarkable than predicting future conditions. In solving the previous type of problem, we predicted a future event by determining the concentrations that will be reached at equilibrium from the system's initial concentration. In solving the type of problem covered in this section, we will do exactly the opposite as we travel back into the past to determine what initial concentrations would have resulted in the current equilibrium concentrations. We've outlined one method of solving this type of problem below but many variations exist.

Sample Problem 5.3.3 — Determining Initial Concentrations from K_{eq} and the Equilibrium Concentrations

Some CH_3OH was injected into a flask where it established equilibrium with a $[CO] = 0.15$ M. What was the initial concentration of CH_3OH?

$$CH_3OH(g) \rightleftharpoons 2 H_2(g) + CO(g) \qquad K_{eq} = 0.040$$

What to Think About	How to Do It

What to Think About

1. Draw an ICE table and fill in the information provided in the question.

2. Use the coefficients in the balanced chemical equation to relate the moles of reactant consumed to the moles of each product formed.
   For each mole of CH_3OH that is consumed, 2 mol of H_2 and 1 mol of CO are produced.

3. Complete the ICE table.

4. Solve for x using the equilibrium expression and constant.

How to Do It

$CH_3OH(g) \rightleftharpoons$		$2 H_2(g)$ +	$CO(g)$
I	x	0	0
C			
E			0.15

$CH_3OH(g) \rightleftharpoons$		$2 H_2(g)$ +	$CO(g)$
I	x	0	0
C	-0.15	$+0.30$	$+0.15$
E			

$CH_3OH(g) \rightleftharpoons$		$2 H_2(g)$ +	$CO(g)$
I	x	0	0
C	-0.15	$+0.30$	$+0.15$
E	$x - 0.15$	0.30	0.15

$$K_{eq} = \frac{[H_2]^2[CO]}{[CH_3OH]} = \frac{(0.30)^2(0.15)}{x - 0.15} = 0.040$$

$$\frac{(0.30)^2(0.15)}{0.040} = x - 0.15$$

$$x = 0.49 \text{ M}$$

Practice Problems 5.3.3 — Determining Initial Concentrations from K_{eq} and the Equilibrium Concentrations

1. NiS reacted with O_2 in a 2.0 L flask. When equilibrium was achieved 0.36 mol of SO_2 were found in the flask. What was the original $[O_2]$ in the flask? $K_{eq} = 0.30$

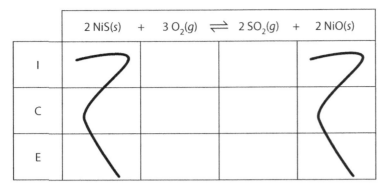

	2 NiS(s) + 3 O_2(g) $\rightleftharpoons$ 2 SO_2(g) + 2 NiO(s)			
I				
C				
E				

2. Some HI is pumped into a flask. At equilibrium, the [HI] = 0.60 mol/L. What was the initial [HI]? $K_{eq} = 0.25$

	2 HI(g) $\rightleftharpoons$ H_2(g) + I_2(g)		
I			
C			
E			

3. Some SO_2 and O_2 are injected into a flask. At equilibrium, the $[SO_2]$ = 0.050 M and the $[O_2]$ = 0.040 M. What was the initial $[O_2]$? $K_{eq} = 100$

	2 SO_2(g) + O_2(g) $\rightleftharpoons$ 2 SO_3(g)		
I			
C			
E			

The Equilibrium Constant and Partial Pressures

The equilibrium position of a reaction is characterized by a mathematical value often referred to as the **mass action expression**. For the reaction:

$$dD + eE \rightleftharpoons fF + gG$$

where D, E, F, and G represent chemical formulas, and d, e, f, and g are coefficients, the mass action expression is:

$$\frac{(aF)^f (aG)^g}{(aD)^d (aE)^e}$$

where a stands for the *activity* of each of the species in the equation.

The activity of a chemical species may be represented by its concentration (e.g., [F]) in the case of species present in solution or as gases, or by its partial pressure (e.g., P_F) in the case of a reaction where all species are present as gases. If the activities are represented by concentrations and the system is at equilibrium, the mass action expression is called an equilibrium constant K_c (as described in section 5.2). If, however, the activities are represented by partial pressures and the system is at equilibrium, the expression is still called an equilibrium constant, but it is represented by K_p. To summarize:

$$K_c = \frac{[F]^f [G]^g}{[D]^d [E]^e} \qquad K_p = \frac{[P_F]^f [P_G]^g}{[P_D]^d [P_E]^e}$$

Note: K_p should always be *calculated* using partial pressures in *atmospheres*.

The numerical values of K_C and K_p are usually different. Their relationship becomes clear if you remember the ideal gas law, which states that $PV = nRT$. Rearrangement of the ideal gas law shows:

Concentration, $C = n/V$ and $n/V = P/RT$, hence $C = P/RT$, thus $P = CRT$

Substitution of CRT for P into the K_p expression above allows you to derive the relationship between K_p and K_C as follows:

$$K_p = K_C(RT)^{\Delta n}$$

Because K_p is determined using partial pressures in atmospheres, it follows that the ideal gas constant value, $R = 0.08206$ L·atm/mol·K. Additionally,

T = temperature in K, and
$\Delta n = (f + g) - (d + e)$ (the difference in the sums of the coefficients for the *gaseous* reactants and products)

Sample Problem 5.3.4 — Conversion Between K_c and K_p

The Haber process for the formation of ammonia establishes equilibrium at 498 K. Under these circumstances, $[N_2] = 0.020$ mol/L, $[H_2] = 0.18$ mol/L, and $[NH_3] = 0.14$ mol/L. Determine the numerical value of K_c and K_p.

What to Think About	How to Do It
1. Determine the balanced chemical equation that describes the equilibrium.	$N_2(g) + 3 H_2(g) \rightleftharpoons 2 NH_3(g)$
2. Write an appropriate K_c expression for the equation.	$K_c = \dfrac{[NH_3]^2}{[N_2][H_2]^3} = \dfrac{(0.14)^2}{(0.020)(0.18)^3} = 170$
3. Substitute concentrations and solve for K_c.	
4. Determine Δn and substitute into the appropriate equation to determine K_p. (Be sure to apply the exponent Δn to the *entire product* of $R \times T$. Also take care with the *sign* of Δn and substitution of the correct R value.)	$\Delta n = 2 - (1 + 3) = -2 \quad K_p = K_c(RT)^{\Delta n}$ $= 170(0.08206 \text{ L atm/mol } K \times 498 K)^{-2}$ $= 170 \times 0.000599 = 0.10$ Notice that NO units are included in a K_c or K_p value.

Practice Problems 5.3.4 — Conversion Between K_c and K_p

1. Given the equilibrium quantities stated below each species, determine K_p for the following reactions at a fixed temperature:

   (a) $N_2O_4(g) \rightleftharpoons 2 NO_2(g)$
       2.71 atm   0.600 atm

   (b) $CaCO_3(s) \rightleftharpoons CaO(s) + CO_2(g)$
       15.6 g/L   0.02 g/L   1.04 atm

2. Given the equilibrium partial pressures stated below each species, and the K_p value at a fixed temperature, determine the missing partial pressure.

   (a) $2 NO(g) + O_2(g) \rightleftharpoons 2 NO_2(g) \quad K_p = 1.6 \times 10^{12}$
       6.5×10^{-5} atm 4.5×10^{-5} atm   ?

   (b) $N_2O_4(g) \rightleftharpoons 2 NO_2(g) \quad\quad K_p = 0.715$
       ?   15.8 atm

3. At 500.°C, the reaction between N_2 and H_2 to form ammonia has a $K_p = 1.5 \times 10^{-5}$. What is the numerical value of K_c for this reaction?

4. For which of the following reactions would $K_p = K_c$? Explain your choice.

   (a) $N_2(g) + O_2(g) \rightleftharpoons 2 NO(g)$

   (b) $2 NO(g) + O_2(g) \rightleftharpoons 2 NO_2(g)$

5.3 Activity: Visualizing Equilibria

Question
How could you determine an equilibrium system's constant if you were able to count the number of molecules present at equilibrium?

Background
The amount of each reactant and product remains constant at equilibrium because each chemical is being produced at the same rate that it is being consumed. The diagrams below represent the interconversion of A (dark) molecules and B (light) molecules:

$$A \text{ (dark)} \rightleftharpoons B \text{ (light)}$$

Procedure
1. Each row of drawings represents a separate trial that results in equilibrium. Answer the questions below about the trials.

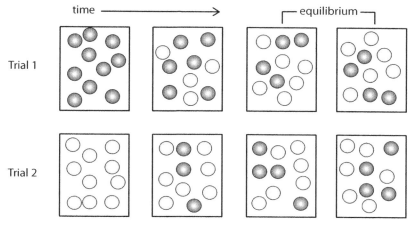

Results and Discussion
1. State a property of chemical equilibrium that is evident by observing trials 1 and 2.

2. What is the equilibrium constant for A $\rightleftharpoons$ B? The container could be any volume because the volumes cancel in this particular equilibrium expression.

3. In another trial, 20 A molecules and 50 B molecules were counted in a reaction vessel. How many A molecules will there be in the vessel when equilibrium is established?

4. After equilibrium was established in trial 2, the temperature was decreased. When equilibrium was restored, there were 7 A molecules and 3 B molecules in the container. State whether A $\rightleftharpoons$ B is exothermic or endothermic.

5.3 Review Questions

1. Complete the following ICE tables.

(a)

	$2 CH_4(g) \rightleftharpoons$	$C_2H_2(g)$	$+$	$3 H_2(g)$
I	6.0	0		0
C				
E		1.5		

(b)

	$N_2(g)$	$+$	$3 H_2(g) \rightleftharpoons$	$2 NH_3(g)$
I			5.0	0
C				
E	2.0			1.0

2. During an experiment, 3.0 mol of NO_2 are injected into a 1.0 L flask at 55°C. At equilibrium, the flask contains 1.2 mol of N_2O_4.

$2 NO_2(g) \rightleftharpoons N_2O_4(g)$

(a) What is the $[NO_2]$ at equilibrium?

(b) What is K_{eq} for this reaction at 55°C?

3. Equal volumes of 3.60 M A^{2+} and 6.80 M B^- are mixed. After the reaction, equilibrium is established with $[B^-] = 0.40$ M.

$A^{2+}(aq) + 3B^-(aq) \rightleftharpoons AB_3^-(aq)$

(a) What is the $[A^{2+}]$ at equilibrium?

(b) Determine K_{eq}.

4. Complete the following ICE tables:

(a)

K_{eq} = 1.20	$H_2(g)$	+ $C_2N_2(g)$	$\rightleftharpoons$ 2 HCN(g)
I			0
C			
E	5.0	1.5	

(b)

K_{eq} = 1.20	$H_2(g)$	+ $C_2N_2(g)$	$\rightleftharpoons$ 2 HCN(g)
I	5.4		0
C			
E			3.6

5. The interconversion of the structural isomers glyceraldehyde-3-phospate (G3P) and dihydroxyacetone phosphate (DHAP) is a biochemical equilibrium that occurs during the breakdown of glucose in our cells. What will their concentrations be at equilibrium if the initial concentration of each isomer is 0.020 M?

G3P(aq) $\rightleftharpoons$ DHAP(aq) K_{eq} = 19

6. A 1.00 L flask is injected with 0.600 mol of each of the following four gases: H_2, CO_2, H_2O, and CO.

$H_2(g) + CO_2(g) \rightleftharpoons H_2O(g) + CO(g)$ K_{eq} = 1.69

(a) What is the $[H_2]$ at equilibrium?

(b) What is the [CO] at equilibrium?

7. A 500 mL flask is injected with 0.72 mol of C_2N_2 and 0.72 mol of H_2. What will the [HCN] be when the system reaches equilibrium?

$H_2(g) + C_2N_2(g) \rightleftharpoons$ 2 HCN(g) K_{eq} = 1.20

8. A 1.0 L flask containing 4.0 mol of H_2 and a 1.0 L flask containing 4.0 mol of F_2 are connected by a valve. The valve is opened to allow the gases to mix in the 2.0 L combined volume.

$$H_2(g) + F_2(g) \rightleftharpoons 2 HF(g) \qquad K_{eq} = 121$$

How many moles of H_2 will be present in the system when it equilibrates?

9. A 250 mL flask containing 1.0 g of excess BN(s) is injected with 0.21 mol of $Cl_2(g)$.

$$2 BN(s) + 3 Cl_2(g) \rightleftharpoons 2 BCl_3(g) + N_2(g) \qquad K_{eq} = 0.045$$

(a) What will the $[BCl_3]$ equal when the system attains equilibrium? (Hint: The math is a bit trickier on this one; you need to take the cube root of each side.)

(b) Would the reaction achieve equilibrium if the flask initially contained 1.0 g of BN(s)? Support your answer with calculations.

10. A flask is injected with 0.60 M C_2H_2 and 0.60 M H_2. Determine the $[H_2]$ at equilibrium by trial and error. Lower the $[C_2H_2]$ and the $[H_2]$ and raise the $[CH_4]$ in appropriate increments until you find a set of concentrations that provides the K_{eq} value when substituted into the equilibrium expression.

$$2 CH_4(g) \rightleftharpoons C_2H_2(g) + 3 H_2(g) \qquad K_{eq} = 2.8$$

11. In a 2.00 L flask, 3.00 M H_2, 3.00 M Cl_2, and 7.50 M HCl coexist at equilibrium. A student removes 7.00 mol of HCl from the flask.

(a) What would the concentration of each gas be when equilibrium re-establishes?

	$H_2(g)$	+	$Cl_2(g)$	$\rightleftharpoons$	2 HCl(g)
E_o					
I					
C					
E_f					

(b) Describe how the system's response is consistent with Le Châtelier's principle.

12. A 200.0 mL solution of 0.10 M Fe^{3+}, 0.10 M SCN^-, and 1.8 M $FeSCN^{2+}$ is at equilibrium. The solution is diluted by adding water up to 500.0 mL. Complete the ICE table below and show the algebraic equation that would allow you to solve for the ion concentrations when equilibrium is restored. Do **NOT** solve for x.

	$Fe^{3+}(aq)$ +	$SCN^-(aq)$ $\rightleftharpoons$	$FeSCN^{2+}(aq)$
E_o	0.10	0.10	1.8
I			
C			
E_f			

13. In a 500.0 mL flask, 2.5 mol of H_2, 2.5 mol of Br_2, and 5.0 mol of HBr coexist at equilibrium. At 35 s, 2.5 mol of Br_2 is injected into the flask, and the system re-establishes equilibrium at 55 s. Use three different-colored plots on the graph below to show how the concentration of each chemical changes during this period. (This question can be solved algebraically without using the quadratic formula despite not providing a perfect square.)

$$H_2(g) + Br_2(g) \rightleftharpoons 2 HBr(g)$$

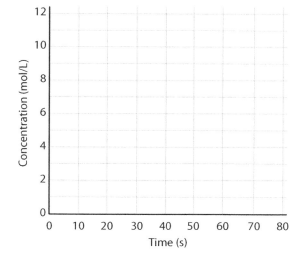

14. Some SO_3 is injected into a 500 mL flask. At equilibrium the $[O_2] = 1.80$ M.

$$2 SO_3(g) \rightleftharpoons 2 SO_2(g) + O_2(g) \qquad K_{eq} = 3.83 \times 10^{-2}$$

(a) What is the $[SO_3]$ at equilibrium?

(b) How many moles of SO_3 were originally injected into the flask?

15. Equal quantities of $H_2(g)$ and $I_2(g)$ are pumped into a flask. At equilibrium the $[HI] = 1.0$ M. What was the initial $[H_2]$?

$$H_2(g) + I_2(g) \rightleftharpoons 2 HI(g) \qquad K_{eq} = 4.0$$

16. Some PCl_5 is pumped into a 500 mL flask. The $[PCl_3] = 1.50$ M at equilibrium. What was the initial $[PCl_5]$?

$$PCl_5(g) \rightleftharpoons PCl_3(g) + Cl_2(g) \qquad K_{eq} = 2.14$$

17. A reaction mixture contains 0.24 mol of NO, 0.10 mol of O_2, and 1.20 mol of NO_2 at equilibrium in a 1.0 L container. How many moles of O_2 would need to be added to the mixture to increase the amount of NO_2 to 1.30 mol when equilibrium is re-established?

$$2 NO(g) + O_2(g) \rightleftharpoons 2 NO_2(g)$$

18. Write the K_p expression for each of the following equations:

(a) $PCl_5(g) \rightleftharpoons PCl_3(g) + Cl_2(g)$

(b) $P_4(s) + 5 O_2(g) \rightleftharpoons 2 P_2O_5(g)$

(c) $CO_2(g) + CaO(s) \rightleftharpoons CaCO_3(s)$

19. Calculate K_p for the equilibria in Review Questions 4, 6, and 7 in section 5.2.

Review Question 4:

Review Question 6:

Review Question 7:

20. Consider the following reaction:

$$2\ SO_2(g) + O_2(g) \rightleftharpoons 2\ SO_3(g) \qquad K_p = 0.14\ \text{at}\ 625°C$$

If a reaction vessel is filled with SO_3 at a partial pressure of 0.10 atm and 0.20 atm each of SO_2 and O_2 gas, is the reaction at equilibrium? If not, in which direction does it proceed to reach equilibrium?

21. The following graph represents partial pressure vs. time for the reaction between A and B gas to form C gas. Gas A is present in excess.

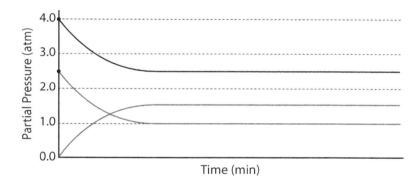

(a) Write a balanced chemical equation for the equilibrium in the question.

(b) Write the equilibrium expression K_p for the reaction.

(c) Calculate the numerical value for K_p for this reaction.

(d) Calculate the numerical value for K_c for this reaction.

22. In a container, 1.00 mol of N_2 and 3.00 mol of H_2 are mixed together to produce ammonia. At equilibrium, the total pressure of the system is 1.8×10^6 Pa and the mixture contains only 50% of the N_2 that was present originally. Calculate K_p for this reaction at this temperature.

23. A lab technician places 0.300 atm of SO_2, 0.400 atm O_2, and 0.020 atm of SO_3 into a 10.0 L bulb. Once equilibrium is established, the partial pressure of SO_3 is found to be 0.140 atm. What is the value of K_p for the reaction under these conditions?

24. $PCl_5(g)$ decomposes into $PCl_3(g)$ and $Cl_2(g)$. A pure sample of phosphorus pentachloride is placed into an evacuated 1.00 L glass bulb. The temperature remains constant while the pure sample decomposes as shown below:

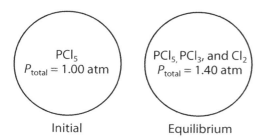

           Initial   Equilibrium

(a) Explain why the pressure increases in the container as the reaction reaches equilibrium.

(b) Determine the partial pressure of each gas when the system reaches equilibrium.

(c) Calculate K_p for the equilibrium system.

(d) If the decomposition were to go to completion, what would the total pressure be in the system?

5.4 Le Châtelier's Principle

Warm Up

Consider the following equilibrium: $2\,SO_2(g) + O_2(g) \rightleftharpoons 2\,SO_3(g)$

1. What is equal at equilibrium?

_____

2. What would happen to the forward rate if some O_2 were removed from this equilibrium?

_____

3. Explain why, in terms of collision theory.

_____

4. Would the reaction still be at equilibrium at this point?

_____

Equilibria Response to Reactant or Product Removal

In 1888, the French chemist Henry Le Châtelier wrote, "Every change of one of the factors of an equilibrium occasions a rearrangement of the system in such a direction that the factor in question experiences a change in a sense opposite to the original change." Le Châtelier's principle has since been expressed in many different ways that are fortunately easier to understand than Le Châtelier's own wording.

> **Le Châtelier's principle**: An equilibrium system subjected to a stress will shift to partially alleviate the stress and restore equilibrium.

In other words, when an equilibrium system is disrupted, it will shift its reactant and product concentrations, changing one into the other, to reduce the disruption and re-establish equilibrium. Le Châtelier's principle allows chemists to predict what will happen to an equilibrium's reactant and product concentrations when its conditions change.

When a quantity of reactant or product is added to an equilibrium system, the system will shift to remove *some* of the added chemical.

When a quantity of reactant or product is removed from an equilibrium system, the system will shift to replace *some* of the removed chemical.

An **equilibrium system** is a reacting system that is at or approaching equilibrium. When we change the concentration of a reactant or a product, we "stress" the equilibrium system by temporarily destroying the equilibrium condition. When a system responds by changing some reactants into products, the response is referred to as a "**shift right**" because the products are on the right side of a chemical equation. When a system responds by changing some products into reactants, the response is called a "**shift left**."

Sample Problem 5.4.1(a) — Predicting How an Equilibrium System Will Respond to the Addition of Reactant or Product

Some HI is added to the system below. In what direction will the system shift to restore equilibrium? When equilibrium is restored, how will the concentration of each substance compare to its concentration before the HI was added?

$$H_2(g) + I_2(g) \rightleftharpoons 2\,HI(g)$$

What to Think About	How to Do It
1. Using Le Châtelier's principle, determine that the system will shift to remove some of the added HI.	The system must *shift left* (toward reactants) to consume some of the added HI.
2. Infer from Le Châtelier's principle that the shift left produces H_2 and I_2. Note that Le Châtelier's principle doesn't explicitly state what happens to the concentrations of H_2 and I_2, but you can infer what happens from your understanding of the principle	Since not all of the added HI will be removed, the [HI] will increase. The [H_2] and [I_2] will also increase

How does a chemist remove chemicals from an equilibrium system? Obviously you can't simply reach in and pick some ions or molecules out. Chemists usually remove one chemical by reacting it with another. The reaction that removes the chemical might also arrive at equilibrium. We'll discuss this situation in later chapters.

Students often state that a stressed equilibrium system "*tries to* restore equilibrium" or "*tries to* remove some of the added chemical." As Yoda of *Star Wars* says, "Do or do not. There is no try." A stressed system doesn't *try to* restore equilibrium; it *does* restore equilibrium. When a reactant or product is added to an equilibrium system, it doesn't *try to* remove some of the added chemical; it *does* remove some of the added chemical.

Sample Problem 5.4.1(b) — Predicting How an Equilibrium System Will Respond to the Removal of Reactant or Product

Some solid calcium hydroxide is in equilibrium with a saturated solution of its ions.

$$Ca(OH)_2(s) \rightleftharpoons Ca^{2+}(aq) + 2\,OH^-(aq)$$

This is a solubility equilibrium. The rate of dissolving equals the rate of recrystallizing. Some OH^- is removed by adding some hydrochloric acid to the solution. (The H^+ in the acid neutralizes some OH^- to produce H_2O.) In what direction will the equilibrium shift? When equilibrium is restored, how will the calcium ion and the hydroxide ion concentrations compare to their concentrations before the acid was added?

What to Think About	How to Do It
1. Using Le Châtelier's principle, determine that the system will shift to replace some of the removed OH^-.	The system must <u>shift right</u> (towards products) to replace some of the removed OH^-.
2. Determine the effect of the shift right. The shift right also produces some Ca^{2+} and causes more of the $Ca(OH)_2(s)$ to dissolve.	Since not all of the removed OH^- is replaced, the [OH^-] will decrease. The [Ca^{2+}] will increase.

Practice Problems 5.4.1 — Predicting How an Equilibrium System Will Respond to the Addition or Removal of Reactant or Product

Use the following system for questions 1 and 2:

$$Fe^{3+}(aq) + SCN^-(aq) \rightleftharpoons FeSCN^{2+}(aq)$$

1. (a) What does Le Châtelier's principle say will occur if some $Fe(NO_3)_3$ is added to the system? ($Fe(NO_3)_3$ dissociates into independent Fe^{3+} and NO_3^- ions in solution.)

   (b) In what direction will the system shift?

   (c) When equilibrium is restored, how will the concentration of each substance compare to its concentration before the $Fe(NO_3)_3$ was added?

2. (a) What does Le Châtelier's principle say will occur if some sodium biphosphate is added to the system? (The HPO_4^{2-} ion reacts with the Fe^{3+} ion to produce $FeHPO_4^+$.)

   (b) In what direction will the system shift?

   (c) When equilibrium is restored, how will the concentration of each substance compare to its concentration before the sodium biphosphate was added?

3. Look at the graph below. At t_1 more H_2 was suddenly added to the closed system as shown. Equilibrium was re-established at t_2. Complete the plots to show how the system would respond.

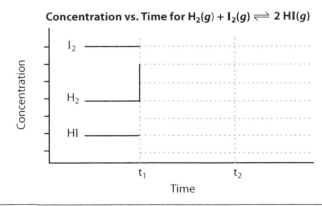

Concentration vs. Time for $H_2(g) + I_2(g) \rightleftharpoons 2\,HI(g)$

The Shift Mechanism: Effects of Stress on Forward and Reverse Reaction Rates

Le Châtelier's principle describes how an equilibrium system responds to a stress without offering any explanation of the response. The explanation is related to the effect of the stress on the equilibrium's forward and reverse reaction rates. To an equilibrium system, a **stress** is any action that has a different effect on the forward reaction rate than it does on the reverse reaction rate, thus disrupting the equilibrium. In other words, a disrupted or stressed equilibrium system is no longer at equilibrium because its forward and reverse reaction rates are not equal.

Sample Problem 5.4.2(a) — Describing the Shift Mechanism

Explain in terms of forward and reverse reaction rates how the following equilibrium system would respond to adding some iron(III) chloride. ($FeCl_3$ dissociates into independent Fe^{3+} and Cl^- ions in solution.)

$$Fe^{3+}(aq) + SCN^-(aq) \rightleftharpoons FeSCN^{2+}(aq)$$

What to Think About	How to Do It
1. Determine the immediate effect of the stress on the forward and/or reverse reaction rates	Adding some Fe^{3+} increases the forward reaction rate (r_f).
2. Decide if this results in a net forward or net reverse reaction.	This results in a net forward reaction, also known as a shift right.

The system in Sample Problem 5.4.2(a) would re-equilibrate in the same manner that it established equilibrium in the first place. Figure 5.4.1(a) shows the rates when the system is initially at equilibrium (E_i), when the system is stressed (S), and when the system restores equilibrium (E_f). The net forward reaction would cause the reactant concentrations and the forward rate (r_f) to decrease, while the product concentrations and the reverse rate (r_r) increase, until r_f once again equals r_r.

The graph in Figure 5.4.1(b) is the more traditional way of depicting the same information shown in the arrow diagram in (a). In (b), the solid line represents the forward rate and the dotted line represents the reverse rate.

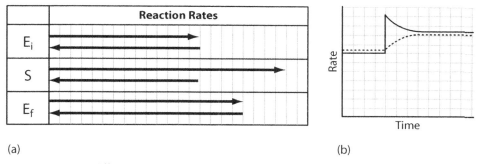

(a)   (b)

Figure 5.4.1 *Two different ways of representing a reaction in a diagram*

Sample Problem 5.4.2(b) — Describing the Shift Mechanism

Explain in terms of forward and reverse reaction rates how the following reaction would respond to removing some SO_2.

$$2\,SO_2(g) + O_2(g) \rightleftharpoons 2\,SO_3(g)$$

What to Think About	How to Do It
1. Determine the immediate effect of the stress on the forward and/or reverse reaction rates.	Removing some SO_2 decreases the forward reaction rate (r_f).
2. Decide if this results in a net forward or net reverse reaction.	This results in a net reverse reaction, also known as a shift left.

The kinetics diagram on the right illustrates the rates at the initial equilibrium, at the time of the stress, and when equilibrium is restored. Note that the rates are lower when equilibrium is restored than they were at the initial equilibrium. This is logical since some chemical was removed from the system.

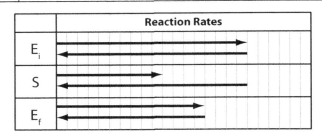

Practice Problems 5.4.2 — Describing the Shift Mechanism

Consider the following equilibrium system:

$$2\,NOCl(g) \rightleftharpoons 2\,NO(g) + Cl_2(g)$$

1. Explain in terms of forward and reverse reaction rates how the equilibrium would respond to each of the following changes.
   (a) adding some NO
   (b) removing some Cl_2
   (c) removing some NOCl

2. Show how the forward and the reverse reaction rates respond to a sudden addition of NO to the system at t_1. Use a solid line for the forward rate and a dotted line for the reverse rate. The system re-equilibrates at t_2. The arrow diagram on the right of the graph is another way of depicting the same information. You may use it to do your rough work.

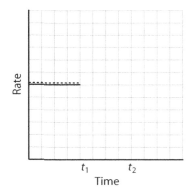

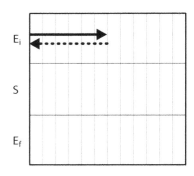

In heterogeneous reactions, an increase in surface area increases the forward and reverse rates equally since both forward and reverse reactions occur at the same surface. Adding more solid or crushing the solid present at equilibrium therefore has no effect on the equilibrium concentrations of the reactants and products in solution. When the initial reactants have a greater surface area, the system reaches equilibrium sooner. Likewise, adding a catalyst increases the forward and reverse rates equally and therefore has no effect on the position of the equilibrium. When a catalyst is added to the initial reactants, the system reaches equilibrium sooner.

The Equilibrium Position

The phrase **equilibrium position** refers to the relative concentrations of reactants and products at equilibrium and is usually expressed as percent yield. In Grade 11, you learned that percent yield is the amount of a product formed or recovered as a percentage of what the complete reaction will theoretically produce.

$$\textbf{percent yield} \ = \ \frac{\text{actual yield}}{\text{theoretical yield}} \times 100$$

An equilibrium system with an increased percent yield is said to have an equilibrium position farther to the right. "The equilibrium *position* shifted right" translates to: "the system has a greater percent yield than it had at the previous equilibrium." It is important to make a distinction between the equilibrium system shifting in response to a stress (as described by Le Châtelier's principle) and the equilibrium position shifting as a possible result. When you lose your balance snowboarding, you shift your weight to regain your balance. Sometimes you also shift your balance farther forward or backward on your board. Likewise, when an equilibrium system shifts to remove some of an added chemical or to replace some of a removed chemical, the system may "overshoot" or "undershoot" the original equilibrium position, depending on the circumstance. Consider the following equilibrium:

$$HP(aq) \ \rightleftharpoons \ H^+(aq) + P^-(aq)$$
$$\text{yellow} \qquad\qquad\qquad \text{blue}$$

A green solution indicates equal concentrations of HP and P^- and therefore a 50% yield. If some yellow HP is added to a green equilibrium mixture, the *system will shift right* to remove some of the added HP. However, when equilibrium is restored, the solution is still yellow so we know that *the equilibrium position has shifted left*.

The expression "products are favored" is sometimes used to describe an equilibrium system. Be careful making inferences from this expression. Let's examine what the phrase does and, perhaps more importantly, does not mean. Products are *favored* when the equilibrium has a greater than 50 percent yield. This means that more than half of the limiting reactant has been converted into product.

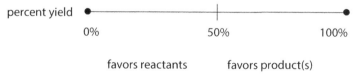

If a reaction has a limiting reactant, you cannot infer that any one reactant or product has a higher or lower concentration than any other reactant or product solely from the products being favored. For example:

$$H_3BO_3(aq) + CN^-(aq) \ \rightleftharpoons \ H_2BO_3^-(aq) + HCN(aq)$$

Even though products are favored in the above equilibrium, the [HCN] may be less than the [CN⁻] if the CN⁻ is in excess. Likewise, the [HCN] may be less than the [H₃BO₃] if the H₃BO₃ is in excess. Furthermore, a reasonable excess of either reactant ensures that the total [reactants] will be greater than the total [products] even though the products are favored.

5.4 Review Questions

1. Consider the following equilibrium system: $2 NO(g) + Cl_2(g) \rightleftharpoons 2 NOCl(g)$

    (a) What does Le Châtelier's principle say will occur if some NO is added to the system?

    (b) In which direction will this system shift in response to the stress?

    (c) Compare the $[Cl_2]$ when equilibrium is reestablished to its concentration before the NO was added.

2. Consider the following equilibrium system: $2 NO(g) + O_2(g) \rightleftharpoons 2 NO_2(g)$
    (a) Explain in terms of forward and reverse reaction rates how the system responds to removing some O_2.

    (b) Compare the rates of the forward and reverse reactions when equilibrium is reestablished with the rates before some O_2 was removed.

3. Silver nitrate is added to the equilibrium system:
    $Ag(S_2O_3)_2{}^{3-}(aq) \rightleftharpoons Ag^+(aq) + 2 S_2O_3{}^{2-}(aq)$

    When equilibrium is restored, how will each ion's concentration compare with its concentration before the silver nitrate was added? Explain how you arrived at your answer.

4. Cholesterol is a component of cell membranes and a building block for hormones such as estrogen and testosterone. About 80% of the body's cholesterol is produced by the liver, while the rest comes directly from our diet. There are two forms of cholesterol: a "good" form (HDL) that helps lubricate blood vessels and a "bad" form (LDL) that deposits on the inside of artery walls where it can restrict blood flow. Suppose these two forms could be converted from one to the other via the following "equilibrium" reaction:
    $LDL + X \rightleftharpoons HDL + Y$

    (a) Briefly explain why a drug that removes the bad cholesterol (LDL) would not be completely effective (i.e., it would have a bad side-effect).

    (b) Referring to the above equilibrium, how could a drug company effectively treat people with too high an LDL:HDL ratio?

5. Sulfur dioxide is an important compound in wines, where it acts as an antimicrobial and antioxidant to protect the wine from spoiling. The following equilibrium exists in wines:

$$SO_2(aq) + H_2O(l) \rightleftharpoons H^+(aq) + HSO_3^-(aq)$$

State whether a winemaker should increase the wine's pH (by removing H^+) or decrease the wine's pH (by adding H^+) to shift the equilibrium toward the active SO_2?

6. Complete the following table using the words "decrease," "same," or "increase" to indicate how the equilibrium concentrations are affected by the stated stress. "Increase" means that when equilibrium is restored, the chemical's concentration is greater than it was before the stress.

$$2 NH_3(g) \rightleftharpoons N_2(g) + 3 H_2(g)$$

		Add NH$_3$	Remove some H$_2$	Add N$_2$
Equilibrium Concentration	N$_2$			
	H$_2$			
	NH$_3$			

7. $$HP \rightleftharpoons H^+ + P^-$$

    red   yellow

The above equilibrium system appears orange due to equal concentrations of HP and P^-.

(a) What action will shift the equilibrium so the solution turns red?

(b) What could be done to shift the equilibrium so the solution turns yellow?

8. Hemoglobin is the protein in red blood cells that transports oxygen to cells throughout your body. Each hemoglobin (Hb) molecule attaches to four oxygen molecules:

$$Hb(aq) + 4 O_2(aq) \rightleftharpoons Hb(O_2)_4(aq)$$

In which direction does the above equilibrium shift in each of the following situations:

(a) At high elevations the air pressure is lowered reducing the $[O_2]$ in the blood.

(b) At high altitude, climbers sometimes breathe pressurized oxygen from a tank to increase the $[O_2]$ in the blood.

(c) People who live at higher altitudes produce more hemoglobin.

(d) Carbon monoxide poisoning occurs when carbon monoxide molecules bind to hemoglobin instead of oxygen molecules. Carboxyhemoglobin is even redder than oxyhemoglobin; therefore, one symptom of carbon monoxide poisoning is a flushed face.

9. Explain why neither adding a catalyst nor increasing the surface area of S(s) stresses the following equilibrium, even though each of these actions increases the forward reaction rate.

$$2\,S(s) + 3\,O_2(g) \rightleftharpoons 2\,SO_3(g)$$

10. The following equilibrium exists in an aqueous solution of copper(II) chloride:

$$CuCl_4{}^{2-}(aq) + 4\,H_2O(l) \rightleftharpoons Cu(H_2O)_4{}^{2+}(aq) + 4\,Cl^-(aq)$$
green   blue

   (a) Some Cl^- is removed by adding some silver nitrate to the solution. The Ag^+ in the silver nitrate precipitates with the Cl^- to produce AgCl(s). In what direction will the equilibrium shift?

   (b) If the initial equilibrium mixture was blue, what would you observe as a sodium chloride solution was added dropwise to the equilibrium mixture?

11. At t_1 some CO was suddenly removed from the closed system shown below. Equilibrium was reestablished at t_2. Complete the plots to show how the system would respond.

$$Ni(s) + 4\,CO(g) \rightleftharpoons Ni(CO)_4(g)$$

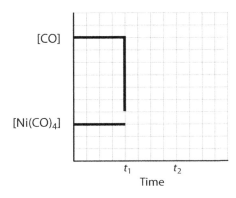

12. Show how the forward and reverse reaction rates respond to having some HOCl suddenly removed from the following system at t_1.

$$H_2O(g) + Cl_2O(g) \rightleftharpoons 2\,HOCl(g)$$

   Use a solid line for the forward rate and a dotted line for the reverse rate. The system re-equilibrates at t_2. The arrow diagram on the right is another way of displaying the same information. You may use it to do your rough work.

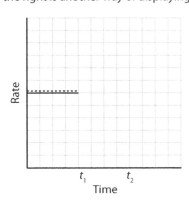
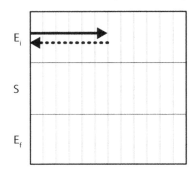

13. Equilibria are often linked through one chemical common to both. Even two equilibria coupled together present an interesting dynamic.

Equilibrium 1

$$Cu^{2+} + 4\,NH_3 \rightleftharpoons Cu(NH_3)_4^{\,2+}$$

$$+$$

$$4\,H^+$$

Equilibrium 2 $\uparrow\downarrow$

$$4\,NH_4^{\,+}$$

How would the $[Cu^{2+}]$ be affected by adding some H^+ to this coupled system? Briefly explain using Le Châtelier's principle.

14. Silver acetate has a low solubility in water. A small amount of solid silver acetate is in equilibrium with a saturated solution of its ions.

Equilibrium 1

$$AgCH_3COO(s) \rightleftharpoons Ag^+(aq) + CH_3COO^-(aq)$$

$$+$$

$$H^+(aq)$$

Equilibrium 2 $\uparrow\downarrow$

$$CH_3COOH(aq)$$

What would you observe occurring in the beaker as $H^+(aq)$ is added dropwise to the solution? Briefly explain using Le Châtelier's principle.

15. Consider the following equilibrium:

$$2\,NO(g) + O_2(g) \rightleftharpoons 2\,NO_2(g)$$

Describe how [NO] could be greater than the $[NO_2]$ despite the products being favored at equilibrium.

16. Because few natural systems are closed, many of nature's reversible reactions are perpetually "chasing after" equilibrium. In *At Home in the Universe*, the author, Stuart Kauffman, describes living systems as "persistently displaced from chemical equilibrium." Describe one way to ensure that a reversible reaction never achieves equilibrium.

5.5 Le Châtelier's Principle and Volume and Temperature Changes

Warm Up

1. What is the scientific meaning of *pressure*?

   _____

2. To increase gas pressure, we _____ the gas into less space.

3. What is temperature a measure of?

   _____

4. An increase in temperature increases the rate of reactions because the molecules collide more
   _____ and _____.

How Equilibria Respond to Volume Changes

We've described and explained how equilibria respond to changing the concentration of a single reactant or product. The concentrations of all the reactants and products can be changed simultaneously by changing the volume of the reacting system. The volume of a gaseous system can be changed by compressing or decompressing it. The volume of an aqueous system can be changed by evaporating water from it or by diluting it. A change in volume changes all the reactants' and products' concentrations.

It isn't possible for a shift to partially restore all the chemicals' concentrations but some equilibria can shift to partially restore the total or combined concentration of the chemicals. For example, if an aqueous equilibrium is diluted then all the chemical concentrations are decreased. A shift can't increase the concentrations of chemicals on both sides of the equation but some equilibria can increase the total chemical concentration by shifting to the side of the equation with the greater number of particles. Le Châtelier views this situation from the perspective of pressure.

> Equilibria respond to volume changes by shifting to relieve some of the added pressure or to replace some of the lost pressure.

You are probably familiar with the concept of gas pressure, but you may not be familiar with the concept of solute (osmotic) pressure. A detailed discussion of osmosis and osmotic pressure is not required here. You need only know that osmotic pressure is to dissolved particles what gas pressure is to gas particles. In 1901, the Dutch chemist Jacobus van't Hoff discovered that dissolved particles in an aqueous solution behave just like gas particles in a container. The relationship between the concentration, temperature, and pressure is the same for gas particles and dissolved particles. Van't Hoff won the first Nobel Prize in chemistry for his work on osmotic pressure and chemical equilibrium. Just as a gas's pressure is proportional to its concentration of gas particles, an aqueous solution's osmotic pressure is proportional to its concentration of solute particles. Decompressing a gas lowers its gas pressure. Diluting a solute lowers its osmotic pressure.

Chemists sometimes refer to the partial pressure of a gas. **Partial pressure** is the gas's part of the total gas pressure or the pressure exerted by this gas alone in a mixture of gases. The sum of the partial pressures equals the total pressure of the gas mixture. A gas's partial pressure is proportional to its concentration. The same concepts and principles apply to solutes and their partial osmotic pressures.

Consider the following equilibrium:

$$H_2(g) + F_2(g) \rightleftharpoons 2HF(g)$$

This equilibrium doesn't respond to a volume change. It cannot partially restore the pressure by shifting in either direction since there are the same number of gas particles on each side of the equation.

Quick Check

1. According to Le Châtelier's principle, how will an equilibrium respond to being compressed?

   _____

2. What is *partial pressure*?

   _____

3. According to Le Châtelier's principle, how will an aqueous equilibrium respond to being diluted?

   _____

Sample Problem 5.5.1(a) — Predicting How an Equilibrium Will Respond to a Decrease in Volume

The system described by the equation below is compressed. In what direction will the system shift to restore equilibrium? When equilibrium is restored, how will the number of each type of molecule and the concentration of each substance compare to those before the system was compressed?

$$PCl_3(g) + Cl_2(g) \rightleftharpoons PCl_5(g)$$

What to Think About

1. Recall that Le Châtelier's principle says the system will shift to relieve *some* of the added pressure.

2. Consider the effect the stress has on the system to determine the number of each type of molecule. The stress changed the amount of space that the particles move around in, not the number of particles. Only the system's response to the stress changes the number of particles. The forward reaction converts two molecules into one molecule. Thus a shift right reduces the total number of particles and the pressure of the system.

3. Determine the effect of compression on the concentrations of the substances in the system. The situation regarding concentration is illustrated below:

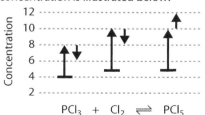

In this diagram, all the original concentrations are doubled by the compression so the volume must have been halved.

How to Do It

The system must <u>shift right</u> to reduce the pressure.

The number of PCl_5 molecules will increase, while the number of PCl_3 and Cl_2 molecules will decrease.

Because the system was compressed, every substance has a higher concentration or partial pressure at the new equilibrium than it did at the initial equilibrium.

(Although the shift can't reduce all the chemicals' concentrations or partial pressures, it is reducing most of them (2/3) by shifting to the right. The result is that some of the added pressure is relieved.)

Sample Problem 5.5.1(b) — Predicting How an Equilibrium Will Respond to an Increase in Volume

The system below is diluted. In what direction will the system shift to restore equilibrium? When equilibrium is restored, how will the number of each type of particle and the concentration of each species compare to those before the system was diluted?

$$H^+(aq) + NO_2^-(aq) \rightleftharpoons HNO_2(aq)$$

What to Think About

1. Recall that Le Châtelier's principle says that equilibrium will be restored by replacing *some* of the lost osmotic pressure.

2. Consider the effect the stress has on the system to determine the number of each type of molecule. Only the system's response to the stress, not the stress itself, changes the number of particles. The reverse reaction converts one particle into two particles thus a shift left increases the total number of particles and the osmotic pressure of the system.

3. Determine the effect of dilution on the concentrations of the substances in the system. The situation regarding concentration is illustrated below:

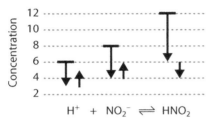

In this diagram, all the original concentrations are halved by the dilution so the volume must have been doubled.

How to Do It

The system must <u>shift left</u> to increase the pressure.

The number of HNO_2 molecules will decrease while the number of H^+ and NO_2^- ions will increase.

Because the system was diluted, every substance has a lower concentration at the new equilibrium than it did at the initial equilibrium.

Practice Problems 5.5.1 — Predicting How an Equilibrium Will Respond to a Volume Change

1. The system below is compressed:

   $$2\,NOCl(g) \rightleftharpoons 2\,NO(g) + Cl_2(g)$$

   In what direction will the system shift to restore equilibrium? When equilibrium is restored, how will the number of each type of molecule and the concentration of each substance compare to those before the system was compressed?

2. The system below is diluted:

   $$Ag(S_2O_3)_2^{3-}(aq) \rightleftharpoons Ag^+(aq) + 2\,S_2O_3^{2-}(aq)$$

   In what direction will the system shift to restore equilibrium? When equilibrium is restored, how will the number of each type of particle and the concentration of each species compare to those before the system was diluted?

Continued opposite

Practice Problems 5.5.1 — *Continued*

3. The volume of the system below is decreased:

$$CO_2(g) + H_2(g) \rightleftharpoons CO(g) + H_2O(g)$$

Will the equilibrium system respond? Explain.

The Shift Mechanism: The Effect of Volume Change on Forward and/or Reverse Reaction Rates

For an explanation of what causes this shift, we must once again turn to chemical kinetics. When the volume of an equilibrium system changes, all the reactant and product concentrations change proportionately. Nevertheless, the forward and reverse reaction rates may change by different amounts. In doing so, they become unequal. From Le Châtelier's predictions, we can infer the following:

> The direction (forward or reverse) that has the greater sum of gaseous or aqueous reactant coefficients is the more sensitive of the two directions to volume changes.

By "more sensitive," we mean that a volume change will decrease or increase the rate of that direction more than that of the opposite direction. At equilibrium, the relationship between concentration and the reaction rate depends only on the coefficients in the balanced equation. For example, consider the following system:

$$Fe^{3+}(aq) + SCN^-(aq) \rightleftharpoons FeSCN^{2+}(aq)$$

Diluting this aqueous system decreases its forward rate more than its reverse rate because the sum of the reactant coefficients for the forward reaction is 2 whereas the lone reactant coefficient for the reverse reaction is only 1. If the sum of gaseous or aqueous reactant coefficients equals the sum of the gaseous or aqueous product coefficients then the equilibrium is not stressed by volume changes. This is because any volume change will have the same effect on the forward and reverse rates. For example, consider the following system:

$$H_2(g) + F_2(g) \rightleftharpoons 2\,HF(g)$$

Compressing this gaseous system increases its forward and reverse rates equally and therefore does not disrupt the equilibrium.

The only external factors that affect reaction rates are the reactant concentrations and temperature. A pressure change only stresses an equilibrium if the pressure change reflects a change in the reactant and product concentrations. The pressure of an equilibrium system can be changed without changing its concentrations by, for example, adding an inert gas to the system. Since this pressure change does not reflect any change of reactant or product concentrations, it does not affect the equilibrium.

Sample Problem 5.5.2(a) — Describing the Shift Mechanism for a Decrease in Volume

Explain in terms of forward and reverse reaction rates how the equilibrium system below would respond to a decrease in volume.

$$2 SO_2(g) + O_2(g) \rightleftharpoons 2 SO_3(g)$$

What to Think About	How to Do It
1. Determine the immediate effect of the stress on the forward and/or reverse reaction rates.	Compressing the system increases the forward rate (r_f) more than the reverse rate (r_r).
2. Decide if this would result in a net forward or net reverse reaction.	This results in a net forward reaction, also known as a shift right.

The arrow diagram on the right illustrates the rates at the initial equilibrium, at the time of the stress, and when equilibrium is restored.

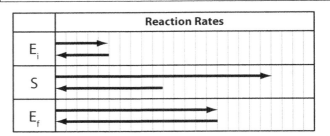

Sample Problem 5.5.2(b) — Describing the Shift Mechanism for a Volume Change

Explain in terms of forward and reverse reaction rates how the equilibrium system below would respond to being diluted.

$$H^+(aq) + SO_4{}^{2-}(aq) \rightleftharpoons HSO_4{}^-(aq)$$

What to Think About	How to Do It
1. Determine the immediate effect of the stress on the forward and/or reverse reaction rates.	Diluting the system decreases the forward rate (r_f) more than the reverse rate (r_r).
2. Decide if this would result in a net forward or net reverse reaction.	This results in a net reverse reaction, also known as a shift left.

The arrow diagram on the right illustrates the rates at the initial equilibrium, at the time of the stress, and when equilibrium is restored.

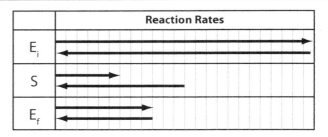

Practice Problems 5.5.2 — Describing the Shift Mechanism for Changes in Volume

1. Explain in terms of forward and reverse reaction rates how the equilibrium system below would respond to a decrease in volume.

$$2\,NOCl(g) \rightleftharpoons 2\,NO(g) + Cl_2(g)$$

2. Explain in terms of forward and reverse reaction rates how the equilibrium system below would respond to being diluted.

$$Ag(S_2O_3)_2{}^{3-}(aq) \rightleftharpoons Ag^+(aq) + 2\,S_2O_3{}^{2-}(aq)$$

3. Show how the forward and reverse reaction rates respond to a sudden compression of the system at t_1. Use a solid line for the forward rate and a dotted line for the reverse rate. The system restores equilibrium at t_2. The arrow diagram on the right is another way of depicting the same information. You may use it to do your rough work.

$$2\,SO_2(g) + O_2(g) \rightleftharpoons 2\,SO_3(g)$$

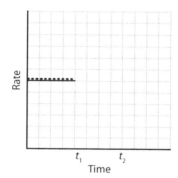
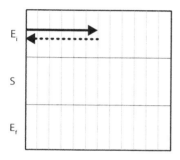

How Equilibria Respond to Temperature Changes

Le Châtelier's principle states the following:

> Equilibria respond to changing temperatures by shifting to remove some of the added kinetic energy or to replace some of the removed kinetic energy.

Sample Problem 5.5.3(a) — Predicting How an Equilibrium Will Respond to an Increase in Temperature

The system below is heated. In what direction will the system shift to restore equilibrium? When equilibrium is restored, how will the concentration of each species compare to its concentration before the system was heated?

$$N_2(g) + O_2(g) \rightleftharpoons 2\,NO(g) \qquad \Delta H = 181 \text{ kJ/mol}$$

What to Think About	How to Do It
1. Recall that Le Châtelier's principle says the system will shift to remove *some* of the added kinetic energy and cool itself.	The system must <u>shift right</u> (in the endothermic direction) to convert some of the added KE into PE.
2. Determine the effect of heating on the concentrations of the substances in the system. Note that 2 NO molecules are formed for each N₂ and O₂ molecule that react.	The [N₂] and [O₂] will decrease and the [NO] will increase.

Note that ΔH can be included as part of a thermochemical equation:

$$N_2(g) + O_2(g) + 181 \text{ kJ} \rightleftharpoons 2 NO(g)$$

In that case, the kinetic energy can be treated just as though it were a chemical. Adding O_2 would cause a shift to the right to remove some of the added O_2. Likewise, adding kinetic energy causes a shift to the right to remove some of the added kinetic energy.

Sample Problem 5.5.3(b) — Predicting How an Equilibrium Will Respond to a Decrease in Temperature

The system below is cooled. In what direction will the system shift to restore equilibrium? When equilibrium is restored, how will the concentration of each species compare to its concentration before the system was cooled?

$$N_2(g) + O_2(g) \rightleftharpoons 2 NO(g) \qquad \Delta H = 181 \text{ kJ/mol}$$

What to Think About	How to Do It
1. Recall that Le Châtelier's principle says the system will shift to replace *some* of the lost kinetic energy and warm itself.	The system must <u>shift left</u> (in the exothermic direction) to convert some PE into KE.
2. Determine the effect of cooling on the concentrations of the substances in the system. Note that 2 NO molecules are consumed for each N_2 and O_2 molecule formed.	The [NO] will decrease. The $[N_2]$ and $[O_2]$ will increase.

Practice Problems 5.5.3 — Predicting How an Equilibrium Will Respond to a Temperature Change

1. The system below is heated. In what direction will the system shift to restore equilibrium? When equilibrium is restored, how will the concentration of each species compare to its concentration before the system was heated?

$$2 SO_2(g) + O_2(g) \rightleftharpoons 2 SO_3(g) \qquad \Delta H = -198 \text{ kJ/mol}$$

2. The system below is cooled. In what direction will the system shift to restore equilibrium? When equilibrium is restored, how will the concentration of each species compare to its concentration before the system was cooled?

$$H_2(g) + I_2(g) \rightleftharpoons 2 HI(g) + 17 \text{ kJ/mol}$$

Effects of Volume and Temperature Changes

Figure 5.5.1 depicts the situation described in Sample Problem 5.5.3(b) above. When the stress is a sudden concentration or volume change it appears as a spike(s) on plots of concentrations versus time. Temperature changes do not appear on these plots so the system responds to an invisible stress. Another difference is that concentration changes, both individual and those resulting from volume changes, can be very sudden. However, the temperature of a system, particularly an aqueous system, cannot change rapidly. This means that chemical systems begin responding while the temperature is still changing. In other words, the response begins before the stress is complete.

Neither volume nor temperature change itself changes the percent yield so a system's response to these stresses shifts its equilibrium position in the same direction that the system shifted in response to the stress.

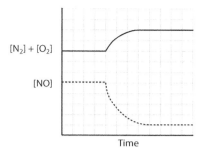

Figure 5.5.1 *Changes in concentration show up in the graph but the temperature change doesn't.*

Pressure-Temperature Relationships

Increasing the temperature of gases in a closed container increases their pressure. The temperature change itself affects the equilibrium. However, the resulting pressure change is irrelevant to the equilibrium because it does not reflect a change of concentrations. The same cannot be said for the reverse. Some of the kinetic energy of gas particles transforms into potential energy as the particles speed up, escaping their mutual attractions and spreading apart.

When a gas is compressed, its temperature rises because some of the particles' potential energy converts to kinetic energy as the particles are forced closer together. The temperature change resulting from compressing or decompressing a gas mixture does affect its equilibrium. In questions where a gaseous equilibrium is compressed or decompressed, assume that its temperature was held constant unless otherwise stated. Such a stipulation allows you to deal with only one variable at a time.

The Shift Mechanism: The Effect of Temperature Change on Forward and Reverse Reaction Rates

If the collision geometry requirements are the same for the forward and reverse reactions, then their rates depend solely on the frequency of collisions possessing the activation energy. The forward and reverse reaction rates are equal at equilibrium. Therefore the frequency of collisions possessing the activation energy must be the same for the forward and reverse reactions. The percentage of the area under a collision energy distribution curve that is at or beyond the activation energy (E_a) represents the percentage of collisions having enough energy to react.

For an endothermic reaction, like that represented in Figures 5.5.2 and 5.5.3, the forward reaction has a lower percentage of collisions with the activation energy needed than the reverse reaction does. The forward reaction must therefore have a greater frequency of collisions to achieve the same frequency of successful collisions as the reverse reaction. For example, 4% of the forward reaction's 800 collisions per second and 20% of the reverse reaction's 160 collisions per second would both equal 32 successful collisions per second. For an endothermic reaction, a higher concentration of reactants is therefore required to generate the same rate as a lower concentration of products because a lower percentage of the reactant collisions are successful.

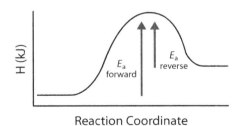

Figure 5.5.2 *Potential energy diagram.*

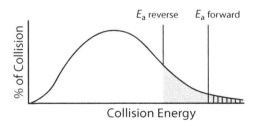

Figure 5.5.3 *Collision energy diagram*

Increases in temperature cause a shift in the endothermic direction because they increase the rate of the endothermic direction more than they increase the rate of the exothermic direction. The endothermic direction has the harder task due to its higher activation energy so it benefits more from the assistance provided by the increased temperature. Likewise, decreases in temperature cause a shift in the exothermic direction because they decrease the rate of the endothermic direction more than they decrease the rate of the exothermic direction. The endothermic direction is hindered more than the exothermic direction by the decreased temperature.

An equilibrium's endothermic direction is more sensitive to temperature changes than its exothermic direction due to the endothermic direction's greater activation energy.

Sample Problem 5.5.4(a) — Describing the Shift Mechanism for an Increase in Temperature

Explain in terms of forward and reverse reaction rates how the system below would respond to being heated.

$$N_2(g) + O_2(g) \rightleftharpoons 2 NO(g) \qquad \Delta H = 181 \text{ kJ/mol}$$

What to Think About	How to Do It
1. Determine the immediate effect of the stress on the forward and/or reverse reaction rates.	Heating the system increases the forward rate (r_f) more than the reverse rate (r_v).
2. Decide if this would result in a net forward or net reverse reaction.	This results in a net forward reaction, also known as a shift right.

The arrow diagram on the right illustrates the rates at the initial equilibrium, at the time of the stress, and when equilibrium is restored.

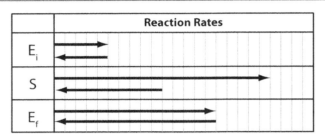

Sample Problem 5.5.4(b) — Describing the Shift Mechanism for a Decrease in Temperature

Explain in terms of forward and reverse reaction rates how the system below would respond to being cooled.

$$N_2(g) + O_2(g) \rightleftharpoons 2 NO(g) \qquad \Delta H = 181 \text{ kJ/mol}$$

What to Think About	How to Do It
1. Determine the immediate effect of the stress on the forward and/or reverse reaction rates?	Cooling the system decreases the forward rate (r_f) more than the reverse rate (r_v).
2. Decide if this would result in a net forward or net reverse reaction.	This results in a net reverse reaction, also known as a shift left.

The arrow diagram on the right illustrates the rates at the initial equilibrium, at the time of the stress, and when equilibrium is restored.

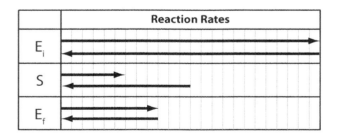

Practice Problems 5.5.4 — Describing the Shift Mechanism for Changes in Temperature

1. Explain in terms of forward and reverse reaction rates how the system below would respond to being heated.

$$2 SO_2(g) + O_2(g) \rightleftharpoons 2 SO_3(g) \qquad \Delta H = -198 \text{ kJ/mol}$$

2. Explain in terms of forward and reverse reaction rates how the system below would respond to being cooled.

$$2 Cl_2(g) + 2 H_2O(g) + 113 \text{ kJ/mol} \rightleftharpoons 4 HCl(g) + O_2(g)$$

3. Show how the forward and reverse reaction rates in the system below would respond to a temperature increase at t_1. Use a solid line for the forward rate and a dotted line for the reverse rate. The system restores equilibrium at t_2. The arrow diagram on the right is another way of depicting the same information. You may use it to do your rough work.

$$2 NCl_3(g) \rightleftharpoons N_2(g) + 3 Cl_2(g) \qquad \Delta H = -460 \text{ kJ/mol}$$

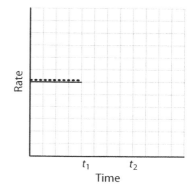
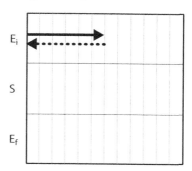

The Haber-Bosch Process

Almost all of the world's ammonia is produced via the Haber-Bosch process and almost all of our inorganic nitrogen compounds are produced from this ammonia. More than 100 million tonnes of ammonia with a value in excess of $600 million are produced annually. About 80% of the world's ammonia is used to produce fertilizers. Other products include explosives, plastics, fibres, and dyes.

German chemist Fritz Haber developed the equipment and procedures for producing ammonia (NH_3) from its constituent elements (N_2 and H_2) in 1910. In 1918, he received the Nobel Prize in chemistry for this accomplishment. In 1931, another German chemist, Carl Bosch, won the Nobel Prize in chemistry, in part for transforming the process to an industrial scale. The balanced equation and enthalpy for the reaction are:

$$N_2(g) + 3 H_2(g) \rightleftharpoons 2 NH_3(g) \qquad \Delta H = -92.4 \text{ kJ/mol}$$

Process Production Rate and Temperature Considerations

Consider the plight of a chemist who wants to produce NH_3 in his or her laboratory by allowing a single set of reactants to achieve equilibrium within a closed container. The percent yield and the reaction rate both need to be considered in choosing the optimal temperature. Lower temperatures produce higher percent yields of NH_3 at equilibrium since lower temperatures shift this equilibrium toward products. However, at lower temperatures the reaction proceeds at slower rates in both forward and reverse directions. Therefore it takes longer to produce any given amount of product. In other words, a higher temperature generates a faster forward rate but sustains it for a much shorter time period, both because the reaction rate is faster and the percent yield is less. To use a racing analogy, at higher temperatures the reaction runs faster toward a closer finish line (lower % yield).

Reactions proceeding at lower temperatures will eventually produce the amount produced at higher temperatures and then just keep rumbling along. This is the chemical version of the familiar tale of the tortoise versus the hare. Maximum productivity might be achieved by initially establishing equilibrium at a high temperature and then shifting the equilibrium toward products by lowering the temperature. Using a catalyst allows chemists to increase the reaction rate at a lower temperature that produces a higher percent yield.

> For the Haber-Bosch process, lower temperatures produce a higher percent yield but at a lower rate.

The chemical industry does not produce ammonia by allowing single sets of reactants to establish equilibria within closed containers. As the reacting mixture is cycled and recycled through a Haber reactor, N_2 and H_2 are continuously fed in at one location while NH_3 is continuously liquefied and removed at another. The ammonia can be selectively removed because hydrogen bonding between NH_3 molecules causes them to condense at a higher temperature than hydrogen and nitrogen. The temperatures in the reactor are adjusted to maximize the concentration of NH_3, when and where it is extracted. The forward rate is kept high by replacing the consumed reactants while the reverse rate is kept low by removing product. Percent yield ceases to be a consideration if the system doesn't achieve equilibrium.

An industrial chemist must strike a compromise between the increased rate provided by a greater temperature and the increased cost to produce it. The reaction rate is also increased by using a catalyst. The "bottom line" for industry is its annual profit, not its annual production of ammonia. A plant strives to generate the greatest possible amount of ammonia for the lowest possible cost. The industry is obviously influenced by a tremendous number of commercial and economic factors as well as chemical factors.

Process Production Rate and Pressure Considerations

Higher pressures generate faster rates and push the reaction toward a higher percent yield.

According to Le Châtelier's principle, the system partially relieves the increased pressure by shifting right as the forward reaction converts four molecules into two. Compressing the gases also raises their temperature. High compression systems are expensive to build and to operate. Most Haber reactors operate at about 3.5×10^4 kPa. The increased yield at this pressure more than compensates for the higher construction and operation costs.

Quick Check

1. Name the chemical produced by the Haber-Bosch process.

   _____

2. What increases the rate of the Haber-Bosch process without decreasing its percent yield?

   _____

5.5 Activity: Dealing With Pressure

Question

What will a gaseous equilibrium mixture look like at the molecular level as it responds to being compressed?

Background

An equilibrium mixture of colorless dinitrogen tetroxide, $N_2O_4(g)$, and orange nitrogen dioxide, $NO_2(g)$, forms when nitric acid is poured over copper. When this equilibrium mixture is compressed in a plugged syringe, the mixture becomes darker orange as a result of concentrating the NO_2 molecules. Within seconds the mixture's color changes slightly, yet unmistakeably, as the equilibrium shifts in response to the stress.

$$N_2O_4(g) + energy \rightleftharpoons 2\,NO_2(g)$$
colorless   orange

Procedure

1. The three diagrams below represent the tube in a syringe. Complete the third diagram by drawing in a possible number of NO_2 and N_2O_4 molecules after the system has responded to the stress and restored equilibrium.
2. Color in the circle underneath each syringe to indicate how pale or dark orange the gas would appear.

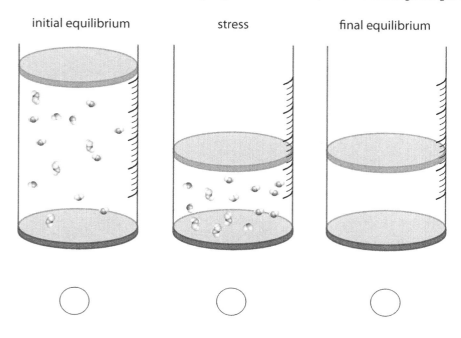

initial equilibrium   stress   final equilibrium

Results and Discussion

1. In response to the compression, the number of NO_2 molecules _____ and the number of N_2O_4 molecules _____.

2. Describe the molecules' behavior when the reaction in the syringe is at equilibrium.

3. How would the color of the equilibrium mixture change when the syringe is plunged into an ice bath? Explain.

5.5 Review Questions

1. Consider the following equilibrium: $Fe^{3+}(aq) + SCN^-(aq) \rightleftharpoons FeSCN^{2+}(aq)$
   (a) In which direction will the system shift if it is diluted? Explain your answer in terms of Le Châtelier's principle.

   (b) Compare the number and the concentration of SCN^- ions when equilibrium is restored to their number and concentration before the system was diluted.

2. Explain *in terms of forward and reverse reaction rates* how this system responds to an increase in volume.
   $$PCl_5(g) \rightleftharpoons PCl_3(g) + Cl_2(g)$$

3. In which direction does the following equilibrium shift when the gas mixture is compressed? Explain using Le Châtelier's principle *and* in terms of forward and reverse reaction rates.
   $$2\,C(s) + O_2(g) \rightleftharpoons 2\,CO(g)$$

4. Describe a situation when equilibrium concentrations change but no stress occurs.

5. Complete the following plots. The system is at equilibrium prior to t_1. At t_1 the volume of the system is suddenly doubled. The system responds to this stress between t_1 and t_2 until it re-equilibrates at t_2.
   $$N_2O_4(g) \rightleftharpoons 2\,NO_2(g)$$

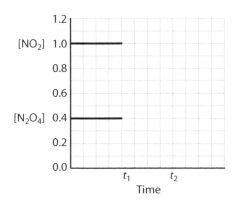

6. Show how the forward and reverse reaction rates respond to a sudden increase in the volume of the system at t_1. Use a solid line for the forward rate and a dotted line for the reverse rate. The system restores equilibrium at t_2. The arrow diagram on the right is another way of depicting the same information. You may use it to do your rough work.

$$N_2O_4(g) \rightleftharpoons 2\,NO_2(g)$$

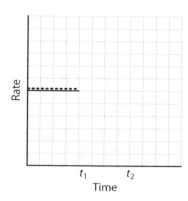
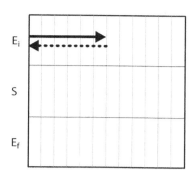

7. The solubility of a substance is its highest possible concentration at a given temperature. Any further solid added to the solution will remain undissolved in equilibrium with the dissolved state. Dissolving sodium sulfate in water is exothermic.

$$Na_2SO_4(s) \rightleftharpoons 2\,Na^+(aq) + SO_4{}^{2-}(aq) + heat$$

State whether sodium sulfate will be less soluble or more soluble when the temperature of the solution is increased. Explain.

8. In which direction will the following equilibrium system shift when it is heated?

$$2\,SO_3(g) + 192\,kJ/mol \rightleftharpoons 2\,SO_2(g) + O_2(g)$$

Provide two ways to arrive at this answer.

9. Complete the following plots. The system below is at equilibrium prior to t_1. The system is suddenly cooled at t_1. The system responds to this stress between t_1 and t_2 until it re-equilibrates at t_2.

$$N_2O_4(g) + 57\,kJ \rightleftharpoons 2\,NO_2(g)$$

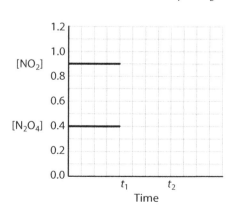

Chapter 5 Chemical Equilibrium

10. Show how the forward and reverse reaction rates respond to a sudden increase in the temperature of the system below at t_1. Use a solid line for the forward rate and a dotted line for the reverse rate. The system restores equilibrium at t_2. The arrow diagram on the right is another way of depicting the same information. You may use it to do your rough work.

$$Ni(s) + 4\,CO(g) \rightleftharpoons Ni(CO)_4(g) \qquad \Delta H = -603\ kJ/mol$$

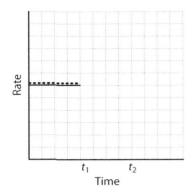 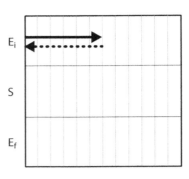

11. $Co(H_2O)_6^{2+}(aq) + 2\,Cl^-(aq) \rightleftharpoons Co(H_2O)_4Cl_2(aq) + 2\,H_2O(l)$
    pink   purple

A flask containing the above equilibrium turns from purple to pink when cooled. State whether the forward reaction is endothermic or exothermic. Explain how you arrived at your answer.

12. $A + B \rightleftharpoons AB + 16.8\ kJ/mol$

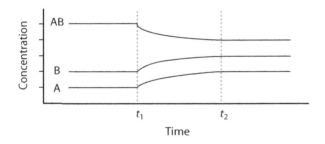

(a) In which direction is the equilibrium system shifting?

(b) What specifically was done to this system at t_1?

13. Explain *in terms of forward and reverse reaction rates* how the equilibrium below responds to a decrease in temperature:

$$N_2(g) + 3\,H_2(g) \rightleftharpoons 2\,NH_3(g) \qquad \Delta H = -92.4 \text{ kJ/mol}$$

14. Why is an equilibrium's endothermic direction more sensitive to temperature changes than its exothermic direction?

15. What conditions of temperature and pressure favor products in the following reaction:

$$PCl_5(g) \rightleftharpoons PCl_3(g) + Cl_2(g) \qquad \Delta H = 238 \text{ kJ/mol}$$

16. Briefly describe the conflicting factors that chemists face when choosing a temperature to perform the Haber-Bosch process.

17. Consider the system below. When equilibrium is restored, how will the number of each type of molecule and the concentration of each substance compare to those before the stress was introduced? Complete the following table using the words "decrease," "same," or "increase."

$$2\,NH_3(g) \rightleftharpoons N_2(g) + 3\,H_2(g) \qquad \Delta H = 92.4 \text{ kJ/mol}$$

		Decrease Volume	Decrease Temperature
Equilibrium concentration	N_2		
	H_2		
	NH_3		
Equilibrium number	N_2		
	H_2		
	NH_3		

18. The graph below shows how forward and reverse reaction rates change as an exothermic reaction goes from initiation to equilibrium. Plot the forward and reverse reaction rates for the same reaction at a higher temperature.

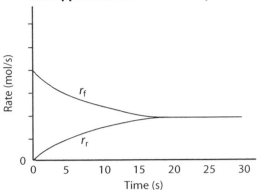

Rate (forward and reverse) vs. Time for a Reaction as It Approaches and Achieves Equilibrium

19. Nitric acid is produced commercially by the Ostwald process. The first step of the Ostwald process is:
$$4\,NH_3(g) + 5\,O_2(g) \rightleftharpoons 4\,NO(g) + 6\,H_2O(g) + energy$$
In which direction will the above system shift in the following situations:

(a) Some NO is added.

(b) Some NH_3 is removed.

(c) The pressure of the system is decreased by increasing the volume.

(d) The temperature of the system is decreased.

20. A piston supported by gas trapped in a cylinder is a fixed pressure apparatus. As long as the gas in the cylinder is supporting the same piston then its pressure must be constant because it is exerting the same force over the same bottom surface of the piston. If the piston weighs more, then the fixed pressure is greater. Consider the following equilibrium system trapped in a cylinder:
$$PCl_5(g) \rightleftharpoons PCl_3(g) + Cl_2(g)$$
(a) In which direction will the system shift when some weight is added to the piston?

(b) How would this shift affect the apparatus?

21. Complete the following review table.

$$N_2(g) + 3 H_2(g) \rightleftharpoons 2 NH_3(g) \qquad \Delta H = -92.4 \text{ kJ/mol}$$

Stress	Le Châtelier Predicts		Chemical Kinetics Explains	
	Response	Shift	Effect	Net Rx
Add H_2	some of the added H_2 removed			
Add NH_3		left		
Remove N_2			r_f decreases	
Decrease volume (compress)				net forward rx
Decrease temperature			r_r decreases more than r_f	

Extension

22. Holding the temperature and pressure constant when a reactant or product is added to an equilibrium system is easier said than done. Some SO_3 is added to the following system. Its temperature and pressure are *not* fixed.

$$2 SO_2(g) + O_2(g) \rightleftharpoons 2 SO_3(g) + 198 \text{ kJ/mol}$$

   (a) In which direction will the system shift in response to the added SO_3?

   (b) In which direction will the system shift in response to the small change in pressure resulting from the added SO_3?

   (c) In which direction will the system shift in response to the small change in temperature resulting from the increased pressure?

   (d) In which direction will the system shift in response to the change in temperature resulting from the system's shift to the added SO_3?

5.6 Pressure, Equilibrium, and Free Energy

Warm Up

In this activity, you will determine if entropy is increased or decreased when you stretch a balloon. Your determination will help you complete the ΔS cells in the table below.

- Stretch a balloon (or a thick rubber band) by pulling and relaxing multiple times.
- Hold the balloon against your upper lip or forehead during a stretch. Keep it in contact with your face while letting the balloon relax slowly.

1. What do you feel when the balloon is stretched? When it is relaxed?

   _____

2. Complete the ΔH portion of the data table below using + or − signs.

	ΔH	ΔG	ΔS	Representation
Stretched				
Relaxed				

3. Does the balloon stretch or relax *spontaneously*? Stretch the balloon and let go of the both ends simultaneously to find out.

   _____

4. Complete the ΔG portion of the table.

5. What MUST the sign of ΔS be? Indicate in the table above.

6. Is the relaxation of the balloon *enthalpy* or *entropy driven*?

   _____

7. Draw a molecular representation to show how the chains of molecules must align themselves when you stretch the balloon and when you relax it.

8. Do the sign of ΔS and the drawings of chain alignment representation portions of your table agree? Why or why not?

   _____

   _____

Dependence of Free Energy on Pressure

The entropy of 1 mole of a gas in a 20.0 L container is larger than the entropy of 1 mole of the same gas in a 10.0 L container. There are more microstates for the gas or ways for the molecules of the gas to arrange themselves in the space in a larger volume. If the entropy of a gas depends on the volume and consequently the pressure, then the free energy of the gas must also depend on these two factors. Experimentally, it can be seen that:

$$G = G° + RT \ln P$$

where $G°$ is the free energy of a gas sample at 1 atm pressure, and G is the free energy of the gas at some pressure P. R is 8.314 J/mol·K, and T is the temperature in Kelvin degrees.

How does the free energy change for a reaction depend upon pressure?

Methane "burns" in oxygen to form carbon dioxide and water:

$$CH_4(g) + 2\,O_2(g) \rightleftharpoons CO_2(g) + 2\,H_2O(g)$$

For this reaction:

$$\Delta G = G_{CO_2} + 2\,G_{H_2O} - G_{CH_4} - 2\,G_{O_2} \text{ (under non-standard conditions)}$$

If we use $G = G° + RT \ln P$ for each component:

$$\Delta G = (G°_{CO_2} + RT \ln P_{CO_2}) + 2(G°_{H_2O} + RT \ln P_{H_2O}) - (G°_{CH_4} + RT \ln P_{CH_4})$$

$$- 2(G°_{O_2} + RT \ln P_{O_2})$$

Collecting all the $G°$ terms and all the $RT \ln P$ terms:

$$\Delta G = G°_{CO_2} + 2\,G°_{H_2O} - G°_{CH_4} - 2\,G°_{O_2} + RT\,(\ln P_{CO_2} + 2 \ln P_{H_2O} - \ln P_{CH_4} - 2 \ln P_{O_2})$$

Since $\Delta G° = G°_{CO_2} + 2\,G°_{H_2O} - G°_{CH_4} - 2\,G°_{O_2}$ and $2 \ln x = \ln x^2$

We have $\Delta G = \Delta G° + RT\,(\ln P_{CO_2} + \ln P^2_{H_2O} - \ln P_{CH_4} - \ln P^2_{O_2})$

Applying log rules: $\ln a + \ln b = \ln (a \cdot b)$ and $\ln c - \ln d = \ln (c/d)$,

we end up with $\Delta G = G° + RT \ln \left[\dfrac{\left(P_{CO_2}\right)\left(P^2_{H_2O}\right)}{\left(P_{CH_4}\right)\left(P^2_{O_2}\right)} \right]$

The expression in square brackets is the reaction quotient Q from section 5.2.

You do not need to be able to derive this equation. We provide the mathematical justification for those who want to understand how the reaction quotient appears in the equation when we consider a change in the Gibbs free energy of a reaction. For any reaction *with species present at non-standard pressures*:

$$\Delta G = \Delta G° + RT \ln Q$$

You can calculate $\Delta G°$ for a reaction from reference values of free energies of formation of reactants and products as in chapter 3. Using $\Delta G°$ and Q, you can determine ΔG.

The sign of ΔG allows you to predict whether the reaction will proceed spontaneously forward (– sign) or reverse (+ sign) to reach equilibrium. If a reaction mixture is at equilibrium ΔG will be 0.

Sample Problem 5.6.1 — Calculation and Use of ΔG

Consider the reaction:

$$2 NO_2(g) \rightleftharpoons N_2O_4(g) \qquad\qquad \Delta G° = -5.39 \text{ kJ/mol}_{rxn} \text{ at } 25°C$$

A mixture contains NO_2 with a partial pressure of 0.10 atm and N_2O_4 with a partial pressure of 0.20 atm. Use ΔG to determine whether the gas mixture is at equilibrium. If it is not, in which direction will the reaction proceed?

What to Think About	How to Do It
1. The pressures are not 1 atm and the question asks for the value of ΔG as opposed to $\Delta G°$, so the equation required is: $$\Delta G = \Delta G° + RT \ln Q$$	Determine the reaction quotient Q by placing the partial pressure of the product over the partial pressure of the reactant and raising the pressure of each species to the power of its coefficient: $$Q = \frac{P_{N_2O_4}}{P^2_{NO_2}} = \frac{0.20 \text{ atm}}{(0.10 \text{ atm})^2} = 20$$
2. The temperature must be expressed in Kelvin degrees.	$$25°C \times \frac{1 \text{ K}}{1°C} + 273 \text{ K} = 298 \text{ K}$$
3. The value of the gas constant must have units of energy. Recall: $$\frac{0.08206 \text{ L·atm}}{\text{mol·K}} \times \frac{101.3 \text{ J}}{\text{L·atm}} = 8.31 \frac{\text{J}}{\text{mol·K}}$$ (or more precisely 8.314)	If K were given in the question, a comparison of Q to K would predict the reaction's preferred direction. However, K is not given, hence
4. Be sure the $G°$ and R units are *the same* (both kJ or both J).	$$\Delta G = \Delta G° + RT \ln Q$$ $$= -5.39 \frac{\text{kJ}}{\text{mol}_{rxn}} + \left(0.008314 \frac{\text{kJ}}{\text{mol·K}} \times 298 \text{ K} \times \ln(20.) \right)$$ $$= -5.39 \text{ kJ/mol}_{rxn} + 7.42 \text{ kJ/mol}$$ $$= 2.03 \text{ kJ/mol}_{rxn} \text{ or } 2.0 \text{ kJ/mol}_{rxn}$$ A non-zero ΔG value indicates the system is not at equilibrium.
5. Be sure to carry the correct signs through the entire calculation.	The system is NOT at equilibrium. Because the sign of ΔG is **positive**, the reaction will proceed in the reverse direction (to the LEFT) to reach equilibrium.

Practice Problems 5.6.1 — Calculation and Use of ΔG

1. What is the value for Gibbs free energy in the production of ammonia from nitrogen and hydrogen:
    $N_2(g) + 3\,H_2(g) \rightleftharpoons 2\,NH_3(g)$, if the pressure of all three gases is 2.00 atm and the temperature is 23°C?
    Begin by determining $\Delta G°$ for this reaction using the reference values from Table A8 in the appendix.

2. $\Delta G°$ for the reaction $H_2(g) + I_2(g) \rightleftharpoons 2\,HI(g)$ is 2.60 kJ/mol$_{rxn}$ at 25°C. Calculate ΔG and predict the direction in which the
    reaction proceeds spontaneously if the initial pressures are 7.0 atm, 3.0 atm, and 3.50 atm for H_2, I_2, and HI respectively.

3. Methanol, a common gasoline additive is also present as a component in windshield washer solution. A common method for
    synthesis of this alcohol is to react carbon monoxide with hydrogen gas:

    $$CO(g) + 2\,H_2(g) \rightleftharpoons CH_3OH(l)$$

    Calculate ΔG for this reaction at 25°C when 2.5 atm of carbon monoxide and 1.5 atm of hydrogen gases react to form liquid
    methanol. Begin by determining $\Delta G°$ for this reaction using the reference values from Table A8 in the appendix.

**Free Energy and the
Equilibrium Constant**

The relationship between the reaction quotient and free energy is:

$$\Delta G = \Delta G° + RT \ln Q$$

At equilibrium, $\Delta G = 0$. The reaction mixture has reached a minimum free energy. Also at
equilibrium, $Q = K_{eq}$, so the reaction quotient is equal to the equilibrium constant.

Then, at equilibrium, $\Delta G = \Delta G° + RT \ln Q$

becomes $\qquad\qquad 0 = \Delta G° + RT \ln K$

Thus, $\qquad\qquad\qquad\qquad\qquad$ **$\Delta G° = -RT \ln K$**

With this expression, we can use the reference values of $\Delta G°_f$ to calculate $\Delta G°$ for a reaction and then calculate K.

Note 1: Some references prefer to deal with logs to the base 10, rather than natural logs to the base e. In that case, since $2.303 \log x = \ln x$, the above expression becomes:

$$\Delta G° = -2.303 \, RT \log K$$

Note 2: Usually the change in Gibbs free energy at equilibrium is calculated from the partial pressures of the reagents in a reaction such as the oxidation of methane gas, so the equilibrium constant is actually K_p. However, occasionally the change in Gibbs free energy at equilibrium may refer to K_c in situations such as low solubility salt equilibria (K_{sp}) or weak acids (K_a).

Using $\Delta G°$ and K to Predict Reaction Direction

There are three possible situations when calculating the change in Gibbs free energy at equilibrium:

1. If $\Delta G°$ is negative, $\ln K$ must be positive. This means that K is greater than 1 and the reaction proceeds spontaneously (is thermodynamically favorable) in the forward direction.
2. If $\Delta G°$ is positive, $\ln K$ must be negative. This means that K is less than 1 and the reverse reaction is spontaneous.
3. If $\Delta G° = 0$, $\ln K = 1$. The reaction is at equilibrium.

If $\Delta G°$ is a large negative number, K will be much greater than one. This means that the forward reaction will go virtually to completion. Conversely, if $\Delta G°$ is a large positive number, K will be a tiny fraction, much less than 1, and the reverse reaction will go nearly to completion. Table 5.6.1 summarizes these relationships.

Table 5.6.1 $\Delta G°$, K, and Reaction Direction

$\Delta G°$ negative	$K > 1$	spontaneous reaction
$\Delta G° = $ zero	$K = 1$	at equilibrium
$\Delta G°$ positive	$K < 1$	reverse reaction is spontaneous
$\Delta G° <<< 0$	K very BIG	spontaneous to near completion
$\Delta G° >>> 0$	K nearly 0	reverse reaction to near completion

---

Sample Problem 5.6.2(a) — Calculating $\Delta G°$ from K Values

The equilibrium constant K for the reaction $PCl_3(g) + Cl_2(g) \rightleftharpoons PCl_5(g)$ is 24.0 at 250.°C. Calculate $\Delta G°$. Is the reaction spontaneous in the forward or reverse direction?

What to Think About	How to Do It
1. Convert the temperature to Kelvin degrees.	$250.°C \times \dfrac{1 \text{ K}}{1°C} + 273 \text{ K} = 523 \text{ K}$
2. Use the equation $\Delta G° = -RT \ln K$ to calculate $\Delta G°$.	$\Delta G° = -RT \ln K$ $= -8.314 \dfrac{J}{mol \cdot K} \times 523 \text{ K} \times \ln (24.0)$
3. It is critical to use the appropriate R value and to carry the negative sign that precedes the equation through each step in the equation.	$= -13\,800 \text{ J/mol}_{rxn}$ $= -13.8 \text{ kJ/mol}_{rxn}$
4. If $K > 1$, $\Delta G°$ must be *negative*.	The forward reaction is spontaneous.

Sample Problem 5.6.2(b) — Conversion of ΔG° to K

Phosphorus pentachloride decomposes as follows: $PCl_5(g) \rightleftharpoons PCl_3(g) + Cl_2(g)$.
$\Delta G° = 26.5$ kJ/mol$_{rxn}$ at 227°C. Calculate the equilibrium constant, K. Does the reaction favor products or reactants under these conditions?

What to Think About	How to Do It
1. Convert the temperature to Kelvin degrees.	$227°C \times \dfrac{1\,K}{1°C} + 273\,K = 500.\,K$
2. As ΔG° and K are in the question, use the equation $\Delta G° = -RT \ln K$.	$\Delta G° = -RT \ln K$ so $\ln K = \dfrac{-\Delta G°}{RT}$
3. It is critical to use the appropriate R value and to carry the *negative sign* that precedes the equation throughout the calculations.	hence, $K = e^{\frac{\Delta G°}{-RT}}$ where $\dfrac{\Delta G°}{-RT} = \dfrac{26.5\ kJ/mol_{rxn}}{-0.008314\ \frac{kJ}{mol\cdot K} \times 500.\,K} = -6.37$
4. Make sure the energy units for ΔG° and R agree.	Thus $K = e^{-6.37} = 1.70 \times 10^{-3}$

Practice Problems 5.6.2 — Conversions of ΔG° to K and K to ΔG°

1. The pollutant gas nitrogen monoxide forms from nitrogen and oxygen gas according to the following equation:
   $N_2(g) + O_2(g) \rightleftharpoons 2\,NO(g)$. K is only 8.44×10^{-3} at 2500°C. Calculate ΔG°. Is the reaction spontaneous in the forward or the reverse direction?

2. (a) Calculate K for a reaction at 25°C that has a ΔG° value of −35.0 kJ/mol$_{rxn}$.

   (b) Repeat the calculation at the same temperature for a reaction with ΔG° equal to +35.0 kJ/mol$_{rxn}$.

   (c) Compare the K values and what they mean for these two reactions.

Variations in Total Free Energy for Reversible Reactions

In an *exergonic* reaction (one in which $\Delta G°$ *is negative*) the products (point 2 in Figure 5.6.1(a)) have less free energy and are more stable than the reactants (point 1 in Figure 5.6.1(a)). The difference between these two points (2 – 1) is $\Delta G°$. All points between 1 and 2 correspond to various mixtures of the reactants and products present as the reaction proceeds. The difference between point 1 (in the forward direction) or point 2 (in the reverse direction) and any point on the curve is ΔG. The mixture of reactants and products present at the *minimum* of the curve (point 3) has the *least free energy* and is the *most stable* of all. This represents the *equilibrium mixture*.

At any point on the curve, a comparison of the *reaction quotient Q* to the *equilibrium constant K* indicates the *direction* in which the reaction must proceed *to reach equilibrium*. This will always be the direction that is *downhill* in a free energy diagram! For an exergonic reaction, because $\Delta G°$ *is negative,* K *must be* > 1 so the *equilibrium mixture will always contain more products than reactants.*

In an *endergonic* reaction (one in which $\Delta G°$ *is positive*) the products (point 2 in Figure 5.6.1(b)) will have more free energy than the reactants (point 1 in Figure 5.6.1(b)). In this case, $K < 1$ and the standard reaction is *reactant favored*, resulting in an equilibrium mixture containing more reactants than products.

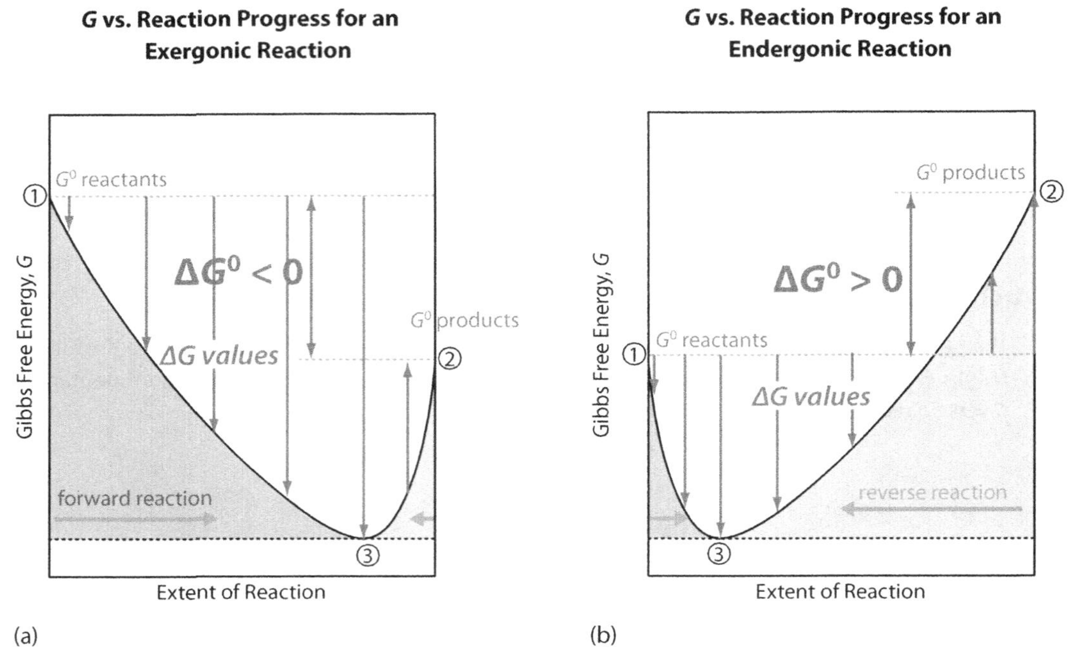

G vs. Reaction Progress for an Exergonic Reaction

G vs. Reaction Progress for an Endergonic Reaction

(a)

(b)

Figure 5.6.1 *Free energy changes during the course of an exergonic and an endergonic reaction at constant temperature.*

5.6 Review Questions

1. Calculate $\Delta G°$ for the conversion of oxygen to ozone:
   $3 O_2(g) \rightleftharpoons 2 O_3(g)$ at 25°C given that $K = 2.50 \times 10^{-29}$

2. Consider the reaction: $MgCO_3(s) \rightleftharpoons MgO(s) + CO_2(g)$
   (a) Is the forward reaction spontaneous at room temperature (25°C)? Give a mathematical justification.

   (b) Is the reaction driven by enthalpy, entropy, both, or neither? Give a mathematical justification.

   (c) What is the value of K at 25°C?

   (d) At what temperature does the direction of the spontaneous reaction change?

   (e) Does high temperature make the reaction more or less spontaneous in the forward direction? Include a full explanation.

3. Methane, $CH_4(g)$, is the main component of natural gas. When the barrel of a Bunsen burner is wide open, more oxygen ($O_2(g)$) is available for the combustion of the methane. The products are entirely $CO_2(g)$ and $H_2O(g)$. When the barrel is nearly closed, the products are $CO_2(g)$ and some $H_2O(l)$.

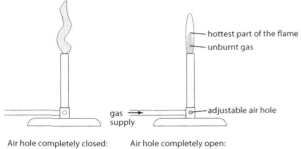

hottest part of the flame
unburnt gas

gas supply

adjustable air hole

Air hole completely closed:
luminous flame

Air hole completely open:
non-luminous roaring flame

(a) Calculate $\Delta G°$ at 25°C for each reaction.

(b) Calculate K for each reaction.

(c) Which burner adjustment gives a hotter flame?

(d) Why does opening the barrel on the burner force a more complete combustion?

4. Use the reference values for $\Delta H_f°$ and $S°$ from Table A8 in the appendix to calculate $\Delta H°$, $\Delta S°$, and $\Delta G°$ for the reaction:

$CO(g) + H_2O(g) \rightleftharpoons CO_2(g) + H_2(g)$ at 25°C.

(a) $\Delta H°$ (Show all work completely.)

(b) $\Delta S°$ (Show all work completely.)

(c) $\Delta G°$ (Use the Gibbs-Helmholtz equation with a temperature of 25°C.)

(d) Calculate the equilibrium constant K for this reaction at 25°C.

(e) Calculate the equilibrium constant K for this reaction at 225°C.

(f) Using your answers to parts (d) and (e), determine whether this reaction is exo- or endothermic? Justify your answer. Does this response agree with the answer to part (a)?

5. Consider what each of the following graphs represent.

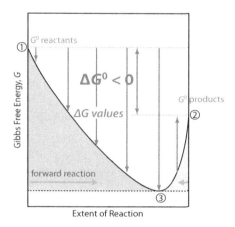

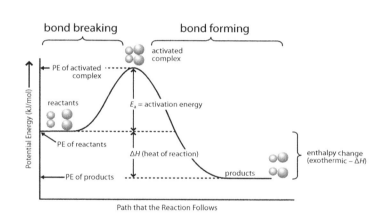

(a) How are the graphs similar? Be specific.

(b) How are the graphs different? Be specific.

6. Consider the following representations of a physical and a chemical change. Answer each question for A and B.

A. A physical change

B. A chemical change

(a) What is the sign of $\Delta H°$?

(b) What is the sign of $\Delta S°$?

(c) How does the sign of $\Delta G°$ vary with temperature?

7. Consider the following reaction:

$N_2O_4(g) \rightleftharpoons 2 NO_2(g)$

(a) Calculate $\Delta G°$.

(b) Examine the following molecular representation. Assume each molecule exerts a partial pressure of 0.010 atm at 25°C. Calculate ΔG.

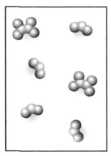

(c) In general, how would the representation change if the system were to achieve equilibrium?

8. Consider the following reaction at 25°C.

$$2\,NO(g) + O_2(g) \rightleftharpoons 2\,NO_2(g) \quad \Delta G° = -71.2 \text{ kJ/mol}_{rxn}$$

(a) Calculate ΔG under the following conditions:

$P_{NO} = 0.0500$ atm $\quad P_{O_2} = 0.0500$ atm $\quad P_{NO_2} = 0.100$ atm

(b) Is the reaction more or less spontaneous under these pressure conditions?

9. (a) Calculate ΔG at 298 K for the reaction $2\,ICl(g) \rightleftharpoons I_2(g) + Cl_2(g)$ in a mixture containing the following partial pressures:

$P_{ICl} = 2.0$ atm $\quad P_{I_2} = 0.0020$ atm $\quad P_{Cl_2} = 0.0020$ atm

(Remember: I_2 is normally a solid under standard conditions.)

(b) Is this reaction more or less spontaneous under these conditions than under standard conditions?

10. At 25°C, acetic acid, CH_3COOH, ionizes in water to form hydrogen and acetate ions. The acid is quite weak and has a small equilibrium constant, K_a, of 1.8×10^{-5}. $CH_3COOH(aq) \rightleftharpoons H^+(aq) + CH_3COO^-(aq)$

(a) Calculate $\Delta G°$ for the ionization of acetic acid.

(b) Calculate ΔG for the reaction if $[CH_3COOH] = 0.10$ mol/L, $[H^+] = 9.5 \times 10^{-5}$ mol/L, and $[CH_3COO^-] = 9.5 \times 10^{-5}$ mol/L.

(c) Compare the spontaneity of ionization under the conditions in part (b) to those under standard conditions.

6 Acid-Base Equilibrium

This chapter focuses on the following AP Big Ideas from the College Board:

- Big Idea 3: Changes in matter involve the rearrangement and/or reorganization of atoms and/or the transfer of electrons.
- Big Idea 6: Any bond or intermolecular attraction that can be formed can be broken. These two processes are in a dynamic competition, sensitive to initial conditions and external perturbations.

By the end of this chapter, you should be able to do the following:

- Identify acids and bases through experimentation
- Identify various models for representing acids and bases
- Analyze balanced equations representing the reaction of acids or bases with water
- Classify an acid or base in solution as either weak or strong, with reference to its electrical conductivity
- Analyze the equilibria that exist in weak acid or weak base systems
- Identify chemical species that are amphiprotic
- Analyze the equilibrium that exists in water
- Perform calculations relating pH, pOH, $[H_3O^+]$, and $[OH^-]$
- Explain the significance of the K_a and K_b equilibrium expressions
- Perform calculations involving K_a and K_b

By the end of this chapter, you should know the meaning of these **key terms**:

- acid
- acid ionization constant (K_a)
- amphiprotic
- Arrhenius
- base
- base ionization constant (K_b)
- Brønsted-Lowry
- conjugate acid-base pair
- electrical conductivity
- ion product constant
- mass action expression
- pH
- pK_w
- pOH
- polarized
- strong acid
- strong base
- water ionization constant (K_w)
- weak acid
- weak base

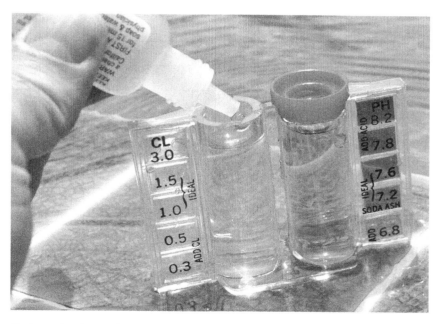

Testing swimming pool water involves acid-base interactions.

6.1 pH and pOH Review Questions

(Assume all solutions are at 25°C unless otherwise indicated.)

1. Define pH and pOH using a statement and an equation for each.

2. Why do we use Sorensen's pH and pOH scales to express hydronium and hydroxide concentrations in aqueous solutions?

3. Complete the following table, expressing each value to the proper number of significant figures.

$[H_3O^+]$	pH	Acidic/Basic/Neutral
3.50×10^{-6} M		
	11.51	
0.00550 M		
	0.00	
6.8×10^{-9} M		

4. Complete the following table, expressing each value to the proper number of significant figures.

$[OH^-]$	pOH	Acidic/Basic/Neutral
7.2×10^{-9} M		
	9.55	
4.88×10^{-4} M		
	14.00	
0.000625 M		

5. Complete the following statements:
   (a) As a solution's pOH value and $[H_3O^+]$ both decrease, the solution becomes more _____ (acidic or basic).

   (b) As a solution's pH value and $[OH^-]$ both decrease, the solution becomes more _____ (acidic or basic)

   (c) The _____ (sum or product) of the $[H_3O^+]$ and $[OH^-]$ equals K_w.

   (d) The _____ (sum or product) of pH and pOH equals pK_w.

6. Complete the following table, expressing each value to the proper number of significant figures.

$[H_3O^+]$	pOH	Acidic/Basic/Neutral
0.0342 M		
	8.400	
7.2×10^{-12} M		
	3.215	

7. For pure water at 60.0°C, the value of $pK_w = 13.02$. Calculate the pH at this temperature and decide if the water is acidic, basic, or neutral.

8. Calculate the pH of a 0.30 M solution of $Sr(OH)_2$.

9. A 2.00 g sample of pure NaOH is dissolved in water to produce 500.0 mL of solution. Calculate the pH of this solution.

10. A sample of HI is dissolved in water to make 2.0 L of solution. The pH of this solution is found to be 2.50. Calculate the mass of HI dissolved in this solution.

11. Complete the following table, expressing each value to the proper number of significant figures.

$[H_3O^+]$	$[OH^-]$	pOH	pH	Acidic/Basic/Neutral
5.620×10^{-5} M				
	0.000450 M			
		12.50		
			10.5	

12. Calculate the pH resulting from mixing 75.0 mL of 0.50 M HNO_3 with 125.0 mL of a solution containing 0.20 g NaOH.

13. Calculate the pH of the solution that results from mixing 200.0 mL of a solution with a pH of 1.50 with 300.0 mL of a solution having a pOH of 1.50.

14. Calculate the pH of a solution that is produced when 3.2 g of HI is added to 500.0 mL of a solution having a pH of 13.00. Assume no volume change.

15. The following three solutions are mixed together:
    25.0 mL of 0.20 M HCl + 35.0 mL of 0.15 M HNO_3 + 40.0 mL of 0.30 M NaOH
    Calculate the pH of the final solution.

16. What mass of HCl should be added to 450.0 mL of 0.0350 M KOH to produce a solution with a pH of 11.750? (Assume no volume change.)

17. What mass of LiOH must be added to 500.0 mL of 0.0125 M HCl to produce a solution with a pH of 2.75? (Assume no volume change.)

6.2 The Ionization of Water

Warm Up

1. Describe the difference between a weak acid and a strong acid.

   _____

   _____

2. Compare the relative electrical conductivities of 1.0 M HCl, 1.0 M CH₃COOH, and distilled water. Explain your reasoning.

   _____

   _____

3. On your K_a table, find the equation for water acting as an acid and reproduce it here. Write the K_a expression for water.

The Ion-Product Constant of Water

Earlier in this course, you saw that water can act as either a Brønsted-Lowry weak acid or weak base. Water is amphiprotic and so can form both hydronium and hydroxide ions. In a Brønsted-Lowry equilibrium, we can see how one water molecule donates a proton to another water molecule (Figure 6.2.1). This is called **autoionization**.

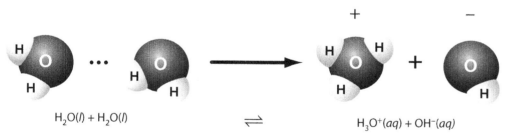

$$H_2O(l) + H_2O(l) \rightleftharpoons H_3O^+(aq) + OH^-(aq)$$

Figure 6.2.1 *Autoionization of water*

As with any equilibrium equation, we can write a corresponding equilibrium constant expression:

$$K_w = [H_3O^+][OH^-]$$

where K_w is the **water ionization constant** or **ion product constant**.

Remember that the value of an equilibrium constant depends on the temperature.

At 25°C, $K_w = 1.00 \times 10^{-14} = [H_3O^+][OH^-]$

From this information, we can calculate the $[H_3O^+]$ and $[OH^-]$ in water at 25°C. It is obvious from the equilibrium that the $[H_3O^+] = [OH^-]$ at any temperature. Because of this, water is neutral.

$$H_2O(l) + H_2O(l) \quad \rightleftharpoons \quad H_3O^+(aq) + OH^-(aq)$$
$$ x \qquad\qquad x$$

$$K_w = 1.00 \times 10^{-14} = [H_3O^+][OH^-]$$
$$= (x)(x) = x^2$$
$$x = 1.00 \times 10^{-7} \text{ M}$$
$$[H_3O^+] = [OH^-] = 1.0 \times 10^{-7} \text{ M}$$

Quick Check

1. The autoionization of water is endothermic. If the temperature of water is increased, what happens to the concentration of hydronium ion, hydroxide ion, and K_w?

    _____

    _____

2. At higher temperatures, how will the concentration of hydronium ion and hydroxide ion compare to each other?

    _____

    _____

3. At 10°C, $K_w = 2.9 \times 10^{-15}$. Calculate $[H_3O^+]$ and $[OH^-]$ in water at this temperature.

Adding Acid or Base to Water

When we add an acid or base to water, we cause the equilibrium present in water to shift in response. In 1.0 M HCl, HCl, which is a strong acid, thus ionizes 100% to produce 1.0 M H_3O^+ and 1.0 M Cl^- ions:

$$HCl(aq) + H_2O(l) \quad \rightarrow \quad H_3O^+(aq) + Cl^-(aq)$$
$$ 1.0 \text{ M} \qquad 1.0 \text{ M}$$

The added hydronium ions cause the water equilibrium to shift left and the concentration of hydroxide to decrease.

Likewise, when a strong base dissolves in water, the added hydroxide ions cause a shift left, and a corresponding hydronium ion concentration to decrease.

An increase in $[H_3O^+]$ causes a decrease in $[OH^-]$, and vise versa. The $[H_3O^+]$ is inversely proportional to $[OH^-]$.

Both H_3O^+ and OH^- ions exist in all aqueous solutions:
*   If $[H_3O^+] > [OH^-]$, the solution is acidic.
*   If $[H_3O^+] = [OH^-]$, the solution is neutral.
*   If $[H_3O^+] < [OH^-]$, the solution is basic.

Sample Problem 6.2.1 — Calculating [H₃O⁺] and [OH⁻] in Solutions of a Strong Acid or Strong Base

What is the $[H_3O^+]$ and $[OH^-]$ in 0.50 M HCl? Justify that the solution is acidic.

What to Think About	How to Do It
1. HCl is a strong acid and so will ionize 100%. Thus $[HCl] = [H_3O^+]$.	$[H_3O^+] = 0.50\ M$
2. The temperature is not specified. Assume 25°C.	$K_w = 1.00 \times 10^{-14} = [H_3O^+][OH^-]$
3. Substitute into K_w and solve for $[OH^-]$.	$1.00 \times 10^{-14} = (0.50\ M)[OH^-]$ $[OH^-] = 2.0 \times 10^{-14}\ M$ Because the $[H_3O^+] > [OH^-]$, the solution is acidic.

Practice Problems 6.2.1 — Calculating [H₃O⁺] and [OH⁻] in Solutions of a Strong Acid or Strong Base (Assume the temperature in each case is 25°C.)

1. Calculate the $[H_3O^+]$ and $[OH^-]$ in 0.15 M $HClO_4$. Justify that this solution is acidic.

2. Calculate the $[H_3O^+]$ and $[OH^-]$ in a saturated solution of magnesium hydroxide. (Hint: this salt has low solubility, but is a strong base.)

3. A student dissolved 1.42 g of NaOH in 250. mL of solution. Calculate the resulting $[H_3O^+]$ and $[OH^-]$. Justify that this solution is basic.

Mixing Solutions of Strong Acids and Bases

When we react strong acids with strong bases, we need to consider two factors: solutions will dilute each other when mixed, and then acids will neutralize bases. The resulting solution will be acidic, basic, or neutral depending on whether more acid or base is present after neutralization.

Sample Problem 6.2.2 — What Happens When a Strong Acid Is Added to a Strong Base?

What is the final $[H_3O^+]$ in a solution formed when 25 mL of 0.30 M HCl is added to 35 mL of 0.50 M NaOH?

What to Think About	How to Do It
1. When two solutions are combined, both are diluted. Calculate the new concentrations of HCl and NaOH in the mixed solution.	HCl is a strong acid, so $[HCl] = [H_3O^+]$ NaOH is a strong base, so $[NaOH] = [OH^-]$ $[HCl] = \dfrac{0.30\ mol}{L} \times \dfrac{0.025\ L}{0.060\ L} = 0.125\ M$ $[NaOH] = \dfrac{0.50\ mol}{L} \times \dfrac{0.035\ L}{0.060\ L} = 0.292\ M$
2. The hydronium ions and hydroxide ions will neutralize each other. Since there is more hydroxide, there will be hydroxide left over. Calculate how much will be left over.	$[H_3O^+]_{initial} = 0.125\ M$ $[OH^-]_{initial} = 0.292\ M$ $[OH^-]_{excess} = [OH^-]_{initial} - [H_3O^+]_{initial}$ $= 0.292\ M - 0.125\ M$ $= 0.167\ M = 0.17\ M$
3. Use K_w to calculate the hydronium ion concentration from the hydroxide ion concentration.	$K_w = [H_3O^+][OH^-]$ $1.00 \times 10^{-14} = [H_3O^+](0.17\ M)$ $[H_3O^+] = 6.0 \times 10^{-14}\ M$

Practice Problems 6.2.2 — What Happens When a Strong Acid Is Added to a Strong Base?

1. Calculate the final $[H_3O^+]$ and $[OH^-]$ in a solution formed when 150. mL of 1.5 M HNO_3 is added to 250. mL of 0.80 M KOH.

2. Calculate the mass of solid NaOH that must be added to 500. mL of 0.20 M HI to result in a solution with $[H_3O^+] = 0.12$ M. Assume no volume change on the addition of solid NaOH.

3. Calculate the resulting $[H_3O^+]$ and $[OH^-]$ when 18.4 mL of 0.105 M HBr is added to 22.3 mL of 0.256 M HCl.

6.2 Activity: Counting Water Molecules and Hydronium Ions

Question

How many water molecules does it take to produce one hydronium ion?

Procedure

1. Calculate the number of water molecules present in 1.0 L of water using the density of water (1.00 g/mL) and its molar mass.
2. Calculate the number of hydronium ions in 1.0 L of water. (Hint: You need the $[H_3O^+]$ in pure water from step 1.)
3. Using the above answers, calculate the ratio of ions/molecules. This is the percentage ionization of water.
4. Using the ratio above, calculate the number of water molecules required to produce one hydronium ion.

Results and Discussion

1. From the ratio of ions to molecules, it is evident that an extremely small percentage of water molecules actually ionize. Because there are an enormously large number of molecules present in the solutions we use, a reasonable number of hydronium and hydroxide ions are present. What volume of water contains only one hydronium ion?

6.2 Review Questions

1. In its pure liquid form, ammonia (NH_3) undergoes autoionization. Write an equation to show how ammonia autoionizes.

2. Complete the following table:

$[H_3O^+]$	$[OH^-]$	Acidic, Basic, or Neutral?
	6.0 M	
3.2×10^{-4} M		
	9.2×10^{-12} M	
2.5 M		
	4.7×10^{-5} M	

3. The autoionization of water has $\Delta H = 57.1$ kJ/mol. Write the equation for the autoionization of water including the energy term. Explain how the value of K_w changes with temperature.

4. The K_w for water at 1°C is 1.0×10^{-15}. Calculate the $[H_3O^+]$ and $[OH^-]$ in 0.20 M HI at this temperature.

5. Human urine has a $[H_3O^+] = 6.3 \times 10^{-7}$ M. What is the $[OH^-]$, and is urine acidic, basic, or neutral?

6. Complete the table:

Temperature	K_w	$[H_3O^+]$	$[OH^-]$	Acidic, Basic, or Neutral?
50° C	5.5×10^{-14}			
100° C	5.1×10^{-13}			

7. Heavy water (D_2O) is used in CANDU reactors as a moderator. In heavy water, the hydrogen atoms are H-2 called *deuterium* and symbolized as D. In a sample of heavy water at 50°C, $[OD^-] = 8.9 \times 10^{-8}$ M. Calculate K_w for heavy water.

8. Calculate the $[H_3O^+]$ and $[OH^-]$ in a saturated solution of calcium hydroxide. ($K_{sp} = 4.7 \times 10^{-6}$)

9. A student combines the following solutions:
   Calculate the $[H_3O^+]$ and $[OH^-]$ in the resulting solution.

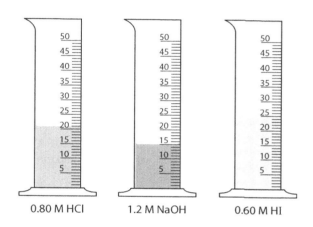

0.80 M HCl   1.2 M NaOH   0.60 M HI

10. What mass of strontium hydroxide must be added to 150. mL of 0.250 M nitric acid to produce a solution with $[OH^-] = 0.010$ M?

6.3 Identifying Acids and Bases

Warm Up

A student tested a number of unknown solutions and recorded the following observations. Based on each observation, place a check mark in the corresponding column that identifies the unknown solution as containing an acid, a base, or either one.

Observation	Acid	Base
Turns phenolphthalein pink		
Feels slippery		
Has pH ≈ 5.0		
Tastes sour		
Conducts electricity		
Reacts with metal to produce a gas		

The Arrhenius Theory of Acids and Bases

In Science 10, you learned how to identify an acid or base using a concept developed by a chemist named Svante Arrhenius. According to the Arrhenius theory, acids release H^+ ions in solution, and bases release OH^- ions.

Typically, when an Arrhenius acid and base react together, a salt and water form. A salt is an ionic compound that does not contain H^+ or OH^- ions. The cation from the base and the anion from the acid make up the salt.

$$\text{Example: } HCl(aq) + NaOH(aq) \rightarrow NaCl(aq) + H_2O(l)$$
$$\text{acid} \qquad \text{base} \qquad \text{salt} \qquad \text{water}$$

Sample Problem 6.3.1 — Identifying Arrhenius Acids and Bases

Classify each of the following substances as an Arrhenius acid, an Arrhenius base, a salt or a molecular compound.
(a) HNO_3
(b) $Al(OH)_3$
(c) $Al(NO_3)_3$
(d) NO_2

What to Think About	How to Do It
(a) An acid releases H^+ ions.	HNO_3 is an acid.
(b) A base releases OH^- ions.	$Al(OH)_3$ is a base.
(c) A salt is an ionic compound not containing H^+ or OH^- ions.	$Al(NO_3)_3$ is a salt.
(d) A molecule is not made up of ions.	NO_2 is a molecular compound.

Practice Problems 6.3.1 — Identifying Arrhenius Acids and Bases

1. Classify each of the following as an Arrhenius acid, an Arrhenius base, a salt, or a molecular compound.

    (a) H_2SO_4 _____

    (b) XeF_6 _____

    (c) CH_3COOH _____

    (d) $NaCH_3COO$ _____

    (e) KOH _____

    (f) NH_3 _____

2. Complete the following neutralization equations. Make sure each equation is balanced, and circle the salt produced.

    (a) $CH_3COOH + LiOH \rightarrow$

    (b) $HI + Ca(OH)_2 \rightarrow$

    (c) $Mg(OH)_2 + H_3PO_4 \rightarrow$

3. Write the formula of the parent acid and the parent base that react to form each salt listed.

	Parent Acid	**Parent Base**
(a) KNO_2		
(b) NH_4Cl		
(c) CuC_2O_4		
(d) $NaCH_3COO$		

Brønsted-Lowry Acids and Bases

Arrhenius' definition worked well to classify a number of substances that displayed acidic or basic characteristics. However, some substances that acted like acids or bases could not be classified using this definition. A broader definition of acids and bases was required.

In the practice problem above, you may have classified NH_3 as molecular. While it is molecular, a solution of NH_3 also feels slippery, has a pH greater than 7, and turns phenolphthalein pink. It clearly has basic characteristics, but it is not an Arrhenius base.

Chemists Johannes Brønsted and Thomas Lowry suggested a broader definition of acids and bases:

Brønsted-Lowry acid — a substance or species that donates a hydrogen ion, H^+ (a proton)
Brønsted-Lowry base — a substance or species that accepts a hydrogen ion, H^+

Consider the reaction that occurs in aqueous HCl:

$$HCl(aq) + H_2O(l) \rightarrow H_3O^+(aq) + Cl^-(aq)$$
acid $\quad$ base $\quad$ hydronium

In this example, the HCl donates a hydrogen ion (H^+) to the water molecule. The HCl is therefore acting as a Brønsted-Lowry acid. The water accepts the H^+ ion so it is acting as a Brønsted-Lowry base.

The H_3O^+ ion is called a **hydronium ion**. It is simply a water molecule with an extra H^+ ion (Figure 6.3.1). It is also called a protonated water molecule.

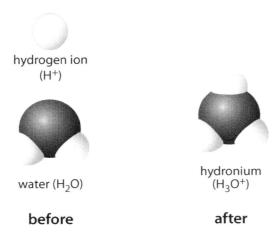

hydrogen ion
(H^+)

water (H_2O)

hydronium
(H_3O^+)

before　　　　　　　**after**

Figure 6.3.1 *A hydronium ion is a water molecule with an extra H+ ion.*

Let's look at NH_3 now. In a solution of ammonia (NH_3) the following reaction occurs:

$$NH_3(aq) + H_2O(l) \rightleftharpoons NH_4^+(aq) + OH^-(aq)$$
base　　　　acid

The ammonia molecule accepted a H^+ ion from the water, so NH_3 is acting as a Brønsted-Lowry base, and water is acting as a Brønsted-Lowry acid.

You may notice that in the equation for HCl, a one-way arrow was used, but in the equation for NH_3, an equilibrium arrow was used. The reasons for this will be explained in the next section. Just remember that if you see an equilibrium arrow, then equilibrium is established. More importantly, in an equilibrium, you have both reactants and products present in the system. Both forward and reverse reactions occur. If we look at the reverse reaction for the ammonia system, we can identify Brønsted-Lowry acids and bases:

$$NH_3(aq) + H_2O(l) \rightleftharpoons NH_4^+(aq) + OH^-(aq)$$
base　　　acid　　　　acid　　　　base

In the reverse reaction, the NH_4^+ ion donates a proton to the OH^- ion. According to Brønsted-Lowry definitions, the NH_4^+ ion is acting as an acid, and the OH^- ion is acting as a base.

In a Brønsted-Lowry equilibrium, there are two acids and two bases: one for the forward reaction, and one for the reverse reaction. An acid and a base react to form a different acid and base.

Two substances that differ by one H^+ ion are called a **conjugate acid-base pair.**

In the example above, the NH_3 and NH_4^+ together form one conjugate acid-base pair, and the H_2O and OH^- form the other conjugate acid-base pair.

Sample Problems 6.3.2 — Identifying Conjugate Acid-Base Pairs

1. In the following equilibrium, identify the acids and bases, and the two conjugate acid-base pairs:

$$HF(aq) + CN^-(aq) \rightleftharpoons HCN(aq) + F^-(aq)$$

2. Complete the following table:

Conjugate Acid	Conjugate Base
$H_2C_2O_4$	
	SO_3^{2-}
HCO_3^-	
	H_2O

3. Complete the following equilibrium, which represents the reaction of a Brønsted-Lowry acid and base. Circle the substances that make up one of the conjugate acid-base pairs.

$$NO_2^-(aq) + H_2CO_3(aq) \rightleftharpoons$$

What to Think About

1. An acid donates a proton and a base accepts a proton.

   In the forward reaction, the HF is the acid and the CN– is the base. In the reverse reaction, the HCN is the acid and the F– is the base.

   The substances in a conjugate acid-base pair differ by one H^+ ion.

2. An acid donates a proton. Find the conjugate base of an acid by removing one H^+. Be careful of your charges on the ions! A base accepts a proton. Find the conjugate acid of a given base by adding one H^+.

3. An acid must be able to donate a H^+ ion. Only the H_2CO_3 has a H^+ to donate. When it donates a H^+ ion, HCO_3^- forms. The NO_2^- ion is forced to accept the H^+, making the NO_2^- a base. When the NO_2^- accepts a proton, it forms HNO_2. The total charge on the reactant side should equal the total charge on the product side. Balance reactions for both.

Note: H_2CO_3 only donates ONE H^+ ion. Substances in a conjugate acid-base pair differ by only ONE H^+ ion. Balance both sides of the equation for number of atoms and charge.

How to Do It

The two conjugate acid-base pairs are: HF/F^- and CN^-/HCN.

$$HF(aq) + CN^-(aq) \rightleftharpoons HCN(aq) + F^-(aq)$$
acid   base   acid   base

Conjugate acid		Conjugate base
$H_2C_2O_4$	$\rightarrow$ remove H^+	$HC_2O_4^-$
HSO_3^-	$\leftarrow$ add H^+	SO_3^{2-}
HCO_3^-	$\rightarrow$ remove H^+	CO_3^{2-}
H_3O^+	$\leftarrow$ add H^+	H_2O

$$NO_2^-(aq) + H_2CO_3(aq) \rightleftharpoons$$
$$HNO_2(aq) + HCO_3^-(aq)$$

Circle around either of the following:
NO_2^-/HNO_2 or H_2CO_3/HCO_3^-

Practice Problems 6.3.2 — Identifying Conjugate Acid-Base Pairs

1. For the following equilibria, label the acids and bases for the forward and reverse reactions.

   (a) $HIO_3 + NO_2^- \rightleftharpoons HNO_2 + IO_3^-$

   (b) $HF + HC_2O_4^- \rightleftharpoons H_2C_2O_4 + F^-$

   (c) $Al(H_2O)_6^{3+} + SO_3^{2-} \rightleftharpoons HSO_3^- + Al(H_2O)_5OH^{2+}$

2. Complete the following table:

Conjugate Acid	Conjugate Base
H_2O_2	
	$H_2BO_3^-$
HCOOH	
	$C_6H_5O_7^{3-}$

3. Complete the following equilibria. Label the acids and bases for the forward and reverse reactions. Circle one conjugate acid-base pair in each equilibria.

   (a) $HNO_2 + NH_3 \rightleftharpoons$

   (b) $H_3C_6H_5O_7 + CN^- \rightleftharpoons$

   (c) $PO_4^{3-} + H_2S \rightleftharpoons$

Amphiprotic Species

Consider the two equilibria below:

$$NH_3(aq) + H_2O(l) \rightleftharpoons NH_4^+(aq) + OH^- (aq)$$
$$\text{acid}$$

$$HF(aq) + H_2O(l) \rightleftharpoons H_3O^+(aq) + F^- (aq)$$
$$\text{base}$$

In the first reaction, water acts as a Brønsted-Lowry acid. In the second reaction, water acts as a Brønsted-Lowry base. An **amphiprotic** species has the ability to act as an acid or a base, depending on what it is reacting with. Water is a common amphiprotic substance. Many anions also display amphiprotic tendencies. For a species to be amphiprotic, it must have a proton to donate and be able to accept a proton. Examples of amphiprotic anions include HCO_3^-, $HC_2O_4^-$, and $H_2PO_4^-$. Uncharged species, with the exception of water, are generally not amphiprotic. For example, HCl will donate one H^+ ion (proton) to form Cl^-, but will not accept a proton to form H_2Cl^+. You should recognize many of the species that form.

Quick Check

1. Write an equation for a reaction between HCO_3^- and CN^- where HCO_3^- acts as an acid.

2. Write an equation for a reaction between HCO_3^- and H_2O where HCO_3^- acts as a base.

3. Circle amphiprotic species in the following list:

   (a) CH_3COOH (b) $H_2PO_4^-$ (c) PO_4^{3-} (d) $H_2C_2O_4$ (e) $HC_2O_4^-$

6.3 Activity: Conjugate Pairs Memory Game

Question
How many conjugate acid-base pairs can you identify?

Materials
- grid of conjugate pairs, cut into cards
- scissors

Procedure
1. Go to edvantagescience.com for a page of symbols and formulae.
2. Cut along the grid lines to make a set of cards. Each card will have one symbol or formula on it.
3. Place the cards face down on the table in a 6 × 6 grid.
4. Play in groups of two or three. The first player turns over two cards. If the two substances are a conjugate acid-base pair, the player keeps the two cards and gets one more turn. If they are not a conjugate acid-base pair, the player turns the cards face down again after everyone has seen them.
5. The next player turns over two cards, again looking for a conjugate pair.
6. The play continues until all conjugate acid-base pair cards are collected. The winner is the player with the most cards.

Results and Discussion
1. Define an acid-base conjugate pair.

2. Explain why H_2SO_3 and SO_3^{2-} are not a conjugate pair.

6.3 Review Questions

1. How are the Arrhenius and Brønsted-Lowry definitions of an acid and base similar? How are they different? Use examples.

2. Explain why the H^+ ion is the same as a proton.

3. A hydronium ion is formed when water accepts a proton. Draw a Lewis structure for water, and explain why water will accept a proton. Draw the Lewis structure for a hydronium ion.

4. In the following equations, identify the acids and bases in the forward and reverse reactions. Identify the conjugate acid-base pairs.

   (a) $NH_3 + H_3PO_4 \rightleftharpoons NH_4^+ + H_2PO_4^-$

   (b) $H_2PO_4^- + SO_3^{2-} \rightleftharpoons HSO_3^- + HPO_4^{2-}$

   (c) $CH_3NH_2 + CH_3COOH \quad CH_3COO^- + CH_3NH_3^+$

5. Formic acid, HCOOH, is the substance responsible for the sting in ant bites. Write an equation showing it acting as an acid when reacted with water. Label the acids and bases in the forward and reverse reactions. Identify the two conjugate acid-base pairs.

6. Pyridine, C_5H_5N, is a Brønsted-Lowry base. It is used in the production of many pharmaceuticals. Write an equation showing it acting as a base when reacted with water. Label the acids and bases in the forward and reverse reactions. Identify the two conjugate acid-base pairs.

7. Sodium hypochlorite solution is also known as bleach. It contains the hypochlorite ion ClO^-.
   (a) Write an equation for the reaction between hypochlorite ion and ammonium ion. Label the acids and bases in the forward and reverse reactions. Identify the two conjugate acid-base pairs.

   (b) This equilibrium favors the reactants. Which of the acids is stronger and donates protons more readily?

8. (a) Explain how to write the formula for the conjugate acid of a given base. Use an example.

   (b) Explain how to write the formula for the conjugate base of a given acid. Use an example.

9. (a) Hydrogen peroxide, H_2O_2, is a Brønsted Lowry acid. It is used as an antiseptic and bleaching agent. Write the formula for the conjugate base of hydrogen peroxide.

(b) Hydrazine, N_2H_4, is a Brønsted-Lowry base used as a rocket fuel. Write the formula for the conjugate acid of hydrazine.

(c) Phenol, HOC_6H_5, is a Brønsted-Lowry acid used to make plastics, nylon, and slimicides. Write the formula for its conjugate base.

(d) Aniline, $C_6H_5NH_2$, is a Brønsted-Lowry base used to make polyurethane. Write the formula for its conjugate acid.

10. Define the term *amphiprotic*. List four amphiprotic species.

11. Baking soda contains sodium bicarbonate.
    (a) Write two equations demonstrating the amphiprotic nature of the bicarbonate ion with water. Describe a test you could perform to identify which equilibrium is more likely to occur.

    (b) Bicarbonate produces CO_2 gas in the batter of cookies or cakes, which makes the batter rise as it bakes. Which of the two equations in (a) represents the action of bicarbonate ion in baking?

12. Water is amphiprotic. Write a reaction showing a water molecule acting as an acid reacting with a water molecule acting as a base. Label the acids and bases for the forward and reverse reactions. Identify the conjugate acid-base pairs.

6.4 The Strengths of Acids and Bases

Warm Up

Consider Figure 6.4.1, which shows electricity being conducted through two solutions of different acids.

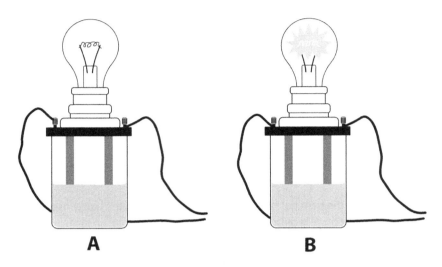

A **B**

Figure 6.4.1 *Although these acids are the same concentration, they don't both conduct electricity.*

One of the solutions is 1.0 M hydrochloric acid and one is 1.0 M acetic acid. Hypothesize which beaker contains which acid, and write a paragraph that explains your reasoning.

_____

_____

_____

The Acid and Base Ionization Constant

Let's go back to our discussion of CH_3COOH. The equilibrium present is:

$$CH_3COOH(aq) + H_2O(l) \; H_3O^+(aq) + CH_3COO^-(aq)$$

As with all equilibria, we can write a K_{eq} expression for acetic acid, which is customized for acids by calling it a K_a expression. The K_a is called the **acid ionization constant**.

$$K_a = \frac{[H_3O^+][CH_3COO^-]}{[CH_3COOH]}$$

Notice that we do not include the $[H_2O]$ in the K_a expression. As you learned earlier, the concentration of water does not change appreciably, so it is treated as part of the constant. For any weak acid in solution, we can write a general equation and K_a expression:

$$HA(aq) + H_2O(l) \rightleftharpoons H_3O^+(aq) + A^-(aq) \qquad K_a = \frac{[H_3O^+][A^-]}{[HA]}$$

In a weak acid solution of appreciable concentration, most of the acid molecules remain intact or un-ionized. Only a few ions are formed. Equal concentrations of different acids produce different H_3O^+ concentrations. The K_a values for weak acids are less than 1.0. The K_a corresponds to the percentage ionization. A greater K_a signifies a greater $[H_3O^+]$ in solution.

Likewise, a weak Brønsted-Lowry base such as ammonia establishes an equilibrium in solution:

$$NH_3(aq) + H_2O(l) \rightleftharpoons NH_4^+(aq) + OH^-(aq)$$

$$K_b = \frac{[NH_4^+][OH^-]}{[NH_3]}$$

where K_b is called the **base ionization constant**. Generally, for a molecule acting as a weak Brønsted-Lowry base in aqueous solution:

$$B(aq) + H_2O(l) \rightleftharpoons HB^+(aq) + OH^-(aq) \qquad K_b = \frac{[HB^+][OH^-]}{[B]}$$

Quick Check

1. HF is a weak acid. Write an equation showing how HF acts in solution; then write the K_a expression for HF.

2. Explain why we would not typically write a K_b expression for NaOH.

   _____

   _____

3. Ethylamine is a weak base with the formula $CH_3CH_2NH_2$. Write an equation showing how ethylamine acts in water, then write the K_b expression.

4. The hydrogen oxalate ion is amphiprotic. Write two equations, one showing how this ion acts as an acid and the other showing this ion acting as a base. Beside each equation, write its corresponding K_a or K_b expression.

Comparing Acid and Base Strengths

Recall that the larger the K_a or K_b, the greater the $[H_3O^+]$ or $[OH^-]$ respectively. To compare the relative strengths of weak acids and bases, we can use in Table A5 in the appendix.
As you look at the table, note the following points:
- Acids are listed on the left of the table, and their conjugate bases are listed on the right.
- The strong acids are the top six acids on the table. Their ionization equations include a one-way arrow signifying that they ionize 100%. Their K_a values are too large to be useful.

- The other acids between, and including, hydronium and water are weak. Their ionization equations include an equilibrium arrow and an associated K_a value.
- Even though OH^- and NH_3 are listed on the left of the table, they do NOT act as acids in water. The reaction arrow does not go in the forward direction. They do NOT give up H^+ ions in water.
- There are two bold arrows along the sides of the table. On the left, acid strength increases going up the table. Notice that this arrow stops for OH^- and NH_3 because they are not weak acids; they will not donate a hydrogen ion in water. On the right, base strength increases going down the table. This arrow stops for the conjugate bases of the strong monoprotic acids because these ions (Cl^-, Br^-, and so on) do not act as weak bases. They will not accept a hydrogen ion from water.
- The K_a values listed are for aqueous solutions at room temperature. Like any equilibrium constant, K_a and K_b values are temperature dependent.
- The table lists the K_a values for weak acids. You will learn how to calculate the K_b of a weak base in section 7.5. For now, you can rank the relative strength of a base from its position on this table. The lower a base is on the right side, the stronger it is. This means that the stronger an acid is, the weaker its conjugate base will be and vice versa. The more willing an acid is to donate a hydrogen ion, the more reluctant its conjugate base will be to take it back.
- Some ions appear on both sides of the table. They are amphiprotic and able to act as an acid or a base. One example of this is the bicarbonate ion, HCO_3^-.

Quick Check

1. Classify the following as a strong acid, strong base, weak acid, or weak base.

    (a) sulfuric acid   _____

    (b) calcium hydroxide   _____

    (c) ammonia   _____

    (d) benzoic acid   _____

    (e) cyanide ion   _____

    (f) nitrous acid   _____

2. For the weak acids or bases above, write an equation demonstrating their behavior in water and their corresponding K_a or K_b expression.

3. A student tests the electrical conductivity of 0.5 M solutions of the following: carbonic acid, methanoic acid, phenol, and boric acid. Rank these solutions in order from most conductive to least conductive.

    _____

    _____

Effects of Structure on Acid Strength

Strong acids ionize to produce more hydronium ions than weak acids when placed in water. That is, strong acids donate their hydrogen ions more readily. Why do some acids ionize more than others? To answer this question, we must examine an acid's structure. The structure of an acid influences how readily a hydrogen ion may leave the molecule (Figure 6.4.2).

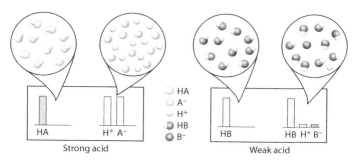

Figure 6.4.2 *Strong acids ionize completely in water. Weak acids ionize only partially. The weaker the acid, the lower the degree of ionization. In this representation, hydronium ion, H_3O^+ is simplified to H^+.*

Binary Acid Strength

The strength of a binary acid, HX depends primarily on the attraction between the nucleus of the hydrogen atom and the electrons that surround the atom X. There is also an attractive force between the electron of the hydrogen atom and the nucleus of X. As the size of X increases, the distance between the nucleus of one atom and the electrons of its neighbor increases. An increased distance results in a longer bond length, less bond strength, and a stronger acid. Binary acids of the halogen family provide a good illustration (Figure 6.4.3).

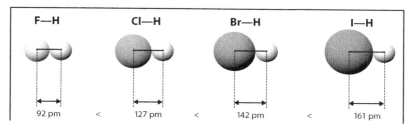

Figure 6.4.3 *Hydrofluoric acid is the weakest member of the hydrohalic acids due to the strong bond between hydrogen and fluorine. Binary acids of the halogen family increase in strength as the bond length increases—the longer the bond length, the more easily they can ionize.*

14 4A	15 5A	16 6A	17 7A
CH_4 Neither acid nor base	NH_3 Weak base $K_a = 1.8 \times 10^{-5}$	H_2O	HF Weak acid $K_a = 6.8 \times 10^{-4}$
SiH_4 Neither acid nor base	PH_3 Very weak base $K_a = 4 \times 10^{-18}$	H_2O Weak acid $K_a = 9.5 \times 10^{-3}$	HCl Strong acid
		H_2Se Weak acid $K_a = 1.3 \times 10^{-4}$	HBr Strong acid

Increasing acid strength →

Increasing acid strength (vertical)

Binary acids containing more than one hydrogen atom are weaker than the hydrohalic acid in the same period (Figure 6.4.4). The presence of more hydrogen atoms bound to the central non-metal strengthens the H–X bonds in an H_nX molecule.

Acids weaker than water do not behave as acids in aqueous solution. Thus ammonia and methane are not commonly considered to be acids. Water is only treated as an acid in the context of aqueous solution chemistry.

Figure 6.4.4 *In general, the acidity of binary acids increases as the non-metal attached to the hydrogen is further to the right in a period or closer to the bottom in a family of the periodic table.*

Ternary Acid Strength

The strength of ternary or oxo-acids depends on two things:

1. the number of oxygen atoms, and
2. the electronegativity of the central non-metal atom

Ternary acids ionize more easily when the O–H bond is readily **polarized** (Figure 6.4.5). The bond is polarized when the pair of electrons shared between the oxygen and hydrogen atoms is drawn away from the hydrogen toward the center of the molecule. This occurs most readily when there are more oxygen atoms and the central non-metal atom is highly electronegative.

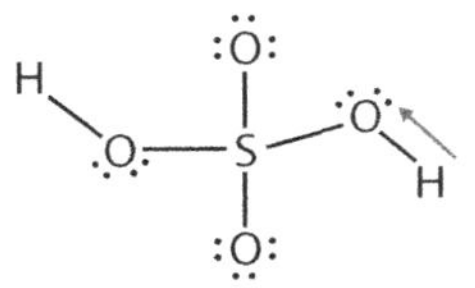

Figure 6.4.5 *Polarization of the O–H bond in an oxo-acid such as sulfuric acid (H$_2$SO$_4$) leads to increased strength*

Carboxylic Acids

The strength of carboxylic acids also depends on polarization of the O–H bond. The bond is more easily polarized if the carbon skeleton is shorter and if there are electronegative atoms attached to the carbon skeleton of the molecule (Figure 6.4.6).

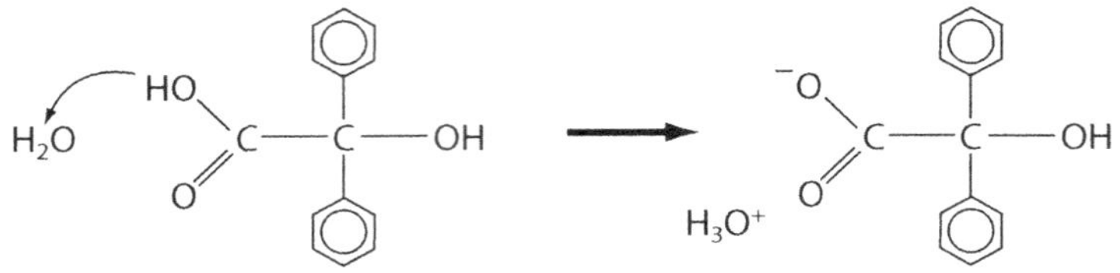

Figure 6.4.6 *The H atom from the carboxylic acid group (–COOH) on the left side of benzillic acid is the most ionizable H atom due to electron withdrawal by the extra oxygen double bonded to the carbon in the group. The electron withdrawal polarizes the H–O bond, causing the acid to ionize.*

Quick Check

1. Study the acids shown here. Which acid is stronger? Clearly explain your answer.

Acid 1   Acid 1

_____

_____

_____

_____

2. Study this table of binary acids. Rank the compounds below from strongest to weakest in terms of acid strength. Give a complete explanation of your reasoning.

Binary compound	Hydro-bromic acid (HBr)	Hydro-chloric acid (HCl)	Hydro-iodic acid (HI)	Hydro-selenic acid(H_2Se)	Hydro-sulfuric acid (H_2S)	Methane (CH_4)	Water (H_2O)
Lewis structure	H—Br:	H—Cl:	H—I :				

_____

_____

3. Study the ternary acids shown here. Rank the compounds below from weakest to strongest in terms of acid strength. Give a complete explanation of your reasoning.

(H_2SO_4)   ($HClO_3$)   ($HBrO_3$)   ($HClO_4$)   (H_2SO_3)

_____

_____

_____

_____

4. Use Table A5 to rank benzoic, ethanoic, and methanoic acids in terms of strength. Arrange the acids from greatest to least polarizable O–H bond.

The Position of Equilibrium and Relative Strengths

When a Brønsted-Lowry acid and base react, the position of the equilibrium results from the relative strengths of the acids and bases involved. If K_{eq} is greater than 1, products are favored. If K_{eq} is less than 1, reactants are favored. Acids that are stronger are more able to donate H^+ ions, so the position of the equilibrium is determined by the stronger acid and base reacting. Consider the reaction between ammonia and methanoic acid:

$$NH_3(aq) + HCOOH(aq) \rightleftharpoons NH_4^+(aq) + HCOO^-(aq)$$
$$\text{base} \qquad \text{acid} \qquad\qquad \text{acid} \qquad \text{base}$$

We can label the acids and bases for the forward and reverse reactions as above. The two acids are methanoic acid and the ammonium ion. According to the K_a table, methanoic acid is a stronger acid than the ammonium ion, so it donates H^+ ions more readily. Therefore, the forward reaction happens to a greater extent than the reverse reaction. Additionally, NH_3 is a stronger base than $HCOO^-$, so it accepts H^+ ions more readily. Therefore, the forward reaction proceeds to a greater extent than the reverse reaction, and products are favored at equilibrium.

Equilibrium favors the reaction in the direction of the stronger acid and base forming the weaker acid and base.

Sample Problem 6.4.1(a) — Predicting Whether Reactants or Products Will Be Favored in a Brønsted-Lowry Acid-Base Equilibrium

Predict whether reactants or products will be favored when HCN reacts with HCO_3^-.

What to Think About	How to Do It
1. Recognize that both HCN and HCO_3^- can act as weak acids, but only HCO_3^- can act as a weak base. This means that HCN will be the acid, and HCO_3^- will be the base. The acid donates a H^+ ion and the base accepts the H^+ ion. We can complete the equilibrium.	$HCN + HCO_3^- \rightleftharpoons CN^- + H_2CO_3$
2. The acid in the forward reaction is HCN, and the acid in the reverse reaction is H_2CO_3.	$acid + base \rightleftharpoons base + acid$
3. According to the K_a table, H_2CO_3 is a stronger acid than HCN. H_2CO_3 will donate H^+ ions more readily than HCN. It is evident from the table that CN^- is a stronger base than HCO_3^-. The stronger acid and base will always appear on the same side of an equilibrium.	weaker acid + weaker base $\rightleftharpoons$ stronger acid + stronger base
4. The equilibrium favors the direction in which the stronger acid and base react to form the weaker conjugate acid and base.	The reverse reaction is favored, so reactants are favored at equilibrium.

Consider the reaction between HSO_4^- and $HC_2O_4^-$. Both of these species are amphiprotic. If two amphiprotic species react, then the stronger acid of the two will donate the H^+ ion, unless one of the species is water. When an amphiprotic species reacts with water, the reaction that occurs to a greater extent is determined by comparing the K_a to the K_b of the amphiprotic species.

Sample Problem 6.4.1(b) — Predicting Whether Reactants or Products Will Be Favored in a Brønsted-Lowry Acid-Base Equilibrium

Predict whether reactants or products will be favored when HSO_4^- reacts with $HC_2O_4^-$.

What to Think About	How to Do It
1. Both substances are amphiprotic. Since HSO_4^- is a stronger acid than $HC_2O_4^-$, the HSO_4^- acts as the acid and donates a H^+ ion to $HC_2O_4^-$.	$HSO_4^- + HC_2O_4^- \rightleftharpoons SO_4^{2-} + H_2C_2O_4$
2. The acid in the forward reaction is HSO_4^-, and the acid in the reverse reaction is $H_2C_2O_4$.	$acid + base \rightleftharpoons base + acid$
3. According to the K_a table, $H_2C_2O_4$ is a stronger acid than HSO_4^-. $H_2C_2O_4$ will donate H^+ ions more readily than HSO_4^-. It is evident from the table that SO_4^{2-} is a stronger base than $HC_2O_4^-$. The stronger acid and base will always appear on the same side of an equilibrium.	$weaker\ acid + weaker\ base \rightleftharpoons$ $stronger\ acid + stonger\ base$
4. The equilibrium favors the direction in which the stronger acid and base react to form the weaker conjugate acid and base.	Reverse reaction favored, so reactants are favored at equilibrium.

Practice Problems 6.4.1 — Predicting Whether Reactants or Products Will Be Favored in a Brønsted-Lowry Acid-Base Equilibrium

1. For the following, complete the equilibrium and predict whether reactants or products are favored at equilibrium.

   (a) hydrogen peroxide + hydrogen sulfite ion $\rightleftharpoons$

   (b) citric acid + ammonia $\rightleftharpoons$

   (c) hydrogen carbonate ion + dihydrogen phosphate ion $\rightleftharpoons$

2. Arsenic acid (H_3AsO_4) reacts with an equal concentration of sulfate ion. At equilibrium, $[H_3AsO_4] > [HSO_4^-]$. Write the equation for this reaction and state which acid is the stronger one.

3. Consider the reaction between the sulfite ion and the hexaaquochromium ion. Write the equation for this reaction, and predict whether K_{eq} is greater or less than 1.

The Levelling Effect

According to the K_a table, all strong acids in water are equally strong. Remember that "strong" means that it ionizes 100%. When each of the strong acids ionizes in water, hydronium ions form:

$$HCl(aq) + H_2O(l) \rightarrow H_3O^+(aq) + Cl^-(aq)$$

$$HBr(aq) + H_2O(l) \rightarrow H_3O^+(aq) + Br^-(aq)$$

Therefore, in a solution of a strong acid, no molecules of the strong acid remain — only the anion and hydronium ion are left. In the same manner, all strong bases dissociate completely to form OH^- ions.

In aqueous solution, the strongest acid actually present is H_3O^+ and the strongest base actually present is OH^-. Water levels the strength of strong acids and bases.

All strong acids in aqueous solution have equal ability to donate a H^+ ion to form H_3O^+. This is analogous to your chemistry teacher and a football player being able to lift a 5 kg weight. Both are able to lift the weight easily, so there is no observed difference in their strengths. Increasing the difficulty of the task (by increasing the amount of weight) would allow us to observe a difference in strength. Likewise, HCl and HI have no observable difference in strength when reacting with water, but when reacting with pure CH_3COOH, their different strengths become apparent.

6.4 Activity: Determining the Relative Strengths of Six Acids

Question

You are given six unknown weak acid solutions of the same concentration. The three weak acid indicators (HIn) are first mixed with HCl and NaOH. Can you build a table of relative acid strengths for six unknown solutions?

Procedure

1. Consider the following data collected when the indicated solutions are mixed:

	HIn_1/In_1^-	HIn_2/In_2^-	HIn_3/In_3^-
HCl	red	yellow	colorless
NaOH	yellow	red	purple
HA_1/A_1^-	red	yellow	purple
HA_2/A_2^-	red	yellow	colorless
HA_3/A_3^-	yellow	yellow	purple

2. There are six unknown weak acid solutions containing a conjugate acid-base pair. Three of the acids are HA_1, HA_2, and HA_3. The other three acids are chemical indicators HIn_1, HIn_2, and HIn_3. A chemical indicator is a weak acid in which its conjugate acid has a different color than its conjugate base. In the indicator solution, both the acid form (HIn) and the base form (In^-) exist in equilibrium.

3. When indicator 1 (HIn_1) is mixed with HCl, the HCl will donate a H^+ ion because it is a strong acid. If HCl acts as an acid, then it will donate a H^+ ion to the base form of the indicator:

   $HCl + In_1^- \rightarrow HIn_1 + Cl^-$

   According to the data in step 1, indicator 1 turns red in HCl. Therefore, HIn must be red. Likewise, In^- must be yellow because the OH^- in NaOH accepts a H^+ ion from HIn to form In^-. We know then that HIn = red and In^- = yellow.

4. When we mix unknown acid 1 (HA_1) with indicator 1 (HIn_1) we see red. The equilibrium established may be written as:

   $HA_1 + In_1^- \rightleftharpoons HIn_1 + A_1^-$
       yellow   red

   Knowing that HIn_1 is red, we conclude that products are favored in this equilibrium. Therefore, HA_1 is a stronger acid than HIn_1.

5. Fill in the table below by comparing the strength of each pair of acids HA to HIn. The first one has been filled in for you from the discussion above.

	HIn_1/In_1^-	HIn_2/In_2^-	HIn_3/In_3^-
HA_1/A_1^-	$HA_1 > HIn_1$		
HA_2/A_2^-			
HA_3/A_3^-			

Results and Discussion

1. Rank the six unknown acids in order from strongest to weakest:

   _____ > _____ > _____ > _____ > _____ > _____

2. Construct a table similar to A5 – Relative Strengths of Brønsted-Lowry Acids and Bases using the six unknown acids. Be sure to include ionization equations and arrows on each side of the table labelled: "Increasing strength of acid" and "Increasing strength of base."

6.4 Review Questions

1. Classify the following as strong or weak acids or bases.
   (a) sodium oxide — used in glass making

   (b) boric acid — used to manufacture fiberglass, antiseptics, and insecticides

   (c) perchloric acid — used to make ammonium perchlorate for rocket fuel

   (d) phosphate ion — present in the cleaner TSP (trisodium phosphate)

2. For any of the substances above that are weak, write an equation showing how they react in water, then write its corresponding K_a or K_b expression.

3. A student tests the electrical conductivity of a 2.0 M oxalic acid solution and compares it to the conductivity of 2.0 M hydroiodic acid. Explain how the hydroiodic acid could have a greater conductivity than the oxalic acid.

4. Calculate the total ion concentration in a solution of 2.0 M nitric acid. Explain why you cannot use this method to calculate the concentration of ions in 2.0 M nitrous acid.

5. Give an example of a
   (a) concentrated weak base

   (b) dilute strong acid

6. (a) Rank the following 0.1 M solutions in order from least electrical conductivity to greatest electrical conductivity: carbonic acid, citric acid, sulfuric acid, sulfurous acid, and water.

   (b) Rank the following bases in order from strongest to weakest: monohydrogen phosphate ion, carbonate ion, fluoride ion, ammonia, nitrite ion, and water.

7. Write the equation for the reaction of each of the following acids in water and its corresponding K_a expression:
   (a) monohydrogen citrate ion

   (b) dihydrogen citrate ion

   (c) aluminum ion

   (d) hydrogen peroxide

8. Write the equation for the reaction of each of the following bases in water and its corresponding K_b expression:
   (a) ammonia

   (b) benzoate ion

   (c) acetate ion

   (d) monohydrogen citrate ion

   (e) pyradine (C_5H_5N).

9. For the following, complete the equilibria, then state whether reactants or products are favored.

(a)

$$Fe(H_2O)_6^{3+}(aq) + HO_2^-(aq) \rightleftharpoons$$

(b)

$$H_2SO_3(aq) + IO_3^-(aq) \rightleftharpoons$$

(c)

$$CN^-(aq) + H_2PO_4^-(aq) \rightleftharpoons$$

10. Using the substances H_2CO_3, HCO_3^-, $H_2C_2O_4$ and $HC_2O_4^-$, write an equilibrium equation with a $K_{eq} > 1$.

11. Consider the following equilibria:

$$H_2SiO_3 + BrO^- \rightleftharpoons HBrO + HSiO_3^- \quad K_{eq} = 0.095$$

$$HClO + BrO^- \rightleftharpoons HBrO + ClO^- \quad K_{eq} = 14$$

Rank the acids H_2SiO_3, HClO, and HBrO from strongest to weakest.

12. Explain why HCl, HBr, and HI are equally strong in water. Use balanced chemical equations in your answer.

6.5 Calculations Involving K_a and K_b

Warm Up

Three of the binary acids containing halogens (hydrohalic acids) are strong acids, while one of them is a weak acid.

1. (a) Write a chemical equation representing the reaction of hydrochloric acid with water and identify the two conjugate acid-base pairs.

   (b) If the concentration of this *strong* acid solution is 0.50 M, what would you expect the $[H_3O^+]$ and the pH of the solution to be?

2. (a) Write a chemical equation representing the reaction of hydrofluoric acid with water and identify the two conjugate acid-base pairs. Which side of this equilibrium is favored?

   (b) If the concentration of this *weak* acid solution is also 0.50 M, would you expect the pH of this solution to be the same as for 0.50 M HCl? Why or why not?

3. Write K_a or K_b expressions for the following species in aqueous solutions:

   (a)

   K_a for $HNO_2 =$

   (b)

   K_b for $C_2O_4^{2-} =$

   (c)

   K_a for $HC_2O_4^- =$

   (d)

   K_b for $NH_3 =$

Part A: Calculations for Weak Acids

Most of the substances that we identify as acids ionize only to a slight extent in water and are therefore considered to be weak acids. As you learned earlier, the following equilibrium exists in an aqueous solution of a weak acid HA:

$$HA(aq) + H_2O(l) \rightleftharpoons A^-(aq) + H_3O^+(aq)$$

In this chemical equilibrium system, the weaker an acid HA is, the less ionization occurs, the more the reactants are favored, and the smaller the value of the acid ionization constant K_a. In strong acids, the ionization is effectively 100%. In weak acids, because most of the original HA remains intact, the concentration of hydronium ions at equilibrium is *much less* than the original concentration of the acid.

Consider the data presented in one of the sample questions in the previous section:

"A 0.10M solution of Aspirin (acetylsalicylic acid) at 25°C is found to have a pH of 2.27."

This pH corresponds to a hydronium ion concentration of only 5.4×10^{-3} M. It tells us that acetylsalicylic acid must be a weak acid because only a small percentage of the original 0.10 mol/L of the acid has ionized. If the ionization were complete, we would expect the hydronium ion concentration to also be 0.10 M, corresponding to a pH of 1.00.

For a strong acid, because almost all of the original acid has been converted to hydronium ions, the $[H_3O^+]$ in the solution is the same as the original acid concentration.

Is there also a way that we could calculate the equilibrium concentration of hydronium ions (and therefore the pH) of a *weak acid* solution if we knew the initial acid concentration? The answer is yes because using an ICE table, you learned how to calculate equilibrium concentrations of chemical species given initial concentrations and a value for the equilibrium constant K_{eq}. Let's begin the discussion of calculating this value and others for weak acid equilibria.

In section 6.4, you were introduced to the acid ionization constant K_a which is given by:

$$K_a = \frac{[A^-][H_3O^+]}{[HA]}$$

This equation will be used to solve the majority of calculations that you will perform, and the three values that we normally care most about are K_a, [HA], and $[H_3O^+]$. Because we are concerned with three variables, there are really three types of problems that you will be expected to solve for weak acids. Let's consider examples of each.

Problem Type 1: Calculating $[H_3O^+]$ (and so usually pH) given K_a and $[HA]_{initial}$

Let's return to our Warm Up example:
Calculate the pH of 0.50 M solution of hydrofluoric acid (HF). K_a for HF = 3.5×10^{-4}

Note the following:
1. The concentration given refers to how the solution *was prepared* — namely, $[HA]_{initial}$.
2. The question is asking us to determine the *equilibrium* concentration of hydronium ions (from which we calculate pH), given the *initial* concentration of the acid and the value of K_a. This suggests the use of an ICE table.
3. We are given the value for K_a. If the value is not given, you will be expected to find that value by referring to the Table of Relative Strengths of Brønsted-Lowry Acids and Bases (Table 5.2.1 and inside back cover).
4. For most weak acid problems, it will be necessary to construct an ICE table underneath the balanced equation for the equilibrium existing in the aqueous solution.
5. Any problem that requires us to calculate a value *on the ICE table itself* will also require us to define a value for that unknown (as *x*, for example). These problems usually involve $[H_3O^+]$ or the $[HA]_{initial}$
6. HF is a monoprotic acid, but even if we are given a polyprotic weak acid, *the first ionization* (donation of the first proton) is *the predominant reaction determining pH*. Subsequent ionizations with much smaller K_a values are of no relative consequence in determining pH and can therefore be considered insignificant.
7. As only the first proton is donated, there is always a 1:1:1 mole ratio in the change line of such problems.
8. You should always read the question carefully — more than once if necessary — so that you are certain of the type of problem you are given, and what you are being asked to calculate.

Let's begin solving this problem: Let *x* equal the equilibrium concentration of hydronium ions: $[H_3O^+]_{eq}$

Now let's construct the ICE table, fill it in, and discuss the entries in Table 6.5.1.

Table 6.5.1 *ICE Table for Example Problem*

		HF +	H_2O	⇌ F^- +	H_3O^+
Initial Concentration	**(I)**	0.50		0	0
Change in Concentration	**(C)**	$-x$		$+x$	$+x$
Equilibrium Concentration	**(E)**	$0.50 - x$		x	x

When filling in the table, we start by making two assumptions:

1. We don't include the concentration of water for the same reason we don't include it in a K_a expression. We can assume the [H$_2$O] remains constant because the extent to which the large concentration of water (55.6 M) actually *changes* is insignificant, given the relatively tiny amount of ionization that actually occurs.

2. We know that the initial [H$_3$O$^+$] in pure water (prior to the ionization of the weak acid) is really 10^{-7} M. However, the fact that the K_a of this acid is so much greater than K_w means that we can assume that this initial [H$_3$O$^+$] (resulting from the autoionization of water) is insignificant compared to the equilibrium [H$_3$O$^+$] resulting from the ionization of this weak acid. Consequently, the initial [H$_3$O$^+$] is given as zero.

At this point we could attempt to solve for x:

$$K_a = \frac{[F^-][H_3O^+]}{HF} = \frac{x^2}{0.50 - x} = 3.5 \times 10^{-4}$$

However, that process would require the use of the quadratic formula. We can avoid this if we make another simplifying assumption based on the relative magnitudes of [HF]$_{initial}$ and K_a. The value of K_a is so small compared to the initial concentration of the acid that the percent of the acid that actually ionizes will not significantly change the original concentration. As a result, we can make the following assumption:

[HF]$_{eq}$ = 0.50 – x ≈ 0.50

It is important to note that the assumption *is not always* justified. This assumption is valid if the percent ionization of the weak acid is ≤ 5%. The percent ionization is given by the following equation:

$$\% \text{ ionization} = \frac{[H_3O^+]_{eq}}{[HA]_{initial}} \times 100\%$$

A good rule-of-thumb is:

If the [HA]$_{initial}$ is at least 10^3 times larger than the K_a value, the assumption is valid.

It may surprise you to know that, as the initial concentration of the acid decreases, the percent ionization *increases*. This means that the assumption is normally only valid for relatively high weak-acid concentrations. Table 6.5.2 demonstrates this, using data for three different concentrations of acetic acid.

Table 6.5.2 *Data for Three Concentrations of Acetic Acid*

[CH$_3$COOH]	Percent Ionization	Assumption
0.15 M	1.1%	valid
0.015 M	3.5%	valid
0.0015 M	11%	invalid

In most, if not all of the problems you will encounter in this course, the assumption will be justified and the use of the quadratic formula can therefore be avoided. However, it is still necessary to *explicitly state the assumption each time you solve such a problem*. If you simply ignore x, it constitutes a chemical error. Having made the assumption, let's return to our example. We now have:

$$\frac{x^2}{0.50} = 3.5 \times 10^{-4} \qquad x = \sqrt{(3.5 \times 10^{-4})(0.50)} = 0.0\underline{13}2 \; M \; H_3O^+$$

pH = –log (0.0$\underline{13}$2) = 1.$\underline{88}$ (two significant figures)

Let's calculate the % ionization as a check to see if our most recent assumption was valid:

$$\% \text{ ionization} = \frac{[H_3O^+]_{eq}}{[HF]_{initial}} \times 100\% = \frac{0.0132 \text{ M}}{0.50 \text{ M}} \times 100\% = 2.6\% \text{ (the assumption was valid)}$$

Quick Check

1. Why don't we include water's concentration when we complete an ICE table?

   _____

   _____

2. Why are we justified in assuming that the initial concentration of hydronium ions prior to the ionization of a weak acid is effectively zero?

   _____

   _____

3. What allows us to assume that $[HA]_{eq} \approx [HA]_{initial}$ in weak acid equilibria?

   _____

   _____

Sample Problem 6.5.1 — Calculating pH given K_a and $[HA]_{initial}$

Hydrogen sulfide is a poisonous flammable gas whose "rotten egg" smell is perceptible at concentrations as low as 0.00047 ppm. It is also a weak acid when dissolved in water. Calculate the pH of 0.0500 M H_2S.

What to Think About

1. The K_a value isn't given. Refer to the table.:
   $K_a = 9.1 \times 10^{-8}$
   This value has two significant figures so our final pH should reflect that.

2. H_2S is a diprotic acid, but the first ionization is all that significantly determines pH.

3. Define x and solve for it using an ICE table.

4. Remember to state the assumption mentioned above.

How to Do It

Let $x = [H_3O^+]_{eq}$

	H_2S	$+$ H_2O	$\rightleftharpoons$ HS^-	$+$ H_3O^+
I	0.0500		0	0
C	$-x$		$+x$	$+x$
E	$0.0500 - x$		x	x

Assume $0.0500 - x \approx 0.0500$

$$K_a = \frac{[HS^-][H_3O^+]}{[H_2S]} = \frac{x^2}{0.0500} = 9.1 \times 10^{-8}$$

$$x = \sqrt{(9.1 \times 10^{-8})(0.0500)} = \underline{6.7}4 \times 10^{-5} \text{ M}$$

$$pH = -\log(\underline{6.7}4 \times 10^{-5}) = 4.\underline{17} \text{ (two sig figs)}$$

Practice Problems 6.5.1 — Calculating pH given K_a and $[HA]_{initial}$

1. Methanoic acid is the simplest carboxylic acid and is found naturally in the venom of bee and ant stings. (It is also called formic acid, from the Latin word for ant, *formica*). Calculate the pH of a 0.50 M solution of methanoic acid.

2. Household vinegar is an aqueous solution of acetic acid. A sample of vinegar is analyzed by titration and found to be 0.850 M CH_3COOH. Calculate the pH of this solution.

3. Calculate the percent ionization in a 0.10 M solution of aspirin with a pH of 2.27. Would our simplifying assumption stated above be valid in this case?

**Problem Type 2:
Calculating $[HA]_{initial}$
given K_a and pH**

In this type of problem, we are given the pH of the solution from which we calculate the equilibrium concentration of hydronium ions. We then use that value and the K_a to calculate the initial concentration of the weak acid.

As we are once again solving for an unknown on the ICE table, we still must define x as that unknown. However, there are a couple of differences between this unknown and the one in the previous problem type:

1. We place this "x" in the "**I**nitial" row, rather than the "**E**quilibrium" row of the table.
2. This unknown will be the largest of any quantity appearing in the ICE table because it's the initial concentration of the acid. Therefore, no assumption regarding its insignificance applies.

Consider the sample problem below. Note that the use of the quadratic isn't necessary to solve this problem. Therefore, there is no need to assume that the amount of ionization of the benzoic acid that occurs relative to the initial concentration is insignificant. However, if the $[H_3O^+]_{eq}$ is sufficiently large relative to the K_a value, the assumption may be valid. Even so, until you have acquired ample experience solving these types of problems, if you don't *have to* make such an assumption to solve the problem, then don't. (Calculate the percentage ionization in the sample problem to see if such an assumption would have been valid in this case.)

Sample Problem 6.5.2 — Calculating $[HA]_{initial}$, given K_a and pH

Benzoic acid is used as a food preservative and a precursor in many organic synthesis reactions. It is the most commonly used chemical standard in calorimetry. What concentration of benzoic acid is required to produce a solution with a pH of 3.30?

What to Think About

1. Once again an ICE table and a "Let $x =$" statement are required.

2. The unknown now represents the initial acid concentration.

3. Use the given pH to calculate the $[H_3O^+]_{eq}$.

4. Look up the value of K_a for benzoic acid: $K_a = 6.5 \times 10^{-5}$

How to Do It

Let $x = [C_6H_5COOH]_{initial}$

$$[H_3O^+]_{eq} = 10^{-3.30} = 0.000501 \text{ M}$$

$$C_6H_5COOH + H_2O \rightleftharpoons C_6H_5COO^- + H_3O^+$$

I	x		0	0
C	-0.000501		$+0.000501$	$+0.000501$
E	$x - 0.000501$		0.000501	0.000501

$$K_a = \frac{[C_6H_5COO^-][H_3O^+]}{[C_6H_5COOH]} = \frac{(0.000501)^2}{(x - 0.000501)}$$

$$= 6.5 \times 10^{-5}$$

$$x - 0.000\underline{501} = \frac{(0.000\underline{501})^2}{6.5 \times 10^{-5}}$$

$$x = 0.00\underline{44} \text{ M (2 significant figures)}$$

Practice Problems 6.5.2 — Calculating $[HA]_{initial}$, given K_a and pH

1. Citric acid is one of the acids responsible for the sour taste of lemons. What concentration of citric acid would be required to produce a solution with a pH of 2.50?

2. Rhubarb's sour taste is due in part to the presence of oxalic acid. A solution of oxalic acid has had the label removed. What concentration should appear on the label if the pH of the solution is found to be 0.55?

3. Nitrous acid is one of the components of acid rain. An aqueous solution of nitrous acid is found to have a pH of 1.85. Calculate the concentration of the acid.

This type of problem does not require us to solve for an unknown x on the ICE table because all of the entries in the table are available directly or indirectly from the information provided in the question. The pH allows us to determine $[H_3O^+]_{eq}$. Although there is *no need* for a simplifying assumption, we are given enough information to calculate percentage ionization to determine if the assumption is justified.

Let's return to acetylsalicylic acid in the following sample problem.

Sample Problem 6.5.3 — Calculating K_a, given $[HA]_{initial}$ and pH

A 0.100M solution of acetylsalicylic acid (Aspirin) is found to have a pH of 2.27. Calculate the K_a for this acid. The formula for acetylsalicylic acid is $C_8H_7O_2COOH$.

What to Think About

1. Use pH to calculate $[H_3O^+]_{eq}$ and then use that value to complete the entries in the ICE table.

   Note that we cannot ignore 0.00537 M compared to 0.10 M.

2. Record the K_a value to two significant figures.

How to Do It

$$[H_3O^+]_{eq} = 10^{-2.27} = 0.00537 \text{ M}$$

$$C_8H_7O_2COOH + H_2O \rightleftharpoons C_8H_7O_2COO^- + H_3O^+$$

	$C_8H_7O_2COOH$	H_2O	$C_8H_7O_2COO^-$	H_3O^+
I	0.100		0	0
C	−0.00537		+0.00537	+0.00537
E	0.0946		0.00537	0.00537

$$K_a = \frac{[C_8H_7O_2COOH^-][H_3O^+]}{[C_8H_7O_2COOH]} = \frac{(0.00537)^2}{0.0946}$$

$$= \underline{3.0} \times 10^{-4} \text{ (2 significant figures)}$$

Practice Problems 6.5.3 — Calculating K_a, given $[HA]_{initial}$ and pH

1. One form of vitamin C is ascorbic acid, $H_2C_6H_6O_6$. The name originates from the fact that ascorbic acid prevents scurvy — a fact first discovered in 1747 by British surgeon John Lind. This subsequently resulted in citrus juice (from limes and lemons) being supplied to sailors in the Royal Navy. A 0.100 M solution of ascorbic acid is found to have a pH of 3.00. Calculate the K_a for ascorbic acid.

2. Lactic acid ($C_3H_6O_3$) is a weak acid produced in muscle tissue during anaerobic respiration and is the acid present in sour milk. It's also responsible for the sour taste of sauerkraut. A 0.025 M solution of lactic acid is found to have a pH of 2.75. Calculate the K_a for lactic acid.

Part B: Calculations for Weak Bases

As with acids, most bases are weak. As you learned earlier, water can both accept and donate a proton (hydrogen ion), so weak bases also participate in equilibria with water. Using the symbol "B" for a weak base, we can represent this as:

$$B(aq) + H_2O(l) \rightleftharpoons HB^+(aq) + OH^-(aq)$$

We can therefore write the following expression for the base ionization constant. K_b:

$$K_b = \frac{[HB^+][OH^-]}{[B]}$$

Although the three main types of problems associated with weak bases that you will be expected to solve are similar to those identified above for weak acids, additional calculations are often required.

For example, if you are given a problem that includes a weak base from the Table of Relative Strengths of Brønsted-Lowry Acids and Bases, you cannot simply look up the K_b value as you are able to with K_a values. Rather, you must *calculate the* K_b *for that base by using the* K_a *value of its conjugate acid.* Let's derive the equation that you will need to perform that calculation below.

Consider the conjugate acid/base pair of NH_4^+ and NH_3 and their respective K_a and K_b expressions:

$$K_a \text{ for } NH_4^+ = \frac{[NH_3][H_3O^+]}{[NH_4^+]} \quad \text{and} \quad K_b \text{ for } NH_3 = \frac{[NH_4^+][OH^-]}{[NH_3]}$$

Note that two common terms appear in each equation. Let's take advantage of that by multiplying the two expressions together and cancelling those common terms:

$$K_a \times K_b = \frac{[NH_3][H_3O^+]}{[NH_4^+]} \times \frac{[NH_4^+][OH^-]}{[NH_3]} = [H_3O^+][OH^-] = K_w$$

This allows us to formulate the following relationship for *conjugate acid-base pairs*:

$$K_a \text{ (conjugate acid)} \times K_b \text{ (conjugate base)} = K_w = 1.00 \times 10^{-14} \text{ (at 25°C)}$$

Taking the negative logarithm of both sides of the above equation, we obtain:

$$pK_a \text{ (conjugate acid)} + pK_b \text{ (conjugate base)} = pK_w = 14.00 \text{ (at 25°C)}$$

This allows us to calculate the K_b value for any weak base in the table. For example:

$$K_b \text{ for } NH_3 = \frac{K_w}{K_a \text{ for } NH_4^+} = \frac{1.00 \times 10^{-14}}{5.6 \times 10^{-10}} = 1.8 \times 10^{-5}$$

You must be careful to use the *correct* K_a value when performing this calculation, especially when dealing with amphiprotic ions. Before you begin the calculation, first locate the weak base on the *right side* of the table. Then look over to the left side of that equation to find the appropriate conjugate acid. The K_a value for *that acid* is the correct value to use in the calculation.

Quick Check

1. Complete the following table by choosing the correct conjugate acid and corresponding K_a value and then calculating the K_b value for each weak base. Consider carefully the first three that are done for you.

	Weak Base	Conjugate Acid	Appropriate K_a Value	Calculated K_b
(a)	$HC_2O_4^-$	$H_2C_2O_4$	5.9×10^{-2}	1.7×10^{-13}
(b)	$H_2PO_4^-$	H_3PO_4	7.5×10^{-3}	1.3×10^{-12}
(c)	HPO_4^{2-}	$H_2PO_4^-$	6.2×10^{-8}	1.6×10^{-7}
(d)	NO_2^-			
(e)	$HC_6H_5O_7^{2-}$			
(f)	HCO_3^-			
(g)	CN^-			

2. Calculate the pK_a and pK_b values for all of the chemical species above. How do the sizes of pK_a values for acids and pK_b values for bases relate to their strength?

Problem Type 1: Calculating [OH⁻] (and usually pH) given K_b and [B]$_{initial}$

In the same way we discussed each of the three main problem types associated with weak acids, let's now begin that discussion for solutions of weak bases.

Remember that if the question involves a weak base from the table, we have to calculate the K_b rather than simply looking it up and also that solving for "x" gives us [OH⁻] rather than [H₃O⁺]. This means that an extra calculation will be necessary if we are asked to determine pH. Remember this point. Consider the sample problems below.

Notice that, in the second sample problem, the cyanide *ion* is reacting with water and functioning as a weak base. Such an event is known as **hydrolysis**. A detailed treatment of hydrolysis will appear in Chapter 7. For now, simply treat ions as you would any other weak base in water.

Note that the only *uncharged* weak base (except for water) in the table of acids and bases is NH_3. Most of the remaining weak bases on the table are anions. Many neutral weak bases are organic compounds called amines containing nitrogen whose lone electron pair is available to accept a proton from water.

Sample Problem 6.5.4(a) — Calculating [OH⁻] and pH using K_b and [B]$_{initial}$

One of the compounds responsible for the odor of herring brine is methylamine, CH_3NH_2.
($K_b = 4.4 \times 10^{-4}$) Calculate the pH of a 0.50 M solution of methylamine.

What to Think About

1. Once again, construct an ICE table. Add the proton from water to the nitrogen in methylamine. Be careful with charges.

2. A value on the ICE table is being solved so, once again, define x.

3. The K_b value is provided so you don't have to calculate it.

4. The relative magnitudes of K_b and [OH⁻]$_{initial}$ allow the assumption to be valid.

How to Do It

Let $x = [OH^-]_{eq}$

$$CH_3NH_2 + H_2O \rightleftharpoons CH_3NH_3^+ + OH^-$$

I	0.50		0	0
C	−x		+x	+x
E	0.50 − x		x	x

Assume $0.50 - x \approx 0.50$

$$K_b = \frac{[CH_3NH_3^+][OH^-]}{[CH_3NH_2]} = \frac{x^2}{0.50} = 4.4 \times 10^{-4}$$

$x = 0.0148$ M OH⁻ so pOH = −log 0.0148 = 1.829

pH = 14.00 − 1.829 = 12.17

Sample Problem 6.5.4(b) — Calculating [OH⁻] and pH using K_b and [B]$_{initial}$

Calculate the pH of a solution containing 0.20 M CN⁻.

What to Think About

1. Calculate the K_b value using the K_a for HCN.

2. As CN⁻ is a relatively strong weak base, expect this solution to have a relatively high pH.

3. Remember to convert the [OH⁻] to pH.

How to Do It

$$K_b \text{ for } CN^- = \frac{K_w}{K_a \text{ for } HCN} = \frac{1.00 \times 10^{-14}}{4.9 \times 10^{-10}}$$

$$= 2.04 \times 10^{-5}$$

Let $x = [OH^-]_{eq}$

$$CN^- + H_2O \rightleftharpoons HCN + OH^-$$

I	0.20		0	0
C	−x		+x	+x
E	0.20 − x		x	x

Assume $0.20 - x \approx 0.20$

$$K_b = \frac{[HCN][OH^-]}{[CN^-]} = \frac{x^2}{0.20} = 2.04 \times 10^{-5}$$

$x = 0.00202$ M OH⁻ so pOH = −log (0.00202)

$$= 2.695$$

pH = 14.00 − 2.695 = 11.31

Practice Problems 6.5.4 — Calculating [OH⁻] and pH using K_b and $[B]_{initial}$

1. Hydrazine, N_2H_4 is used in rocket fuel, in producing polymer foams, and in the production of air bags. The K_b for hydrazine is 1.7×10^{-6}. Calculate the pH of the solution prepared by dissolving 12.0 g of hydrazine in 500.0 mL of solution.

2. Calculate the $[OH^-]$, $[H^+]$, pOH, and pH of a 0.60 M solution of $HCOO^-$.

3. Calculate the K_a and pK_a values for the following:
   (a) methylammonium, $CH_3NH_3^+$

   (b) hydrazinium, $N_2H_5^+$

Problem Type 2: Calculating [B]$_{initial}$, given K_b and pH (or pOH)

This type of problem may require us to calculate both $[OH^-]_{eq}$ (from pH) and K_b (from a K_a) at the beginning of the solution process. We then continue in much the same way as we would for this type of problem when dealing with weak acids. Consider the sample problem below.

Sample Problem 6.5.5 — Calculating [B]$_{initial}$, given K_b and pH (or pOH)

What concentration of NH_3 would be required to produce a solution with a pH = 10.50?

What to Think About

1. Calculate both the K_b for NH_3 (using the K_a for NH_4^+) and the $[OH^-]_{eq}$ (from the given pH).

2. The unknown x will represent the $[NH_3]_{initial}$.

3. No assumption regarding x is part of solving this problem.

How to Do It

$$K_b \text{ for } NH_3 = \frac{K_w}{K_a \text{ for } NH_4} = \frac{1.00 \times 10^{-14}}{5.6 \times 10^{-10}} = 1.78 \times 10^{-5}$$

$$pOH = 14.00 - 10.50 = 3.50$$

$$[OH^-]_{eq} = 10^{-3.50} = 3.16 \times 10^{-4} \text{ M}$$

Let $x = [NH_3]_{initial}$

$$NH_3 + H_2O \rightleftharpoons NH_4^+ + OH^-$$

I	x		0	0
C	-3.16×10^{-4}	✕	$+3.16 \times 10^{-4}$	$+3.16 \times 10^{-4}$
E	$x - 3.16 \times 10^{-4}$		3.16×10^{-4}	3.16×10^{-4}

$$K_b = \frac{[NH_4^+][OH^-]}{[NH_3]} = \frac{(3.16 \times 10^{-4})^2}{x - 3.16 \times 10^{-4}}$$

$$= 1.78 \times 10^{-5}$$

$$x - 3.16 \times 10^{-4} = \frac{(3.16 \times 10^{-4})^2}{1.78 \times 10^{-5}}$$

$$x = 0.0059 \text{ M}$$

Practice Problems 6.5.5 — Calculating [B]$_{initial}$ given K_b and pH (or pOH)

1. Ethylamine ($C_2H_5NH_2$) is a pungent colorless gas used extensively in organic synthesis reactions. It is also a weak base with K_b = 5.6×10^{-4}. What mass of ethylamine is dissolved in 250.0 mL of a solution having a pH of 11.80?

Continued on the next page

Practice Problems 6.5.5 (Continued)

2. What concentration of CN^- would produce a solution with a pH of 11.50?

3. Using the K_b provided above for hydrazine, calculate the $[N_2H_4]$ required to produce a solution with a $[H_3O^+] = 1.0 \times 10^{-10}$ M.

Problem Type 3: Calculating K_b given $[B]_{initial}$ and pH (or pOH)

As was the case with an acidic system, this final type of problem requires no simplifying assumption (although it may prove to be justified), and no unknown to be solved in the ICE table. All of the entries in the table are available, either directly or indirectly, from the information provided in the question. Consider the sample problem below.

Sample Problem 6.5.6 — Calculating K_b, given $[B]_{initial}$ and pH (or pOH)

A solution is prepared by dissolving 9.90 g of the weak base hydroxylamine, NH_2OH, in enough water to produce 500.0 mL of solution. The pH of the solution is found to be 9.904. Calculate the K_b for hydroxylamine.

What to Think About	**How to Do It**
1. Convert grams of the compound dissolved in 500.0 mL to moles per liter to determine $[NH_2OH]_{initial}$.	$[NH_2OH]_{initial} = 9.90\ g\ \dfrac{NH_2OH}{0.5000\ L} \times \dfrac{1\ mol}{33.0\ g} = 0.600\ M$
2. Use the pH to determine $[OH^-]_{eq}$. That value shows that the % ionization is small enough to assume $0.600 - x \approx 0.600$.	$pOH = 14.000 - 9.904 = 4.096$ $[OH^-]_{eq} = 10^{-4.096} = 8.0168 \times 10^{-5}\ M$
3. Record the final answer to three significant figures.	

$$NH_2OH + H_2O \rightleftharpoons NH_2OH_2^+ + OH^-$$

I	0.600		0	0
C	-8.0168×10^{-5}		$+8.0168 \times 10^{-5}$	$+8.0168 \times 10^{-5}$
E	≈ 0.600		8.0168×10^{-5}	8.0168×10^{-5}

$$K_b = \frac{[NH_2][OH_2^-]}{[NH_2OH]} = \frac{(8.0168\ 10^{-5})^2}{0.600} = 1.07 \times 10^{-8}$$

Practice Problems 6.5.6 — Calculating K_b, given $[B]_{initial}$ and pH (or pOH)

1. A 0.400 M solution of the weak base methylamine, CH_3NH_2, is found to have a pH of 12.90. Calculate the K_b of methylamine and the percentage ionization. Compare your calculation of this K_b value with the sample problem above involving methylamine. What might this indicate about the temperature of this solution?

2. One of the most effective substances at relieving intense pain is morphine. First developed in about 1810, the compound is also a weak base. In a 0.010 M solution of morphine, the pOH is determined to be 3.90. Calculate the K_b and pK_b for morphine. (Let "Mor" and "HMor$^+$" represent the conjugate pair in your equilibrium reaction.)

3. Quinine, $C_{20}H_{24}N_2O_2$, is a naturally occurring white crystalline base used in the treatment of malaria. It is also present in tonic water. Calculate the K_b for this weak base if a 0.0015 M solution has a pH of 9.84. (Let "Qui" and "HQui$^+$" represent the conjugate pair in your equilibrium reaction.)

6.5 Activity: An Organically Grown Table of Relative Acid Strengths

Question

Can you construct your own table of relative acid strengths using the relationships you have learned in this section to calculate the K_a values for a series of organic compounds?

Background

The vast majority of chemical compounds are organic (carbon-based) compounds and some of those are weak acids and bases. Given sufficient data, you can use various calculations to organize a collection of these compounds into a table from strongest to weakest acids similar to the Table of Relative Strengths of Brønsted-Lowry Acids and Bases (Table A5), which you have already seen.

Procedure

1. You will be given data relating to 15 organic compounds, 9 of which are weak acids, and 6 of which are weak bases. The data could include K_b, pK_b, pK_a, pH, and pOH information. None of the compounds appear on Table of Relative Strengths of Brønsted-Lowry Acids and Bases (Table 5.2.1 and Table A5). The data will not be presented in any particular order.

2. If given the acid, write the formula for the conjugate base and vice versa.

3. Use the data given to calculate the K_a value for each weak acid or for the conjugate acid of each weak base using any of the relationships discussed in this section. Before beginning, you may want to review the relationships below.

4. Place the equilibrium equation for each weak acid (or conjugate acid) reacting with water in order from strongest down to weakest acid as in an example provided.

5. Include in the right-hand section of the table you construct the K_a value you have calculated.

6. All of the acids are monoprotic carboxylic acids (containing –COOH) and so all of their conjugate bases will appear as –COO⁻ following donation of the proton to water.

7. All of the weak bases are neutral amines containing nitrogen and so all of their conjugate acids will have an extra "H" on the nitrogen and a "+" charge following acceptance of a proton from the hydronium ion.

8. Consider the following when calculating the K_a values (Assume 25°C):

   - For conjugate acid-base pairs: $K_a \times K_b = K_w = 1.00 \times 10^{-14}$

   - For conjugate acid-base pairs: $pK_a + pK_b = pK_w = 14.00$

   - Review how to calculate K_a and K_b, given pH (or pOH) and $[HA]_{initial}$ (or $[B]_{initial}$).

9. Fill in the missing items in the table below and use the data provided to calculate the K_a values for all the acids and conjugate acids of the bases given in the table.

10. Then arrange all of the acids and conjugate acids in the correct order in the table, including the appropriate equilibrium equation for the examples given. Note that "soln" stands for "solution."

Compound Name	Formula for Conjugate Acid	Formula for Conjugate Base	Calculate K_a for Acid or Conjugate Acid Given
Acids			
chloroacetic acid	$ClCH_2COOH$		$pK_a = 2.85$
phenylacetic acid	C_7H_7COOH		pH of 1.0 M soln = 2.155
propanoic acid	C_2H_5COOH		K_b for conjugate base = 7.7×10^{-10}
pyruvic acid	C_2H_3OCOOH		pK_b for conjugate base = 11.45
lactic acid	C_2H_5OCOOH		pOH of 0.10 M soln = 11.57
acetylsalicylic acid	$C_8H_7O_2COOH$		K_b for conjugate base = 2.8×10^{-11}
glycolic acid	CH_3OCOOH		$pK_a = 3.82$
glyoxylic acid	$CHOCOOH$		pK_b for conjugate base = 10.54
glyceric acid	$C_2H_5O_2COOH$		pH of 1.0 M soln = 1.77
Bases			
pyridine		C_5H_5N	$K_b = 1.7 \times 10^{-9}$
trimethylamine		$(CH_3)_3N$	pOH of 0.10 M soln = 2.60
piperidine		$C_5H_{10}NH$	$pK_b = 2.89$
tert-butylamine		$(CH_3)_3CNH_2$	pH of a 1.0 M soln = 12.34
ethanolamine		$C_2H_5ONH_2$	pK_a of conjugate acid = 9.50
n-propylamine		$C_3H_7NH_2$	$pK_b = 3.46$

Relative Strengths of Some Organic Acids and Bases

Strength of Acid	Equilibrium Reaction With Water						K_a Value	Strength of Base
	Acid	+	H_2O	$\rightleftharpoons$	H_3O^+	+ Base		
Stronger ↑				$\rightleftharpoons$				Weaker
				$\rightleftharpoons$				
				$\rightleftharpoons$				
				$\rightleftharpoons$				
				$\rightleftharpoons$				
				$\rightleftharpoons$				
				$\rightleftharpoons$				
				$\rightleftharpoons$				
				$\rightleftharpoons$				
				$\rightleftharpoons$				
				$\rightleftharpoons$				
				$\rightleftharpoons$				
				$\rightleftharpoons$				
				$\rightleftharpoons$				
				$\rightleftharpoons$				
Weaker				$\rightleftharpoons$				Stronger

Sample:

HCOOH (given an acid)	+	H_2O	$\rightleftharpoons$	H_3O^+	+	$HCOO^-$	1.8×10^{-4}	
NH_4^+	+	H_2O	$\rightleftharpoons$	H_3O^+	+	**NH_3** (given a base)	5.6×10^{-10}	

Results and Discussion

1. Are the K_a values for these monoprotic carboxylic acids significantly different from each other in their orders of magnitude? _____

2. Which acid is the strongest and which base is the strongest? _____

3. Use the K_a vlaues you have calculated to expand the Table of Relative Strengths of Acids and Bases, if you want to include these organic compounds.

6.5 Review Questions

1. Calculate the $[H_3O^+]$, $[OH^-]$, pH, and pOH that results when 23.0 g of HCOOH is dissolved in enough water to produce 500.0 mL of solution.

2. At standard temperature and pressure, 5.6 L of H_2S is dissolved in enough water to produce 2.50 L of solution. Calculate the pH of this solution and percent ionization of H_2S.

3. The percent ionization of 0.100 M solution of an unknown acid is 1.34%. Calculate the pH of this solution and identify the acid.

4. Because of its high reactivity with glass, hydrofluoric acid is used to etch glass. What mass of HF would be required be required to produce 1.5 L of an aqueous solution with a pH of 2.00?

5. Phosphoric acid is used in rust removal and also to add a tangy sour taste to cola soft drinks. A solution of phosphoric acid is found to have a pOH of 12.50. Calculate the concentration of this acid.

6. Oxalic acid is a white crystalline solid. Some of its uses include rust removal, bleaching pulpwood, and even as an ingredient in baking powder. A 250.0 mL sample of an oxalic solution is found to have a pH of 2.35. What mass of oxalic acid would remain if this aqueous solution were evaporated to dryness?

7. Hypochlorous acid (HClO) is used mainly as an active sanitizer in water treatment. A 0.020 M solution of hypochlorous acid is found to have a pH of 4.62. Calculate the K_a for hypochlorous acid.

8. Phenylacetic acid ($C_6H_5CH_2COOH$) is used in some perfumes and in the production of some forms of penicillin. A 0.100 M solution of phenylacetic acid has a pOH of 11.34. Calculate the K_a of phenylacetic acid.

9. Complete the following table:

Conjugate Acid	Conjugate Base	K_a for Acid	pK_a	K_b for Base	pK_b
	NO_2^-				
H_2O_2					
	$C_6H_5O^-$				
HSO_4^-					

10. Complete the following table of amphiprotic ions:

Conjugate Acid	Conjugate Base	K_a for Acid	pK_a	K_b for Base	pK_b
	HPO_4^-				
$H_2C_6H_5O_7^-$					
	$H_2BO_3^-$				
HCO_3^-					

11. An aqueous solution is prepared by dissolving 5.6 L of NH_3 gas, measured at STP, in enough water to produce 750.0 mL of solution. Calculate the pH of this solution.

12. Isopropylamine, $(CH_3)_2CHNH_2$, is a weak base ($K_b = 4.7 \times 10^{-4}$) used in herbicides such as Roundup and some chemical weapons. Calculate the pOH and pH of a 0.60 M solution of isopropylamine.

13. What concentration of sulfite ions will produce a solution with a pH of 10.00?

14. Trimethylamine, $(CH_3)_3N$ is a weak base ($K_b = 6.3 \times 10^{-5}$). It is one of the compounds responsible for the smell of rotting fish and is used in a number of dyes. What volume of this gas, measured at STP, must be dissolved in 2.5 L of solution to give that solution a pOH of 2.50?

15. A 0.10 M solution of ethylamine, $C_2H_5NH_2$, is found to have a pOH of 2.14. Calculate the K_b for ethylamine.

7 Applications of Acid-Base Reactions

This chapter focuses on the following AP Big Ideas from the College Board:

- Big Idea 3: Changes in matter involve the rearrangement and/or reorganization of atoms and/or the transfer of electrons.
- Big Idea 6: Any bond or intermolecular attraction that can be formed can be broken. These two processes are in a dynamic competition, sensitive to initial conditions and external perturbations.

By the end of this chapter, you should be able to do the following:

- Demonstrate an ability to design, perform, and analyze a titration experiment involving the following:
  - primary standards
  - standardized solutions
  - titration curves
  - appropriate indicators
- Describe an indicator as an equilibrium system
- Perform and interpret calculations involving the pH in a solution and K_a for an indicator
- Describe the hydrolysis of ions in salt solutions
- Analyse the extent of hydrolysis in salt solutions
- Describe buffers as equilibrium systems
- Describe the preparation of buffer systems
- Predict what will happen when oxides dissolve in rain water

By the end of this chapter, you should know the meaning of these **key terms**:

- acid rain
- buffers
- dissociation
- equation
- equivalence point (stoichiometric point)
- hydrolysis
- hydrolysis reaction
- indicator
- primary standards
- salt
- titration
- titration curve
- transition point

The freshwater African chichlid requires water having a pH between 8.0 and 9.2 to survive. The South American chichlid requires water with a pH between 6.4 and 7.0.

7.1 Hydrolysis of Salts — The Reactions of Ions with Water

Warm Up

Consider the neutralization reactions described below.

1. (a) When equal volumes of 0.10 M HNO_3 and 0.10 M KOH solutions react together, what salt solution exists in the reaction vessel following the reaction?

_____

   (b) Consider the dissociated ions of this salt. Is either of the ions located on the table of relative strengths of Brønsted-Lowry acids and bases (Table A5, at the back of the book)? If so, where? Does this help you predict if the pH of this solution will be equal to, above, or below 7?

_____

_____

2. (a) When equal volumes of 0.10 M CH_3COOH and 0.10 M NaOH solutions react together, what salt solution exists in the reaction vessel following the reaction?

_____

   (b) Consider the dissociated ions of the salt. Is either of the ions located on the table of relative strengths of acids and bases (Table A5)? If so, where? Does this help you predict if the pH of this solution will be equal to, above, or below 7?

_____

_____

Neutralization Reactions

In previous years you were introduced to several reaction types, which were then discussed in more detail in Grade 11. One of those reaction types is *neutralization* in which an acid and a base react to produce a salt and water. The name suggests that when an equal number of moles of hydronium ions from an acid and hydroxide ions from a base react together, the resulting solution will be neutral and thus have a pH of 7.

It might surprise you to know that many such neutralizations produce salt solutions that are actually acidic or basic. This phenomenon occurs because one or both of the dissociated *ions of the product salt* behave as weak acids or bases and thus react with water to generate hydronium or hydroxide ions. This is known as hydrolysis.

Hydrolysis is the reaction of an ion with water to produce either the conjugate base of the ion and *hydronium ions* or the conjugate acid of the ion and *hydroxide ions*.

Whether or not the ions of a salt will hydrolyze can often be determined by considering the acids and bases from which the salt was produced. In each case, we look at the dissociated ions of each type of salt individually and assess their ability to either donate protons to or accept protons from water. This allows us to predict if aqueous solutions of those salts will be acidic, basic, or neutral. Let's begin that discussion below.

A. Neutral Salts: Salts Containing the Anion of a Strong Acid and the Cation of a Strong Base

Consider the first Warm Up question above. When equal amounts of nitric acid and potassium hydroxide solutions are combined, an aqueous solution of potassium nitrate is produced. The dissociated ions present in this solution are the K^+ cations from the strong base and the NO_3^- anions from the strong acid.

Like all aqueous ions, the alkali ions in the solution become surrounded by water molecules in the hydration process, but no reaction between those ions and water occurs. The same is true for all alkali (Group 1) ions and most alkaline earth (Group 2) ions (except beryllium). *These are the cations of strong bases and they do not hydrolyze.* We therefore consider them *spectator ions.*

Like all ions that are the conjugate bases of strong acids, NO_3^- ions have no measurable ability to accept protons from water. Notice on the table of relative strengths of Brønsted-Lowry acids and bases (Table A5) that all such anions of strong acids are located at the top right corner of the table and on the receiving end of a *one-way arrow* — they are thus incapable of accepting protons and so cannot function as bases. Like the cations mentioned above, all anions of strong monoprotic acids are hydrated in water, but no further reaction occurs. *The anions of strong monoprotic acids do not hydrolyze.* They are considered *spectator ions in water.* (Note that the bisulphate anion, HSO_4^-, although unable to *accept* protons from water, is a relatively strong weak acid and therefore *donates* protons to water.) We can generalize these results into the conclusion stated below.

> A salt containing the anion of a strong monoprotic acid and the cation of a strong base will produce a neutral solution in water because neither of the ions undergoes hydrolysis.

Quick Check

1. Circle the ions in the following list that represent cations of strong bases.

   Al^{3+} Rb^+ Fe^{3+} Cr^{3+} Ca^{2+} Sn^{4+} Cs^+ Ba^{2+}

2. Circle the ions in the following list that represent the conjugate bases of strong acids.

   F^- ClO_2^- ClO_4^- SO_4^{2-} Cl^- NO_2^- CH_3COO^- CN^- NO_3^-

3. Circle the following salts whose ions will not hydrolyze when dissociated in water.

   NH_4Cl Na_2CO_3 $RbClO_4$ Li_2SO_3 BaI_2 NH_4HCOO KIO_3 CsF $CaBr_2$

B. Basic Salts: Salts Containing the Anion of a Weak Acid and the Cation of a Strong Base

Look at the second Warm Up question at the beginning of this section. When equal amounts of acetic acid and sodium hydroxide solutions are combined, an aqueous solution of sodium acetate is produced. The dissociated ions present in this solution are the Na^+ ions from the strong base and the CH_3COO^- ions from the weak acid. We have already stated that alkali ions are incapable of undergoing hydrolysis and thus cannot affect the solution's pH.

However, the acetate anion is the conjugate base of a weak acid and therefore has a measurable ability to accept protons from water. Being a weak base, the acetate anion will react with water by accepting protons in the following hydrolysis reaction:

$$CH_3COO^-(aq) + H_2O(l) \rightleftharpoons CH_3COOH(aq) + OH^-(aq)$$

As a result of the hydrolysis, this solution will be basic with a pH above 7.

A salt containing the anion of a weak monoprotic acid and the cation of a strong base will produce a basic solution in water because the anion acts as a weak base, producing hydroxide ions, and the cation does not react.

Quick Check

1. Which of the following salts contain the anion of a weak acid?

   NH_4Cl $NaClO_4$ $Fe(CH_3COO)_3$ KF $LiCl$

   $Al(NO_3)_3$ NH_4HSO_4 $Pb(NO_2)_2$ NH_4I $Ba(CN)_2$

2. Which of the following salts will produce a basic aqueous solution due to anionic hydrolysis?

   $AlBr_3$ $Ca(HCOO)_2$ $RbClO_4$ $SrCO_3$ $Mg(CN)_2$

   $NaCH_3COO$ $Cr(NO_3)_3$ LiC_6H_5COO FeI_3 K_3PO_4

Qualitatively, we can predict that such solutions will be basic due to anionic hydrolysis, but we can also perform all of the same types of calculations for these dissolved anions that we introduced in the previous section for any weak base in water. Consider Sample Problem 7.1.1 below.

Sample Problem 7.1.1 — Calculating the pH of a Basic Salt Solution

A 9.54 g sample of $Mg(CN)_2$ is dissolved in enough water to make 500.0 mL of solution. Calculate the pH of this solution.

What to Think About

1. First calculate the concentration of the compound and then write the dissociation equation to determine the initial concentration of each ion.

2. Then consider each of the dissociated ions separately and decide if either is capable of hydrolyzing.

3. Mg^{2+} will not hydrolyze, but CN^- is the conjugate base of a very weak acid and is therefore a relatively strong weak base. Consequently, expect the pH of this solution to be well above 7.

4. Write an equilibrium equation under which you can construct an ICE table.

5. To calculate the $[OH^-]_{eq}$, first calculate the K_b of the cyanide anion.

6. Remember that you are solving for $[OH^-]_{eq}$ on the ICE table and so an extra step is required to determine pH.

How to Do It

$$\frac{9.54\ \cancel{g}}{0.5000\ L} \times \frac{1\ mol\ Mg(CN)_2}{76.3\ \cancel{g}} = 0.250\ M$$

$$Mg(CN)_2(s) \rightarrow Mg^{2+}(aq) + 2\ CN^-(aq)$$
$$0.250\ M \qquad\qquad 0.250\ M \qquad\quad 0.500\ M$$

$$K_b\ for\ CN^- = \frac{K_w}{K_a\ for\ HCN} = \frac{1.00 \times 10^{-14}}{4.9 \times 10^{-10}}$$

$$= 2.04 \times 10^{-5}$$

Let $x = [OH^-]_{eq}$

$$CN^- + H_2O \rightleftharpoons HCN + OH^-$$

I	0.500		0	0
C	$-x$		$+x$	$+x$
E	$0.500 - x$		x	x

Assume $0.500 - x \approx 0.500$

$$K_b = \frac{[HCN][OH^-]}{[CN^-]} = \frac{x^2}{0.500} = 2.04 \times 10^{-5}$$

$$x = 3.19 \times 10^{-3}\ M = [OH^-]_{eq}$$

$$pOH = -log\ (0.00319) = 2.496$$

$$pH = 14.00 - 2.496 = 11.50\ (2\ sig.\ figures)$$

Practice Problems 7.1.1 — Basic Salt Solutions

1. Without performing any calculations, rank the following salts in order of decreasing pH of their 0.10 M aqueous solutions:

   Na_2SO_3 LiF KNO_2 RbCN $Na_2C_2O_4$ K_2CO_3

   _____ > _____ > _____ > _____ > _____ > _____

2. Sodium carbonate is used in the manufacture of glass and also as a laundry additive to soften water. A 200.0 mL aqueous solution of 0.50 M Na_2CO_3 is diluted to 500.0 mL. Calculate the pH of the resulting solution.

3. What concentration of NaHCOO would be required to produce an aqueous solution with a pH of 9.20? Begin by writing the equation for the predominant equilibrium present in the solution.

C. Acidic Salts I: Salts Containing the Conjugate Base of a Strong Acid and the Conjugate Acid of a Weak Base

When equal amounts of NH_3 (a weak base) and HCl (a strong acid) are combined, the neutralization reaction that occurs is:

$$NH_3(aq) + HCl(aq) \rightarrow NH_4Cl(aq)$$

Following the reaction, the two ions present in the solution are NH_4^+ and Cl^-. We have already noted that chloride ions, like all conjugate bases of the strong acids, are incapable of accepting protons by reacting with water. However, the ammonium cation is the conjugate acid of a weak base and is therefore a weak acid capable of donating protons to water in the cationic hydrolysis reaction shown below:

$$NH_4^+(aq) + H_2O(l) \rightleftharpoons NH_3(aq) + H_3O^+(aq)$$

As a result of the hydrolysis, this solution will be acidic with a pH below 7.

A salt containing the cation of a weak base and the anion of a strong monoprotic acid will produce an acidic solution in water because the cation acts as a weak acid producing hydronium ions and the anion does not react.

Quick Check

1. Write the hydrolysis equation for the conjugate acids of the following weak bases reacting with water and the appropriate K_a expressions:

    (a) methylamine, CH_3NH_2

    (b) n-propylamine, $C_3H_7NH_2$

    (c) trimethylamine $(CH_3)_3N$

2. Calculate the K_a for the conjugate acids of the above weak bases given the following data:

    (a) K_b for methylamine $= 4.4 \times 10^{-4}$

    (b) K_b for n–propylamine $= 3.5 \times 10^{-4}$

    (c) K_b for trimethylamine $= 6.3 \times 10^{-5}$

Sample Problem 7.1.2 — Calculating the pH of an Acidic Salt

The K_b for pyridine, C_5H_5N, is 4.7×10^{-9}. Calculate the pH of a 0.10 M solution of $C_5H_5NHNO_3$.

What to Think About	How to Do It
1. The dissociation equation yields $C_5H_5NH^+$ and NO_3^- ions, each at 0.10 M concentrations. The NO_3^- ion will not hydrolyze as it is the conjugate base of a strong acid. The $C_5H_5NH^+$ cation, however will donate protons to water as it is the conjugate acid of a weak base. That hydrolysis will make the solution acidic. 2. Calculate the K_a for the cation using K_w and the given K_b for pyridine. 5. Construct an ICE table under the equilibrium equation for hydrolysis of the cation. 6. Calculate the pH.	$C_5H_5NHNO_3 (s) \rightarrow C_5H_5NH^+ (aq) + NO_3^- (aq)$ $\qquad\qquad\qquad\quad$ 0.10 M $\qquad\quad$ 0.10 M K_a for $C_5H_5NH^+ = \dfrac{K_w}{K_b \text{ for } C_5H_5N} = \dfrac{1.00 \times 10^{-14}}{4.7 \times 10^{-9}}$ $\qquad\qquad\qquad\qquad = 2.13 \times 10^{-6}$ Let $x = [H_3O^+]_{eq}$ $C_5H_5NH^+ + H_2O \rightleftharpoons C_5H_5N + H_3O^+$

	$C_5H_5NH^+$		C_5H_5N	H_3O^+
I	0.10		0	0
C	$-x$		$+x$	$+x$
E	$0.10 - x$		x	x

Assume $0.10 - x \approx 0.10$

K_a for $C_5H_5NH^+ = \dfrac{[C_5H_5N][H_3O^+]}{[C_5H_5NH^+]} = \dfrac{x^2}{0.10}$

$\qquad\qquad\qquad\qquad = 2.13 \times 10^{-6}$

$x = \sqrt{2.13 \times 10^{-7}} = 4.61 \times 10^{-4}$

$pH = -\log(4.61 \times 10^{-4}) = 3.34$ (2 sig. figures)

Practice Problems 7.1.2 — Acidic Salt Solutions

1. Ammonium nitrate is used in fertilizers, the production of explosives, and instant cold packs. Calculate the pH of the solution produced when 16.0 g of NH_4NO_3 is dissolved in enough water to produce 500.0 mL of solution.

2. The pH of a 0.50 M solution of N_2H_5Cl is found to be 4.266. Calculate the K_a for $N_2H_5^+$. Check your answer, given that the K_b for $N_2H_4 = 1.7 \times 10^{-6}$.

3. What mass of C_5H_5NHCl would be required to produce 250.0 mL of an aqueous solution with a pH = 3.00? (See Sample Problem 6.1.2 above for K_a value.)

D. Acidic Salts II: Salts Containing the Anion of a Strong Acid and a Small Highly Charged Metal Cation

Look closely at the table of relative strengths of acids and bases (Table A5) that you were introduced to earlier in this text. Notice that several of the weak acids are actually hydrated metal cations that are capable of donating protons to water. For example, consider the Al^{3+} cation. The ion itself is not a Brønsted-Lowry acid. However, when it is surrounded by six water molecules in its hydrated form, the combination of its small size and relatively high charge (called a high "charge density" by chemists) draws the oxygens of the attached water molecules very close. This further polarizes their O–H bonds. This increases the tendency of those molecules to donate protons, making the hydrated cation complex a weak acid. Consider the diagram of the hydrated cation in Figure 7.1.1.

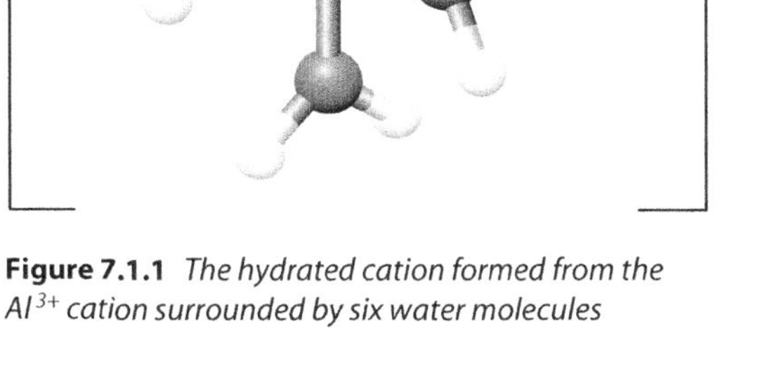

We would not expect this to occur when larger cations with a smaller charge are hydrated. This explains why the alkali metals and all but one of the alkaline earth cations do not hydrolyze. Can you suggest a reason why Be^{2+} *does* react with water to some extent?

The hydrolysis reaction for the hexaaquoaluminum cation is shown below:

$$Al(H_2O)_6^{3+}(aq) + H_2O(l) \rightleftharpoons Al(H_2O)_5OH^{2+}(aq) + H_3O^+(aq)$$

Figure 7.1.1 *The hydrated cation formed from the Al^{3+} cation surrounded by six water molecules*

Note that in the hydrolysis reaction, the number of bound water molecules decreases by one (from six to five) when the proton is donated to water and generates an OH^-. This reduces the overall charge of the cation from 3+ to 2+.

Other hydrated cations such as Fe^{3+}, Cr^{3+}, Sn^{2+}, and Cu^{2+} show similar behavior. Generally, each ion will form an acidic hydrate with the number of water molecules equal to twice the magnitude of the charge on the cation. As a result, a salt containing one of these cations and an anion from a strong monoprotic acid would produce an acidic aqueous solution.

A salt containing the anion of a strong monoprotic acid and a small highly charged metal cation will produce an acidic solution in water because the hydrated cation acts as a weak acid producing hydronium ions and the anion does not react.

Quick Check

1. Circle the salts below that will produce acidic aqueous solutions.

   $NaNO_2$ NH_4I $CaBr_2$ $CrCl_3$ $Sr(CN)_2$ $RbCH_3COO$ $Fe(NO_3)_3$ Li_2SO_3

2. Write the hydrolysis reactions for the following hydrated cations:

   (a) $Sn(H_2O)_4^{2+}$

   (b) $Cu(H_2O)_4^{2+}$

   (c) $Fe(H_2O)_6^{3+}$

Sample Problem 7.1.3 — Acidic Salts II

What mass of $CrCl_3$ would be required to produce 250.0 mL of an aqueous solution with a pH of 2.75?

What to Think About

1. The aqueous solution contains Cl^- ions which will not hydrolyze and hydrated Cr^{3+} ions which will react with water to produce H_3O^+ ions.

2. Use the pH to determine the $[H_3O^+]_{eq}$. Use the $[H_3O^+]_{eq}$, together with the K_a value for $Cr(H_2O)_6^{3+}$ from the table, to calculate the $[Cr^{3+}]_{initial}$.

How to Do It

$$[H_3O^+]_{eq} = 10^{-pH} = 10^{-2.75} = 0.00178\ M$$

$$Let\ x = [Cr^{3+}]_{initial} = [Cr(H_2O)_6^{3+}]_{initial}$$

$$Cr(H_2O)_6^{3+} + H_2O \rightleftharpoons Cr(H_2O)_5OH^{2+} + H_3O^+$$

	x		0	0
C	−0.00178		+0.00178	+0.00178
E	x − 0.00178		0.00178	0.00178

Continued opposite

Sample Problem 7.1.3 (Continued)

What to Think About	**How to Do It**
3. $[CrCl_3]_{initial} = [Cr^{3+}]_{initial} = [Cr(H_2O)_6^{3+}]_{initial}$	$K_a = \dfrac{[Cr(H_2O)_5OH^{2+}][H_3O^+]}{[Cr(H_2O)_6^{3+}]} = \dfrac{(0.00178)^2}{x - 0.00178}$ $= 1.5 \times 10^{-4}$ $1.5 \times 10^{-4}x - 2.67 \times 10^{-7} = 3.17 \times 10^{-6}$ $x = 2.29 \times 10^{-2}\ mol/L$ $2.29 \times 10^{-2}\ \dfrac{mol\ CrCl_3}{\cancel{L}} \times \dfrac{158.5\ g}{\cancel{mol}} \times 0.2500\ \cancel{L}$ $= 0.91\ g\ (2\ sig.\ figures)$

Practice Problems 7.1.3 — Acidic Salts II

1. Iron(III) nitrate solutions are used by jewellers to etch silver and silver alloys. Calculate the pH of a 6.0 M $Fe(NO_3)_3$ solution.

2. What concentration of $AlBr_3$ would be required to produce an aqueous solution with a pH of 3.25?

3. Unlike the other alkaline earth cations, the hydrated beryllium ion will hydrolyze by donating protons to water. The K_a for $Be(H_2O)_4^{2+}$ is 3.2×10^{-7}. Calculate the pH of a 0.400 M aqueous solution of BeI_2.

Magnitudes of K_a and K_b Values

Whether the two remaining classes of salts produce acidic, basic, or neutral solutions depends on the relative magnitudes of the K_a and K_b values for their ions. For the most part, you will not be expected to calculate the pH of such solutions, but calculations will be necessary to determine if those pH values will be above, below, or equal to 7.

E. Salts Containing Weakly Acidic Cations and Weakly Basic Anions

Consider the ions present in a 0.10 M solution of NH_4CN. The ammonium ion is the conjugate acid of a weak base (NH_3), and the cyanide ion is the conjugate base of a weak acid (HCN). As a result, both dissociated ions will react with water and influence the pH of the salt solution. Those two hydrolysis reactions and the corresponding equilibrium constant values are shown below:

$$NH_4^+(aq) + H_2O(l) \rightleftharpoons NH_3(aq) + H_3O^+(aq) \qquad K_a = 5.6 \times 10^{-10}$$

$$CN^-(aq) + H_2O(l) \rightleftharpoons HCN(aq) + OH^-(aq) \qquad K_b = 2.0 \times 10^{-5}$$

Note that the K_b of the cyanide ion is greater than the K_a of the ammonium ion. This tells us that the anionic hydrolysis reaction that generates hydroxide ions occurs to a much greater extent than the cationic hydrolysis reaction that produces hydronium ions. Consequently the [OH$^-$] will exceed the [H$_3$O$^+$] and the solution will be basic with a pH greater than 7.

Thus by comparing the K_a and the K_b values of the ions which hydrolyze, we can determine if the solution will be acidic, basic, or neutral. Below are guides for using this comparison to determine the acidity of a solution.

A salt containing a weakly acidic cation and a weakly basic anion will produce a solution that is:

acidic if K_a for the cation $>$ K_b for the anion
basic if K_a for the cation $<$ K_b for the anion
neutral if K_a for the cation $=$ K_b for the anion

Quick Check

1. Which of the following salts will dissociate into ions that will *both* react with water?

   KI   NH$_4$NO$_2$ Fe(CN)$_3$ Sn(NO$_3$)$_2$ Rb$_2$C$_2$O$_4$ CrBr$_3$ NaCH$_3$COO   AlF$_3$

2. Write out the two hydrolysis reactions that occur when a sample of NH$_4$F dissolves in water.

3. Which of the two hydrolysis reactions in question 2 above will occur to a greater extent? How do you know?

_____

_____

Sample Problem 7.1.4 — Determining if a Salt Solution is Acidic, Basic, or Neutral
Determine if an aqueous solution of Cr(CH$_3$COO)$_3$ will be acidic, basic, or neutral and include the hydrolysis reactions that occur.

What to Think About	How to Do It
1. Both of the dissociated ions will hydrolyze.	$Cr(H_2O)_6^{3+}(aq) + H_2O(l) \rightleftharpoons Cr(H_2O)_5OH^{2+}(aq) + H_3O^+(aq)$ $K_a = 1.5 \times 10^{-4}$
2. Use the K_a for the hydrated Cr^{3+} ion from Table A5.	$CH_3COO^-(aq) + H_2O(l) \rightleftharpoons CH_3COOH(aq) + OH^-(aq)$ $K_b = \dfrac{K_w}{K_a \text{ for } CH_3COOH} = \dfrac{1.00 \times 10^{-14}}{1.8 \times 10^{-5}} = 5.6 \times 10^{-10}$
3. Calculate the K_b for the acetate ion using K_w and the K_a for acetic acid.	As the value of K_a for $Cr(H_2O)_6^{3+}$ is greater than the value of K_b for CH_3COO^-, the hydrolysis of the cation-producing hydronium ions predominates. We would expect this solution to be acidic.

Practice Problems 7.1.4 — Determining if a Salt Solution is Acidic, Basic, or Neutral

1. Determine if a solution of NH_4CH_3COO will be acidic, basic, or neutral, and include the hydrolysis reactions that occur. Can you predict the approximate pH of this solution?

2. Ammonium phosphate is used in fire extinguishers and also in bread making to promote the growth of the yeast. Determine if an aqueous solution of $(NH_4)_3PO_4$ will be acidic, basic, or neutral and include the hydrolysis reactions that occur.

3. Arrange the following 0.10 M salt solutions in order of decreasing pH:

   $FeCl_3$ $(NH_4)_2CO_3$ $Al(CH_3COO)_3$ $NaNO_3$

   _____ > _____ > _____ > _____

F. Salts Containing the Cation of a Strong Base and an Amphiprotic Anion

When aqueous solutions containing an equal number of moles of NaOH and H_3PO_4 are combined, only a *partial neutralization* of the triprotic acid occurs, producing an aqueous solution of NaH_2PO_4. This solution contains sodium ions, which we know will not hydrolyze, and the amphiprotic dihydrogen phosphate ion, which is capable of both donating protons to and accepting protons from water. To determine which hydrolysis reaction predominates, we must once again compare a K_a to a K_b value, except in this case those values are for the *same ion*.

> A salt containing a cation of a strong base and an amphiprotic anion will produce a solution that is: acidic if K_a for the anion > K_b for the anion
> basic if K_a for the anion < K_b for the anion

Table 7.1.1 *Summary Table of Hydrolysis*

| Type of Salt | | Examples | Ion That Hydrolyzes | Result for Solution |
Cation	Anion			
A. Of a strong base	Of a strong acid	KNO_3, NaCl	neither	neutral
B. Of a strong base	Of a weak acid	KCN, $NaCH_3COO$	anion	basic
C. Of a weak base[†]	Of a strong acid	NH_4I, NH_4Br	cation	acidic
D. Small highly charged	Of a strong acid	$FeCl_3$, $Al(NO_3)_3$	cation	acidic
E. Weakly acidic	Weakly basic	NH_4CN, $Fe(NO_2)_2$	both	acidic or basic*
F. Of a strong base	Amphiprotic	$NaHCO_3$, $KHSO_3$	anion	acidic or basic*

[†] *Conjugate acid of* weak base
*Acidic if $K_a > K_b$, basic if $K_a < K_b$

Sample Problem 7.1.5 — Determining if a Salt Solution Containing the Cation of a Strong Base and an Amphiprotic Anion Will be Acidic or Basic

Determine if a 0.10 M solution of NaH_2PO_4 will be acidic or basic and include the hydrolysis reactions that occur.

What to Think About	How to Do It
1. The sodium ions will not hydrolyze, but the dihydrogen phosphate anion can. It is amphiprotic.	$H_2PO_4^-(aq) + H_2O(l) \rightleftharpoons HPO_4^{2-}(aq) + H_3O^+(aq)$ $K_a = 6.2 \times 10^{-8}$ $H_2PO_4^-(aq) + H_2O(l) \rightleftharpoons H_3PO_4(aq) + OH^-(aq)$
2. Use the K_a for the anion from Table A5. Calculate the K_b using K_w and the K_a for phosphoric acid.	$K_b = \dfrac{K_w}{K_a \text{ for } H_3PO_4} = \dfrac{1.00 \times 10^{-14}}{7.5 \times 10^{-3}} = 1.3 \times 10^{-12}$ As the value of K_a is greater than the value of K_b for the anion, the hydrolysis reaction producing hydronium ions is the predominant one and the solution will therefore be slightly acidic.

Practice Problems 7.1.5 — Determining if a Salt Solution Containing the Cation of a Strong Base and an Amphiprotic Anion Will be Acidic or Basic

1. Determine if a 0.10 M solution of K_2HPO_4 will be acidic or basic and include the hydrolysis reactions that occur.

2. Arrange the following 0.10 M aqueous solutions in order of increasing pH:

   $NaHSO_3$ $LiHCO_3$ $KHSO_4$

   _____ < _____ < _____

3. Are any calculations required to determine if an aqueous solution of $KHSO_4$ will be acidic or basic? Why or why not?

7.1 Activity: Hydrolysis — A Rainbow of Possibilities

Question

Can you predict the color that a universal indicator solution will display when added to a series of 10 different 0.1 M aqueous salt solutions?

Background

A universal indicator solution is a mixture of several chemical indicators, each of which undergoes a different color change over a different pH range. When the indicators are mixed, their colors and color changes combine over the entire range of the pH scale to display a series of rainbow-like hues depending on the hydronium concentration of the particular solution as shown in the table below.

pH	1	2	3	4	5	6	7	8	9	10	11	12	13	14
Colour	RED		ORANGE		YELLOW		GREEN			BLUE		PURPLE-VIOLET		

Procedure

1. Calculate the pH of the following 0.1 M aqueous solutions to determine the color displayed by the universal indicator when added to that solution. (The pH values for the first two salts are provided for you.)

    (a) $NaHSO_4$ (pH ≤ 3)

    (b) K_3PO_4 (pH ≥ 11)

    (c) NH_4NO_3

    (d) $Na_2C_2O_4$

2. Write the formula for each salt underneath the appropriate pH value and color in the diagram below.

3. Determine if the following 0.1 M aqueous solutions are acidic, basic, or neutral by comparing the K_a value for the cation to the K_b value for the anion in each salt.

    (a) $(NH_4)_2CO_3$

(b) $Fe_2(SO_4)_3$

(c) $(NH_4)_2C_2O_4$

4. The three solutions above have the following three pH values: 3.8, 6.5, and 8.5. Match each solution above to one of the pH values and write the formula for that salt underneath the appropriate pH value and color in the diagram below.

5. Determine if the following 0.1 M aqueous solutions should be acidic, basic, or neutral by comparing the K_a value to the K_b value for the anion in each salt.
   (a) KH_2PO_4

   (b) $NaHSO_3$

   (c) $KHCO_3$

6. The three solutions above have the following three pH values: 5.5, 4.0, and 9.0. Match each solution above to one of the pH values and write the formula for that salt underneath the appropriate pH value and color in the diagram below.

pH	1	2	3	4	5	6	7	8	9	10	11	12	13	14
Colour	RED		ORANGE		YELLOW		GREEN			BLUE		PURPLE-VIOLET		

_____

_____

_____

Formulas

Results and Discussion

1. If possible, ask your teacher if you can test the results of your calculations by preparing as many of the above solutions as possible. Add a few drops of universal indicator to each and/or measure the pH values with a pH meter.

7.1 Review Questions

1. Three separate unmarked beakers on a lab bench each contain 200 mL samples of 1.0 M clear, colorless aqueous solutions. You are told that one beaker contains $Ca(NO_3)_2$, one beaker contains K_3PO_4, and one beaker contains $Al(NO_3)_3$. Using the principles learned in this section, describe a simple test to identify the solutes in each solution.

2. Complete the following table for the six aqueous solutions by filling in the missing entries.

Salt Formula	Ion(s) that Hydrolyze(s)	Result for Aqueous Solution (Acidic, Basic, or Neutral)	Equation(s) for Hydrolysis Reaction(s) (if any)
$(NH_4)_2SO_3$			
$Al(IO_3)_3$			
RbF			
SrI_2			
KHC_2O_4			
$Fe_2(SO_4)_3$			

3. A 50.0 mL solution of 0.50 M KOH is combined with an equal volume of 0.50 M CH_3COOH.
   (a) Write the chemical equation for this neutralization reaction.

   (b) What salt concentration exists in the reaction vessel following the reaction?

(c) Calculate the pH of this solution. Begin by writing the equation for the predominant equilibrium that exists in the solution.

4. A 25.2 g sample of Na_2SO_3 is dissolved in enough water to make 500.0 mL of solution. Calculate the pH of this solution.

5. Copper(II) chloride dihydrate is a beautiful blue-green crystalline solid. The K_a for the tetraaquocopper(II) ion is 1.0×10^{-8}. What mass of $CuCl_2 \cdot 2\,H_2O$ would be required to produce 250.0 mL of an aqueous solution with a pH of 5.00?

6. Sodium cyanide is mainly used to extract gold and other precious metals in mining. Cyanide salts are also among the most rapidly acting of all poisons. A 300.0 mL aqueous solution of sodium cyanide is found to have a pH of 9.50. What mass of NaCN exists in this solution?

7. One of the main uses for ammonium perchlorate is in the production of solid rocket propellants. Calculate the pH of the solution produced by dissolving 470 g of the salt in enough water to make 5.0 L of solution.

8. Without performing any calculations, arrange the following 0.1 M aqueous solutions in order of increasing pH.

RbI NH_4Br KCN Li_2CO_3 $NaHSO_4$ $Cr(NO_3)_3$ Na_3PO_4 $FeCl_3$

_____ < _____ < _____ < _____ < _____ < _____ < _____ < _____

9. (a) What mass of KNO_2 will remain when 350.0 mL of an aqueous solution with a pH of 8.50 is evaporated to dryness?

(b) How will you observe the pH change as the volume of the solution decreases? Why?

10. Calculate the pH of a 0.500 M aqueous solution of N_2H_5Cl. The K_b for $N_2H_4 = 1.7 \times 10^{-6}$.

7.2 The Chemistry of Buffers

Warm Up

1. Consider a 1.0 L aqueous solution of 0.10 M CH_3COOH. Calculate the pH of this solution and begin by writing the equation for the predominant chemical equilibrium in the solution.

2. From the $[H_3O^+]$ calculated above, determine the percent ionization of the acetic acid.

3. A student adds 0.10 mol of $NaCH_3COO$ to the solution described in question 1.

   (a) In which direction will the equilibrium shift after the addition of the salt?

   _____

   (b) What is the name of this type of effect? (Hint: You learned about this effect in Chapter 4.)

   _____

   (c) How will the percent ionization of the acetic acid and the pH of the solution be affected?

   _____

   (d) What two chemical species participating in the equilibrium will predominate in the solution following the addition of the salt? Can these species react *with each other*?

   _____

Definition of a Buffer

Most biological fluids are solutions whose pH must be maintained within a very narrow range. In your body for example, the ability of your blood to transport oxygen depends on its pH remaining at or very near 7.35. If the pH of your blood were to deviate much more than one-tenth of a unit beyond that, it would lose the capacity to perform its vital function. Yet many products of the multiple metabolic processes occurring right now in your body are acidic compounds, each potentially able to lower your blood pH to fatal levels. In addition, many of the foods you enjoy are full of acidic compounds. If your blood were a solution incapable of effectively and continually resisting changes to its pH level, these foods would kill you. A solution capable of maintaining a relatively constant pH is known as a buffer.

> An acid-base **buffer** is a solution that resists changes in pH following the addition of relatively small amounts of a strong acid or strong base.

To understand how (and how well) a buffer solution resists pH changes, we must first discuss the *components* of a buffer. Let's start with the same 1.0 L solution of 0.10 M CH_3COOH from the Warm Up above. Only a very small percent of the weak acid is ionized, symbolized using enlarged and reduced fonts in the reaction shown below.

$$\textbf{CH}_\textbf{3}\textbf{COOH}(aq) + H_2O(l) \rightleftharpoons CH_3COO^-(aq) + H_3O^+(aq)$$

If a relatively small amount of a strong base such as NaOH is added to this solution, a "reservoir" of *almost all* of the original 0.10 mol of acetic acid is available to neutralize the added hydroxide ions. However, this same minimal ionization means that the solution has *almost no ability* to counter the effects of added hydronium ions from an acid because the concentration of the conjugate base in this solution is so low. This solution therefore cannot be considered to be a buffer.

To give this solution the ability to also absorb *added acid*, we must increase the concentration of the conjugate base. We can do this by adding a soluble salt of that anion in the form of, for example, sodium acetate. The weak base added is normally *the conjugate base of the weak acid already in solution*. This prevents the two species from neutralizing each other.

Let's now add 0.10 mol of $NaCH_3COO$ to this acidic solution with no volume change and consider the effects. The Na^+ is a spectator ion in the solution, but according to Le Châtelier's principle, the added acetate ions will shift the weak acid equilibrium to the left in favor of the molecular acid and further suppress its already minimal ionization. This qualifies as the common ion effect that you learned about earlier. As the shift occurs, the percent ionization of the acetic acid drops from the original 1.3% to only 0.018%. The corresponding decrease in hydronium concentration results in a pH increase in the solution from 2.87 to 4.74.

Recall the pH calculations for weak acids. There, we assumed that the equilibrium concentrations of those acids were effectively equal to the initial concentrations if the percent ionization was less than 5%. In this solution, the assumption is even more justified. Also, the equilibrium concentration of the acetate ion in this solution is slightly more than 0.10 M because of that very small percent ionization. However, because the ionization is so minimal, the equilibrium concentration of the acetate ion is effectively equal to the concentration of that anion resulting from the added salt. Also any hydrolysis of the acetate ion can be ignored because of the presence of the acetic acid.

Our solution is therefore effectively a 0.10 M solution of both acetic acid and its conjugate base, the acetate anion. Appreciable quantities of each component give the solution the capacity to resist large pH changes equally well following the addition of relatively small amounts of either a strong base or a strong acid.

This is because significant (and approximately equal) reservoirs of *both* a weak acid *and* a weak base are available in the solution to neutralize those stresses. Thus, the buffer has the ability to shift to the left or the right in response to either acidic or basic stress.

$$\textbf{CH}_\textbf{3}\textbf{COOH}(aq) + H_2O(l) \rightleftharpoons \textbf{CH}_\textbf{3}\textbf{COO}^-(aq) + H_3O^+(aq)$$
$$\approx 0.10\text{ M} \qquad\qquad\qquad \approx 0.10\text{ M}$$

A buffer solution normally consists of a weak acid and its conjugate weak base in appreciable and approximately equal concentrations.

We refer to this solution as an **acidic buffer** because it will buffer a solution in the acidic region of the pH scale. Note that it's not necessary for the concentrations of the weak acid and its conjugate base to be equal — only that they are each relatively large. Normally, however, we attempt to keep those concentrations as close to equal as possible so as to give the buffer the ability to resist both acid and base stresses equally well. We'll discuss this in more detail below.

To understand how these components allow the buffer to resist significant pH changes, we begin by manipulating the K_a expression for this weak acid. Our goal is to derive an equation that tells us what determines the hydronium concentration of this buffer solution.

Because: $K_a = \dfrac{[CH_3COO^-][H_3O^+]}{[CH_3COOH]}$ then: $[H_3O^+] = K_a\,\dfrac{[CH_3COOH]}{[CH_3COO^-]}$

Or in general: $[H_3O^+] = K_a\,\dfrac{[HA]}{[A^-]}$

This simple but important equation means that the hydronium ion concentration (and therefore the pH) of a buffer solution depends on two factors:
- the K_a value for the weak acid and
- the *ratio* of the concentration of that weak acid to its conjugate base in the solution

Examining the above equation more closely reveals some additional details:

1. If the concentrations of the acid and its conjugate base are equal, a ratio of 1 means that the hydronium concentration in the buffer solution is simply equal to the K_a value for the weak acid. Thus, in our example, the $[H_3O^+] = K_a$ for acetic acid = 1.8×10^{-5} M.

2. At a constant temperature, only one of the two factors determining $[H_3O^+]$ (and therefore its maintenance) is variable. As the value of K_a is a constant, only the weak acid/conjugate base concentration ratio can be changed. Specifically: if the $[HA]/[A^-]$ ratio *increases*, the $[H_3O^+]$ *increases*, and if the $[HA]/[A^-]$ ratio *decreases*, the $[H_3O^+]$ *decreases*.

3. When we dilute a buffer solution, the concentrations of both the weak acid and its conjugate base are reduced equally. Therefore, their ratio remains constant. This means that the hydronium ion concentration (and so the pH) *does not change* when a buffer solution is diluted.

Quick Check

1. Why do we normally attempt to make the concentrations of the weak acid and its conjugate base in a buffer solution approximately equal?

   _____

2. In a buffer containing HA and A⁻, the conjugate base A⁻ will react to neutralize added acid. As a result, following the addition of a small amount of strong acid to a buffer solution, the $[HA]/[A^-]$ ratio will _____ (increase or decrease), the $[H_3O^+]$ will _____ (increase or decrease) slightly, and the pH will _____ (increase or decrease) slightly.

3. Circle the pairs of chemical species below that could be used to prepare a buffer solution.

   HNO_3 and $NaNO_3$ KF and HF HNO_2 and HNO_3 HCOOH and LiHCOO

   $NaHSO_4$ and Na_2SO_4 K_2CO_3 and $K_2C_2O_4$ HCl and NaCl KH_2PO_4 and K_2HPO_4

pH Change Resistance after the Addition of a Strong Acid to an Acidic Buffer

Let's use some of the above points as we discuss the chemistry of buffers in more detail.

We'll begin by using our acetic acid/acetate ion buffer as an example. First, we'll consider how the components of a buffer allow it to resist pH changes after the addition of a relatively small amount of either a strong acid or a strong base.

When a small amount of strong acid is added to a buffer, the reservoir of conjugate base (resulting from the added salt) reacts with the hydronium ions from the acid. In our example, this yields the following net ionic equation:

$$CH_3COO^-(aq) + H_3O^+(aq) \rightarrow CH_3COOH(aq) + H_2O(l)$$

All of the hydronium ions from the strong acid are converted to the weak acid and water in the reaction. This increases the [CH_3COOH] and decreases the [CH_3COO^-] by a stoichiometric amount equal to the number of moles of hydronium ions added from the strong acid. The result is that the buffer component *ratio* increases, which increases the overall [H_3O^+] but *only by a very small amount.*

Although a quantitative treatment of buffer chemistry will likely not be expected in this course, discussing some numbers will demonstrate how effective a buffer is at maintaining a relatively constant pH.

In our original buffer solution, the component ratio was equal to 1. Therefore, the [H_3O^+] was equal to the K_a for acetic acid, namely 1.8×10^{-5} M. We now add 0.010 mol HCl to 1.0 L of our buffer solution containing 0.10 M CH_3COOH and 0.10 M CH_3COO^- with no volume change. The 0.010 mol H_3O^+ will be consumed according to the above reaction and therefore decrease the [CH_3COO^-] by 0.010 mol/L and increase the [CH_3COOH] by 0.010 mol/L. The result for our 1.0 L buffer solution will be as shown in Table 7.2.1.

Table 7.2.1 *Results of Adding 0.010 mol H_3O^+ to the Buffer Solution*

	[CH_3COOH]	[CH_3COO^-]	[CH_3COOH]/[CH_3COO^-] Ratio
Before 0.010 M H_3O^+ added	0.10 M	0.10 M	0.10 M/0.10 M = 1.0
After 0.010 M H_3O^+ added	0.11 M	0.09 M	0.11 M/0.09 M = 1.222

The initial and final [H_3O^+] are calculated below according to the equation:

$$[H_3O^+] = (K_a \text{ for acetic acid}) \times \frac{[CH_3COOH]}{[CH_3COO^-]}$$

Initial [H_3O^+] = $(1.8 \times 10^{-5}$ M$) \times (1.0)$ = **1.8×10^{-5} M** so pH = $-\log (1.8 \times 10^{-5})$ = **4.74**

Final [H_3O^+] = $(1.8 \times 10^{-5}$ M$) \times (1.22)$ = **2.20×10^{-5} M** so pH = $-\log (2.196 \times 10^{-5})$ = **4.66**

The pH has indeed decreased, but *only* by 0.08 units. To appreciate how effective this buffer is at maintaining the pH, consider the result of adding 0.010 mol HCl to 1.0 L of pure water. The [H_3O^+] would increase from 1.0×10^{-7} M to 1.0×10^{-2} M. This represents a *100 000 times increase* in hydronium ion concentration and a *5 unit decrease* in pH from 7.00 to 2.00!

pH Change Resistance after the Addition of a Strong Base to a Buffer Solution

When a small amount of strong base is added to a buffer, the reservoir of weak acid reacts with the hydroxide ions from the base. For our example, this results in the following net ionic equation:

$$CH_3COOH(aq) + OH^-(aq) \rightarrow CH_3COO^-(aq) + H_2O(l)$$

All of the hydroxide ions from the strong base are converted to the conjugate base of the weak acid and water in the reaction. This decreases the [CH_3COOH] and increases the [CH_3COO^-] by a stoichiometric amount equal to the number of moles of hydroxide ions added from the strong base. The result is that the buffer component *ratio* decreases, which decreases the overall [H_3O^+] but once again, *only by a very small amount.*

Using the same 1.0 L buffer solution containing 0.10 M CH_3COOH and 0.10 M CH_3COO^-, we add 0.010 mol NaOH with no volume change. The 0.010 mol OH^- will be consumed according to the above reaction and therefore decrease the [CH_3COOH] by 0.010 mol/L and increase the [CH_3COO^-] by 0.010 mol/L. The result for our 1.0 L buffer solution is shown in Table 8.2.2.

Table 7.2.2 *Results of Adding 0.010 mol OH^- to the Buffer Solution*

	[CH_3COOH]	[CH_3COO^-]	[CH_3COOH]/[CH_3COO^-] Ratio
Before 0.010 M OH^- added	0.10 M	0.10 M	0.10 M/0.10 M = 1.0
After 0.010 M OH^- added	0.09 M	0.11 M	0.09 M/0.11 M = 0.82

We can once again calculate the final $[H_3O^+]$ by multiplying the K_a for acetic acid by the new reduced ratio:

Final $[H_3O^+]$ = $(1.8 \times 10^{-5}$ M$) \times (0.82)$ = **1.48×10^{-5} M** so final pH = $-\log (1.48 \times 10^{-5})$ = **4.83**

The pH value has increased, but once again only slightly — by just 0.09 units. The effectiveness of this buffer at maintaining a relatively constant pH is again evident if we consider that adding 0.010 mol NaOH to 1.0 L of pure water would reduce the $[H_3O^+]$ from 1.0×10^{-7} M to 1.0×10^{-12} M. This represents a *100 000 times decrease* in hydronium ion concentration and a *5 unit increase* in pH from 7.00 to 12.00!

Figure 7.2.1 summarizes our examples above. Note the appropriate net ionic equation below each section of the diagram.

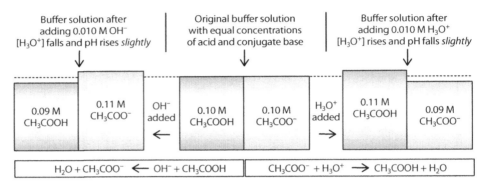

Figure 7.2.1 *The effects on pH of adding a strong base or a strong acid to an acidic buffer*

Sample Problem 7.2.1 — Acidic Buffers

Consider a 1.0 L buffer solution composed of 1.0 M HNO_2 and 1.0 M $NaNO_2$.
(a) Write the equation for the weak acid equilibrium in this solution and highlight the predominant species in that equilibrium.
(b) Write the net ionic equation for the reaction that occurs when a small amount of HCl is added to this solution.
(c) How will the $[HNO_2]/[NO_2^-]$ ratio, the $[H_3O^+]$, and the pH change following the addition of this acid? What equation do you use to make these decisions?

What to Think About

1. The concentrations of both HNO_2 and NO_2^- can be safely assumed to be $\approx$ 1.0 M, making these the major species.

2. The addition of a small amount of the strong acid HCl introduces H_3O^+ ions into the solution, which react with the nitrite anions to form HNO_2 and water.

3. This reduces the $[NO_2^-]$ and increases the $[HNO_2]$ increasing the concentration ratio of weak acid to conjugate base.

   This increases the $[H_3O^+]$ and lowers the pH slightly according to the equation given earlier.

How to Do It

(a) $HNO_2 (aq) + H_2O (l) \rightleftharpoons NO_2^- (aq) + H_3O^+ (aq)$

(b) $NO_2^- (aq) + H_3O^+ (aq) \rightarrow HNO_2 (aq) + H_2O (l)$

(c) The above equation means that the $[HNO_2]/[NO_2^-]$ ratio will increase. This causes the $[H_3O^+]$ to increase slightly and the pH to decrease slightly as per the following equation:

$[H_3O^+] = (K_a$ for $HNO_2) \times \dfrac{[HNO_2]}{[NO_2^-]}$

Practice Problems 7.2.1 — Acidic Buffers

1. (a) Fill in the blanks in the statement below.
    Following the addition of a small amount of strong base to a buffer solution, the [HA]/[A⁻] ratio _____
    (increases or decreases), the [H_3O^+] _____ (increases or decreases) slightly, and the pH _____
    (increases or decreases) slightly.

    (b) Write the net ionic equation for the reaction occurring when a small amount of NaOH is added to the buffer solution
    discussed in Sample Problem 8.2.1 above.

    (c) How will the [HNO_2]/[NO_2^-] ratio, the [H_3O^+], and the pH of this solution change following the addition of this strong
    base?

2. (a) If 100.0 mL of the buffer solution discussed in the sample problem is diluted to 1.0 L, the pH will be the same as the
    original buffer solution. How many moles of HNO_2 and NO_2^- are available to neutralize added H_3O^+ and OH⁻ ions in 1.0 L
    of this diluted solution compared with 1.0 L of the undiluted buffer solution?

    (b) If 0.11 mol HCl is now added to each of these 1.0 L buffer solutions, would they be equally able to resist a significant
    change in their pH levels? Why or why not?

3. Determine if each of the following solutions qualifies as a buffer. Briefly explain your answer in each case.
    (a) 0.10 M HI/0.10 M NaI

    (b) 0.50 M NaF/0.50 M NaCN

    (c) 1.0 M $K_2C_2O_4$/1.0 M KHC_2O_4

    (d) 0.20 M HF/0.20 M HCN

We can also prepare a solution that buffers in the basic region of the pH scale. This is called a **basic buffer**. Although some minor differences exist, the chemistry associated with the maintenance of solution pH is very similar to the chemistry for an acidic buffer.

Consider 1.0 L of an aqueous solution of 0.10 M $NH_3(aq)$ and 0.10 M NH_4Cl (aq). The equilibrium and predominant participating species can be represented as shown below:

$$\underset{\approx 0.10\text{ M}}{NH_3(aq)} + H_2O(l) \rightleftharpoons \underset{\approx 0.10\text{ M}}{NH_4^+(aq)} + OH^-(aq)$$

This solution has appreciable quantities of both a weak base and its conjugate acid in approximately equal amounts. (Note that the chloride ion from the salt is simply a spectator ion in this aqueous solution.) The buffer solution has the capacity to resist large pH changes equally well following the addition of relatively small amounts of both a strong acid and a strong base because significant (and approximately equal) reservoirs of *both* a weak base and a weak acid are available in the solution to neutralize those stresses.

In terms of the hydroxide concentration in a solution of this basic buffer, we can derive an equation similar to the one when we began with an acid ionization earlier. In our example:

Because: $K_b = \dfrac{[NH_4^+][OH^-]}{[NH_3]}$ then: $[OH^-] = K_b\dfrac{[NH_3]}{[NH_4^+]}$

Or in general for any buffer containing a weak base B: $[OH^-] = K_b\dfrac{[B]}{[HB^+]}$

The hydroxide ion concentration (and therefore the pH) of this buffer solution depends on two factors:
- the K_b value for the weak base and
- the *ratio* of the concentration of that weak base to its conjugate acid in the solution

Similar to an acidic buffer, the equation tells us that the hydroxide ion concentration and ultimately the pH of the solution depend on a constant and the ratio of the concentrations of a conjugate acid-base pair. The equation tells us that *if* the [B]/[HB$^+$] ratio *increases*, the [OH$^-$] *increases*, and *if* the [B]/[HB$^+$] ratio *decreases*, the [OH$^-$] *decreases*.

As noted earlier, only a qualitative treatment of buffer chemistry will be expected in this course. However, we can appreciate the effectiveness of this basic buffer by quantitatively investigating the results of adding a relatively small amount of both a strong acid and strong base to 1.0 L of the solution. We will add the same amount of each to the basic buffer as we did to the acidic buffer discussed earlier.

When a small amount of strong acid is added, the reservoir of weak base reacts with the hydronium ions from the acid. In our example, this yields the following net ionic equation:

$$NH_3(aq) + H_3O^+(aq) \rightarrow NH_4^+(aq) + H_2O(l)$$

All of the hydronium ions from the strong acid are converted to the conjugate acid of the weak base and water in the reaction. This increases the [NH$_4^+$] and decreases the [NH$_3$] by a stoichiometric amount equal to the number of moles of hydronium ions added from the strong acid. The result is that the buffer component *ratio* decreases, which decreases the overall [OH$^-$] but *only by a very small amount*.

Assume that we add 0.010 mol HCl to this solution with no volume change. The 0.010 mol H_3O^+ will be consumed according to the above reaction. It will therefore decrease the [NH$_3$] by 0.010 mol/L and increase the [NH$_4^+$] by 0.010 mol/L. The result for our 1.0 L buffer solution is shown in Table 8.2.3.

Table 7.2.3 *Results of Adding 0.010 mol H_3O^+ to the Buffer Solution*

	$[NH_3]$	$[NH_4^+]$	$[NH_3]/[NH_4^+]$ Ratio
Before 0.010 M H_3O^+ added	0.10 M	0.10 M	0.10 M/0.10 M = 1.0
After 0.010 M H_3O^+ added	0.09 M	0.11 M	0.09 M/0.11 M = 0.82

The initial and final $[OH^-]$ along with the initial and final pH values are calculated below:

$$[OH^-] = (K_b \text{ for } NH_3) \times \frac{[NH_3]}{[NH_4^+]} \quad (\text{Remember: } K_b \text{ for } NH_3 = K_w / K_a \text{ for } NH_4^+)$$

Initial $[OH^-] = (1.8 \times 10^{-5} \text{ M}) \times (1.0) = \textbf{1.8} \times \textbf{10}^{-5} \textbf{ M}$

So initial $[H_3O^+] = \dfrac{1.00 \times 10^{-14}}{1.8 \times 10^{-5}} = \textbf{5.6} \times \textbf{10}^{-10} \textbf{ M}$ so initial pH $= -\log (5.6 \times 10^{-10}) = \textbf{9.25}$

Final $[OH^-] = (1.8 \times 10^{-5} \text{ M}) \times (0.82) = \textbf{1.48} \times \textbf{10}^{-5} \textbf{ M}$

So final $[H_3O^+] = \dfrac{1.00 \times 10^{-14}}{1.48 \times 10^{-5}} = \textbf{6.76} \times \textbf{10}^{-10} \textbf{ M}$ so final pH $= -\log (6.76 \times 10^{-10}) = \textbf{9.17}$

Contrast this minimal increase in hydronium concentration and corresponding minimal decrease in pH with the huge changes to both after the addition of 0.010 mol HCl to 1.0 L of pure water, discussed earlier in the section.

pH Change Resistance after the Addition of a Strong Base

When a small amount of strong base is added, the reservoir of the weak conjugate acid (from the added salt) reacts with the hydroxide ions from the base. For our example, this results in the following net ionic equation:

$NH_4^+ (aq) + OH^-(aq) \rightarrow NH_3(aq) + H_2O(l)$

All of the hydroxide ions from the strong base are converted to the weak base and water in the reaction. This increases the $[NH_3]$ and decreases the $[NH_4^+]$ by a stoichiometric amount equal to the number of moles of hydroxide ions added from the strong base. The result is that the buffer component *ratio* increases, which increases the overall $[OH^-]$ once again by a very small amount.

Using the same 1.0 L basic buffer solution above, we add 0.010 mol NaOH with no volume change. The 0.010 mol OH^- will be consumed according to the above reaction. It will therefore increase the $[NH_3]$ by 0.010 mol/L7and decrease the $[NH_4^+]$ by 0.010 mol/L. The result for our 1.0 L buffer solution is shown in Table 7.2.4.

Table 7.2.4 *Results of Adding 0.010 mol OH^- to the Buffer Solution*

	$[NH_3]$	$[NH_4^+]$	$[NH_3]/[NH_4^+]$ Ratio
Before 0.010 M OH^- added	0.10 M	0.10 M	0.10 M/0.10 M = 1.0
After 0.010 M OH^- added	0.11 M	0.09 M	0.11 M/0.09 M = 1.22

We can once again calculate the final $[OH^-]$ according to the following:

Final $[OH^-] = (1.8 \times 10^{-5} \text{ M}) \times (1.222) = \textbf{2.20} \times \textbf{10}^{-5} \textbf{ M}$

So final $[H_3O^+] = \dfrac{1.00 \times 10^{-14}}{2.20 \times 10^{-5}} = \textbf{4.55} \times \textbf{10}^{-10} \textbf{ M}$ and final pH $= -\log (4.55 \times 10^{-10}) = \textbf{9.34}$

Obviously, if *less* than a 0.10 pH unit change occurs in our basic buffer solution after adding either 0.010 mol of strong acid or 0.010 mol of strong base, the buffer is extremely efficient at maintaining a reasonably constant pH compared to pure water.

Consider once again that the same maintenance of relatively constant pH occurs whether we discuss an acid ionization or a base ionization. Figure 7.2.2 summarizes the changes we have just discussed for this basic buffer. Note again the appropriate net ionic equations beneath each section of the diagram.

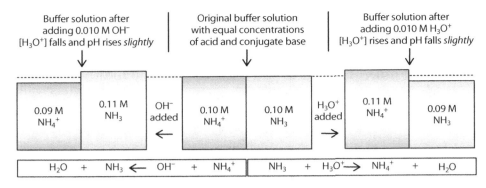

Figure 7.2.2 *The effects on pH of adding a strong base or a strong acid to a basic buffer*

Sample Problem 7.2.2 — Basic Buffers

1. Hydrazine, N_2H_4, is a weak base with a $K_b = 1.7 \times 10^{-6}$. What compound could you add to a 0.50 M solution of hydrazine to make a basic buffer solution?
2. Extension: If the concentration of that compound in the final solution were also 0.50 M, what $[H_3O^+]$ would exist in the buffer solution?

What to Think About	How to Do It
1. To make this solution a buffer, add a soluble salt of the conjugate acid of hydrazine.	The conjugate acid of N_2H_4 is $N_2H_5^+$. Therefore an appropriate compound to add to this solution would be N_2H_5Cl.
2. If the concentration of that conjugate acid is also 0.50 M, then according to the equation discussed above, the hydroxide ion concentration in the solution is equal to the K_b for hydrazine. Calculate the hydronium concentration based on that.	If the solution contained 0.50 M N_2H_4 and also 0.50 M N_2H_5Cl, then in the buffer solution: $[OH^-] = K_b$ for $N_2H_4 = 1.7 \times 10^{-6}$ M Thus: $[H_3O^+] = \dfrac{K_w}{[OH^-]} = \dfrac{100 \times 10^{-14}}{1.7 \times 10^{-6}} = 5.9 \times 10^{-9}$ M

Practice Problems 7.2.2 — Basic Buffers

1. Each of the following solutions contains a weak base. What compounds (in what concentrations ideally) would make each a buffer solution?

Weak Base	Added Compound
(a) 1.0 M CH_3NH_2	
(b) 0.80 M N_2H_4	
(c) 0.20 M $(CH_3)_2NH$	

2. Write the six net ionic equations representing the reactions occurring when a small amount of strong acid and also a small amount of strong base are added to each of the above basic buffer solutions.

	Net Ionic Equation When Acid Added	Net Ionic Equation When Base Added
(a)		
(b)		
(c)		

The Henderson-Hasselbalch Equation (Extension)

A very useful relationship for buffers can be derived from the equation we have discussed in this section, namely:

$$[H_3O^+] = K_a \times \frac{[HA]}{[A^-]}$$

Taking the negative logarithm of both sides of this equation yields:

$$-\log [H_3O^+] = -\log K_a + -\log\left[\frac{[HA]}{[A^-]}\right]$$

(Note the inversion of the ratio when the sign of the log is changed.)

From which we can obtain: $pH = pK_a + \log\left[\frac{[A^-]}{[HA]}\right]$

If we generalize the ratio for any conjugate acid-base pair, we write what is known as the **Henderson-Hasselbalch equation:**

$$\mathbf{pH = pK_a + \log\left[\frac{[base]}{[acid]}\right]}$$

Again, buffer calculations will not likely be required in this course, but any discussion of buffers should include some reference to this equation because, as we will see below, it represents a convenient tool for both analyzing and preparing buffer solutions.

The Capacity of a Buffer

The above equation reinforces that the pH of a given buffer is dependent only on the component ratio in the solution resulting from the relative concentrations of the conjugate base and weak acid. For example, a 0.010 M CH_3COO^-/0.010 M CH_3COOH buffer solution will have the same pH as a buffer solution containing 1.0 M CH_3COO^- and 1.0 M CH_3COOH. However, their ability to *resist changes* to those pH values will be different because that ability depends on the absolute concentrations of their buffer components. The former solution can neutralize only a small amount of acid or base before its pH changes significantly. The latter can withstand the addition of much more acid or base before a significant change in its pH occurs.

Buffer capacity is defined as the amount of acid or base a buffer can neutralize before its pH changes significantly.

A more concentrated or *high-capacity* buffer will experience less of a pH change following the addition of a given amount of strong acid or strong base than a less concentrated or *low-capacity* buffer will. Stated another way, to cause the same pH change, more strong acid or strong base must be added to a high-capacity buffer than to a low-capacity buffer.

Following the addition of an equal amount of H_3O^+ or OH^- ions, the $[A^-]/[HA]$ ratio (and hence the pH) changes more for a solution of a low-capacity buffer than for a high-capacity buffer.

Preparation of a Buffer

The buffer solutions we have discussed in this section contain equal concentrations of conjugate acid-base pairs. There is a reason for that. The Henderson-Hasselbalch equation clearly shows that the more the component ratio changes, the more the solution pH changes. In addition, simple calculations with the same equation show that the more similar the component concentrations are to each other (the closer the $[A^-]/[HA]$ ratio is to 1) in a buffer solution, the less that ratio changes after the addition of a given amount of strong acid or strong base. Conversely, a buffer solution whose component concentrations are very different will experience a greater change in pH following the addition of the same amount of H_3O^+ or OH^- ions. Practically speaking, if the $[A^-]/[HA]$ ratio is less than 0.1 or greater than 10, the buffer can no longer maintain its pH level when a small amount of strong acid or base is added. This means that a buffer is effective only if the following condition is met:

$$10 \geq \frac{[\text{A}^-]}{[\text{HA}]} \geq 0.1$$

As a result, when we prepare a buffer, we attempt to find a weak acid whose pK_a is as close as possible to the desired pH so that the component ratio is within the desired range and ideally as close as possible to 1.

More on Buffer Preparation (Extension)

Preparations of buffer solutions for biological and environmental purposes are a common task for researchers and laboratory technicians. The Henderson-Hasselbalch equation and the above rules are routinely employed in the process. The desired pH of the solution usually dictates the choice of the conjugate acid-base pair. Because a buffer is *most effective* when the component concentration ratio is *closest to 1*, the *best weak acid* will be the one whose pK_a is *closest* to that target pH value. Once that acid is chosen, the Henderson-Hasselbalch equation is used to choose the appropriate ratio of $[\text{A}^-]/[\text{HA}]$ that achieves the desired pH. As mentioned at the beginning of this section, the equilibrium and initial concentrations of the buffer components are almost the same. This allows the equation to yield the following:

$$\text{Desired pH} = pK_a + \log\left[\frac{[\text{A}^-]_{\text{initial}}}{[\text{HA}]_{\text{initial}}}\right]$$

When the actual concentrations are chosen, the fact that higher concentrations make better buffers means that low concentrations are normally avoided. For most applications, concentrations between 0.05 M and 0.5 M are sufficient. Sample Problem 8.2.3 is offered for demonstration purposes only.

Sample Problem 7.2.3 — Extension: Preparing a Buffer

An environmental chemist requires a solution buffered to pH 5.00 to study the effects of acid rain on aquatic microorganisms. Decide on the most appropriate buffer components and suggest their appropriate relative concentrations.

What to Think About	How to Do It
1. Choose an acid whose pK_a value is close to 5.00. The sodium salt of its conjugate base will then be the second buffer component.	The K_a for acetic acid $= 1.8 \times 10^{-5}$. This corresponds to a $pK_a = 4.74$. Therefore this buffer solution can be prepared from acetic acid and sodium acetate. According to the Henderson-Hasselbalch equation, $$pH = 5.00 = 4.74 + \log\left[\frac{[\text{CH}_3\text{COO}^-]_{\text{initial}}}{[\text{CH}_3\text{COOH}]_{\text{initial}}}\right]$$
2. Determine the proper $[\text{A}^-]/[\text{HA}]$ ratio according to the Henderson-Hasselbalch equation to obtain the desired buffer pH.	so $\log\left[\frac{[\text{CH}_3\text{COO}^-]_{\text{initial}}}{[\text{CH}_3\text{COOH}]_{\text{initial}}}\right] = 0.26$ and thus $\left[\frac{[\text{CH}_3\text{COO}^-]_{\text{initial}}}{[\text{CH}_3\text{COOH}]_{\text{initial}}}\right] = 10^{0.26} = 1.8$ A ratio of 1.8 to 1.0 could be accomplished with many combinations. For example: 1.8 M and 1.0 M, 0.18 M and 0.10 M, and 0.90 M and 0.50 M are all correct concentrations for CH_3COO^- and CH_3COOH respectively in this buffer. The choice depends on the required capacity of the buffer.

Practice Problems 7.2.3 — Buffer Capacity and Preparation

1. Rank the following four buffer solutions (by letter) in order from lowest to highest capacity.
   - (a) 0.48 M HF and 0.50 M NaF
   - (b) 0.040 M HCOOH and 0.060 M KHCOO
   - (c) 1.0 M CH$_3$COOH and 1.0 M LiCH$_3$COO
   - (d) 0.10 M H$_2$S and 0.095 M NaHS

   _____ < _____ < _____ < _____

2. *Buffer range* is the pH range over which a buffer acts effectively. Given that the [A⁻]/[HA] ratio should be no less than 0.1 and no more than 10 for a buffer to be effective, use the Henderson-Hasselbalch equation to determine how far away the pH of a buffer solution can be (+ or –) from the pK_a of the weak acid component before that buffer becomes ineffective. Your answer represents the normally accepted range of a buffer.

3. Prior to being used to measure the pH of a solution, pH meters are often calibrated with solutions buffered to pH = 7.00 and also pH = 4.00 or pH = 10.00. Use the table of relative strengths of acids and bases (Table A5) and the Henderson-Hasselbalch equation to select three appropriate conjugate acid-base pairs that could be used to prepare these buffer solutions and complete the table below.

Desired pH	Weak Acid	Weak Acid pK_a	Salt of Conjugate Base
4.00			
7.00			
10.00			

The Maintenance of Blood pH

Two of the most important functions of your blood are to transport oxygen and nutrients to all of the cells in your body and also to remove carbon dioxide and other waste materials from them.

This essential and complex system could not operate without several buffer systems.

The two main components of blood are blood plasma, the straw-colored liquid component of blood, and red blood cells, or *erythrocytes*. Erythrocytes contain a complex protein molecule called hemoglobin, which is the molecule that transports oxygen in your blood. Hemoglobin (which we will represent as HHb) functions effectively as a weak monoprotic acid according to the following equilibrium:

$$HHb(aq) + O_2(aq) + H_2O(l) \rightleftharpoons HbO_2^-(aq) + H_3O^+(aq)$$
hemoglobin   oxyhemoglobin

The system functions properly when oxygen binds to hemoglobin producing oxyhemoglobin. That oxygen is eventually released to diffuse out of the red blood cells to be absorbed by other cells to carry out metabolism. For this to occur properly, several buffer systems maintain the pH of the blood at about 7.35.

If the [H$_3$O$^+$] is too low (pH greater than about 7.50), then the equilibrium shown above shifts so far to the right that the [HbO$_2^-$] is too high to allow for adequate release of O$_2$. This is called *alkalosis*.

If the [H$_3$O$^+$] is too high (pH lower than about 7.20), then the equilibrium shifts far enough to the left that the [HbO$_2^-$] is too low. The result is that the hemoglobin's affinity for oxygen is so reduced that the molecules won't bind together. This is called *acidosis*.

The most important buffer system managing blood pH involves H$_2$CO$_3$ and HCO$_3^-$. CO$_2$(aq) produced during metabolic processes such as respiration is converted in the blood to H_2CO_3 by an enzyme called carbonic anhydraze. The carbonic acid then rapidly decomposes to bicarbonate and hydrogen ions. We can represent the process in the equation shown below:

$$CO_2(aq) + H_2O(l) \rightleftharpoons H_2CO_3(aq) \rightleftharpoons HCO_3^-(aq) + H^+(aq)$$

We can clearly see the buffer components in the above equilibrium system. For example, any addition of hydrogen ions will reduce the $[HCO_3^-]/[H_2CO_3]$ ratio and lower the pH only slightly. Coupled with the above system is the body's remarkable ability to alter its breathing to modify the concentration of dissolved CO_2. In the above example, rapid breathing would increase the loss of CO_2 to the atmosphere in the form of gaseous CO_2. This would then lower the concentration of $CO_2(aq)$ and further help to remove any added H^+ by driving the above equilibrium to the left.

Quick Check

1. Another buffer system present in blood and in other cells is the $H_2PO_4^-/HPO_4^{2-}$ buffer system.
   (a) Write the net ionic equation representing the result of adding hydronium ions to a solution containing this buffer system.

   (b) Write the net ionic equation representing the result of adding hydroxide ions to a solution containing this buffer system.

2. People under severe stress will sometimes hyperventilate, which involves rapid inhaling and exhaling. This can lower the $[CO_2]$ in the blood so much that a person may lose consciousness.
   (a) Consider the above equilibrium and suggest the effect of hyperventilating on blood pH if the concentration of carbon dioxide is too low.

   (b) Why might breathing into a paper bag reduce the effects of hyperventilation?

7.2 Activity: Over-The-Counter Buffer Chemistry

Question
What kinds of buffers are used in over-the-counter medicines?

Background
Many common over-the-counter medicines employ chemical principles that you are learning about. One of the most common and effective pain relievers or "analgesics" is the weak acid acetylsalicylic acid (ASA), $C_8H_7O_2COOH$. This product is marketed under various brands but the best-known one is Aspirin by the Bayer Corporation. (*Note that anyone under the age of 18 should not use ASA as children may develop Reye's syndrome, a potentially fatal disease that may occur with ASA use in treating flu or chickenpox.*)

One form of the product contains a "buffering agent" because some people are sensitive to the acidity level of this medication. That same "buffering agent" is used in several antacid remedies to neutralize excess stomach acid (HCl).

Procedure
1. Consider the advertisement shown here and answer the questions below.

   (a) Identify the ion in the compound listed on the box that acts as the "acid neutralizer" and buffers the ASA.

ASA PLUS Extra Strength
with Calcium Carbonate
500 mg

- Buffered with acid neutralizers
- Bottles of 80 caplets

   (b) Write the net ionic equation corresponding to the reaction involving the "acid neutralizer" reacting with a small amount of strong acid.

   (c) Write the net ionic equation corresponding to the reaction occurring when a small amount of strong base is added to a relatively concentrated solution of ASA.

   (d) Consider the above net ionic equations and decide if a solution containing significant quantities of ASA and the ion identified as the acid neutralizer in question 1 would function well as a buffer solution? Why or why not?

2. Consider the antacid label shown here and note that the active ingredient is the same compound used to buffer the ASA above.

(a) Determine the pH of a buffer solution containing a 0.10 M solution of both the anion in the compound listed on the label and its conjugate acid.

(b) Would this solution be considered an acidic or a basic buffer?

3. Next time you're in a pharmacy, locate other antacid or "buffered" products on the shelves. Read the labels to determine if the active ingredient is the same or different than in the products listed here. If different, think about the chemistry associated with that ingredient and try to figure out how it works. (Thinking about the chemistry you encounter every day is *always* a good idea!)

7.2 Review Questions

1. What is the purpose of an acid-base buffer?

2. Why do you think that the components of a buffer solution are normally a conjugate acid-base pair rather than any combination of a weak acid and a weak base?

3. Explain why a solution of 0.10 M HNO_3 and 0.10 M $NaNO_3$ cannot function as a buffer solution.

4. Each of the following compound pairs exists at a concentration 0.50 M in their respective solutions. Circle the solutions that represent buffers:

Na_2CO_3/KOH   NaCl/HCl C_6H_5COOH/KC_6H_5COO HNO_3/KNO_2

N_2H_4/NH_3 $CH_3NH_3NO_3$/CH_3NH_2 K_2SO_3/$KHSO_3$ CH_3COOH/HI

HBr/NaOH KIO_3/HIO_3 NaHS/H_2S HF/LiF H_2O_2/$RbHO_2$

5. Consider a buffer solution containing 0.30 M HCN and 0.30 M NaCN.
   (a) Without performing any calculations, state the $[H_3O^+]$ in the solution.

   (b) Is this solution considered to be an acidic or a basic buffer? Why?

   (c) Write the net ionic equation for the reaction occurring when a small amount of HCl is added to the solution. What happens to the pH of the solution after the HCl is added?

   (d) Write the net ionic equation for the reaction occurring when a small amount of NaOH is added to the solution. What happens to the pH of the solution after the NaOH is added?

6. Complete the following table for a buffer solution containing equal concentrations of HA and A⁻ when a small amount of strong acid is added and when a small amount of strong base is added.

Stress Applied	Net Ionic Equation	How [HA]/[A⁻] Changes	How pH Changes
H_3O^+ added			
OH^- added			

7. Without performing any calculations, consult the table of K_a values (Table A5) and arrange the following buffer solutions (by letter) in order from lowest $[H_3O^+]$ to highest $[H_3O^+]$:
   (a) 1.0 M H_2S/1.0 M NaHS
   (b) 0.50 M HCN/0.50 M KCN
   (c) 0.25 M $NaHC_2O_4$/0.25 M $Na_2C_2O_4$
   (d) 2.0 M HCOOH/2.0 M LiHCOO

   _____ < _____ < _____ < _____

8. What is meant by the term *buffer capacity* and what does it depend upon? Which of the buffer solutions listed in question 7 above would have the highest capacity?

9. List the following four buffer solutions (by letter) in order from highest to lowest capacity.
   (a) 0.010 M KNO_2/0.010 M HNO_2
   (b) 0.10 M CH_3COOH/0.10 M $NaCH_3COO$
   (c) 0.0010 M NH_3/0.0010 M NH_4Cl
   (d) 1.0 M HF/1.0 M NaF

   _____ > _____ > _____ > _____

10. What is meant by the term *buffer range*? How is it related to the pK_a value for the weak acid component of a buffer solution?

11. Describe the effect of lowering the $[CO_2]$ in blood on the pH of the blood.

12. Describe the effect of *alkalosis* on the ability of hemoglobin to transport oxygen.

13. Describe the effect of *acidosis* on the ability of hemoglobin to transport oxygen.

14. **Challenge:** Consider carefully the components of a buffer solution and decide if a buffer solution could be *prepared* from 1.0 L of 1.0 M HNO_2 and sufficient NaOH? If so, how?

15. Use the Henderson-Hasselbalch equation to calculate the pH of each of the buffers mentioned in question 9 above.

16. Use the Henderson-Hasselbalch equation to answer the following:
    (a) A student requires a solution buffered to pH = 10.00 to study the effects of detergent runoff into aquatic ecosystems. She has just prepared a 1.0 L solution of 0.20 M $NaHCO_3$. What mass of Na_2CO_3 must be added to this solution to complete the buffer preparation? Assume no volume change.

    (b) Calculate the pH of this buffer solution following the addition of 0.0010 mol HCl.

17. Calculate the pH of the following buffer solutions:
    (a) 75.0 mL of 0.200 mol/L CH_3COOH mixed with 75.0 mL of 0.300 mol/L $NaCH_3COO$

    (b) 300. mL of 0.100 mol/L NH_3 combined with 200. mL of 0.200 mol/L NH_4Cl

18. A buffer solution contains 0.400 mol/L of CH_3COOH and 0.400 mol/L of $NaCH_3COO$. What is the pH of the buffer under the following conditions?
    (a) Before any acid or base is added

    (b) After adding 0.050 mol of HCl to 1.00 L of the buffer. Assume the total volume remains constant.

    (c) After adding 0.050 mol of NaOH to 1.00 L of the buffer. Assume the total volume remains constant.

19. A solution contains 0.0375 mol of HCOOH and 0.0325 mol of NaHCOO in a total volume of 1.00 L. Determine the pH following the addition of 0.0100 mol of HCl with no significant change in volume.

20. What ratio of [NaF]/[HF] is required to produce a buffer with a pH of 4.25?

21. How many grams of NH_4Br must be added to 0.500 mol of NH_3 to produce 1.00 L of buffer with a pH of 9.05?

22. (a) What is the pH of 1.00 L of buffer containing 0.180 mol of CH_3COOH and 0.200 mol of $NaCH_3C$

   (b) How many moles of HCl must be added to this buffer to change the pH to:
   (i) 4.600

   (ii) 0.900

   (c) The purpose of a buffer is to maintain a relatively constant pH when strong acids or bases are added. What caused the large drop in pH in (b)(ii)?

7.3 Acid-Base Titrations — Analyzing with Volume

Warm Up

1. What is the typical purpose of a titration?

_____

2. Determine the pH of the following solutions:

0.10 M HCl	0.10 M HCN

3. Assume that 25.0 mL of each of the above solutions is reacted with a 0.10 M NaOH solution. How will the volume of the NaOH solution required to neutralize the HCl compare with that required to neutralize the HCN?

_____

Criteria for Titration

Titrations are among the most important of all the analytical procedures that chemists use. A titration is a form of volumetric analysis. During a titration, the number of moles of solute in a solution is determined by adding a sufficient volume of another solution of known concentration to *just produce a complete reaction*. Once determined, that number of moles can then be used to calculate other values such as concentration, molar mass, or percent purity.

Any reaction being considered for a titration must satisfy three criteria:
1. Only one reaction can occur between the solutes contained in the two solutions.
2. The reaction between those solutes must go rapidly to completion.
3. There must be a way of signaling the point at which the complete reaction has been achieved in the reaction vessel. This is called the **equivalence point** or **stoichiometric point** of the titration.

The equivalence point in an acid-base titration occurs in the reaction vessel when the total number of moles of H_3O^+ from the acid equals the total number of moles of OH^- from the base.

To ensure that the reaction between the acid and the base goes to completion, at least one of the two reacting species must be strong. A complete reaction means that *the volume of added solution required to reach the equivalence point depends only on the moles of the acid and base present and the stoichiometry of the reaction*. Prior to the titration, a small amount of an appropriate chemical indicator is added to the reaction vessel containing the solution being analyzed. The correct indicator is one that will undergo a color change *at or very near* the pH associated with the equivalence point. This color change signals when the titration should stop. A pH meter used to monitor the pH of the reaction mixture during the course of a titration will also indicate when the equivalence point has been reached.

Titration Accuracy

Recall from your introduction to titrations in the M4 Chemistry textbook that quantitative analytical procedures such as titrations require precise instruments and careful measurements to ensure the accuracy of the results. Let's review the equipment and procedures associated with a titration. Figure 7.3.1 shows the apparatus used for a typical titration.

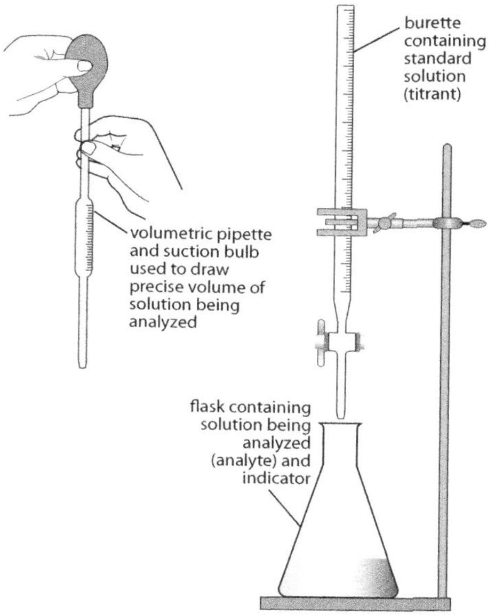

A precise volume of the solution to be analyzed is drawn into a volumetric pipette and transferred into an Erlenmeyer (conical) flask. The shape of the flask allows for swirling of the reaction mixture during the course of the titration without loss of contents. A small amount of an appropriate indicator is then added to this solution. The flask is placed under a burette containing the solution of known concentration called a **standard** or **standardized solution**. The solution in the burette is referred to as the *titrant* and the solution in the flask is called the *analyte*. Normally, the approximate concentration of the analyte is known, which allows a titrant of similar concentration to be prepared. If the titrant is too concentrated, then only a few drops might be required to reach the equivalence point. If the titrant is too dilute, then the volume present in the burette may not be enough to reach the equivalence point.

The standard solution is carefully added to the solution in the flask until the first permanent color change just appears in the indicator. This is called the **transition point** or **endpoint** of the indicator. It should signal when the equivalence point in the titration has been reached.

Figure 7.3.1 *Titration apparatus*

Labels: burette containing standard solution (titrant); volumetric pipette and suction bulb used to draw precise volume of solution being analyzed; flask containing solution being analyzed (analyte) and indicator

> The transition point is the point in a titration at which the indicator changes color.

At the transition point, the valve on the burette is closed to stop the titration and the volume of standard solution added from the burette is determined.

It is important to remember that *the pH at the transition point is dependent only on the chemical nature of the indicator* and is independent of the equivalence point. The *pH at the equivalence point is dependent only on the chemical nature of the reacting species.* As mentioned above, the pH at which the endpoint occurs should be as close as possible to the pH of the solution at the equivalence point. (Each of these topics will be discussed in greater detail in section 7.4.)

A titration should always be repeated as an accuracy check. Incomplete mixing of solutions, incorrect pipetting techniques, or errors made when reading burettes can contribute to inaccuracies in the data collected, particularly for beginning students.

Those experienced at performing titrations normally expect that the volumes added from the burette in each trial should agree with each other within 0.02 mL (less than a drop). Students performing titrations for the first time should expect agreement within 0.1 mL.

If the volumes delivered from the burette in the first two trials do not agree within the desired uncertainty, then the titration must be repeated until they do. Once agreement between two trials occurs, the volumes added in those trials are averaged, and the other data is discarded. For example, consider Table 7.3.1, which lists the volumes of standard solution required to reach the equivalence point in three separate titration trials.

Table 7.3.1 *Volumes of Standard Solution Required for Equivalence Points*

Titration Trial	Volume of Std. Solution
1	21.36 mL
2	21.19 mL
3	21.21 mL

Note that a third trial was required because the first two volumes differed by 0.17 mL, which is beyond the range of acceptable agreement. The volume recorded for trial 3 agrees well with that of trial 2 and so those two volumes are averaged to obtain the correct volume of standard solution, while the data from trial 1 is discarded. (It is common to overshoot a titration on the first trial.)

$$\text{Average volume of standard solution} = \frac{21.19 \text{ mL} + 21.21 \text{ mL}}{2} = 21.20 \text{ mL}$$

Quick Check

1. What ensures that an acid-base titration goes to completion?

   _____

2. Distinguish between an endpoint and an equivalence point in an acid-base titration.

   _____

   _____

3. A student performing a titration for the first time lists the volumes of standard solution required to reach the equivalence point in three separate titration trials.

Titration Trial	Volume of Std. Solution
1	23.88 mL
2	23.67 mL
3	23.59 mL

   What is the correct volume of standard solution that should be recorded by the student?

   _____

Standard Solutions

A successful titration requires that the concentration of the standard solution be very accurately known. There are two ways to obtain a standard solution.

1. A standard solution can be prepared if the solute is a stable, non-deliquescent, soluble compound available in a highly pure form. Such a compound is known as a **primary standard**.
   - Two examples of **acidic primary standards** are:
   (a) potassium hydrogen phthalate, $KHC_8H_4O_4$, a monoprotic acid often abbreviated as simply KHP.
   (b) oxalic acid dihydrate, $H_2C_2O_4 \cdot 2 \ H_2O$, a diprotic acid.
   - A common example of a **basic primary standard** is anhydrous sodium carbonate, Na_2CO_3, which will accept two protons in a reaction with an acid.
   - Each of the above stable, pure compounds can be used to prepare a standard solution whose concentration can be accurately known directly.

2. If the solute is not available in a highly pure form and/or readily undergoes reaction with, for example, atmospheric water vapor or carbon dioxide, then the solution must be *standardized* to accurately determine its concentration before it can be used in a titration. This is accomplished by titrating the solution in question against a primary standard.

   For example, a solution of the strong base sodium hydroxide is often used as a standard solution in a titration. However, solid NaOH rapidly absorbs water vapor from the air. Both solid and aqueous NaOH readily react with atmospheric CO_2 as shown in the equation below:

$$2\,NaOH + CO_2 \rightarrow Na_2CO_3 + H_2O$$

This means that before a solution of NaOH can be used as a standard solution in a titration, its concentration must first be accurately determined by titrating it against an acidic primary standard such as KHP or $H_2C_2O_4 \cdot 2\,H_2O$. For each titration, phenolphthalein is a suitable indicator. KHP reacts with NaOH as shown in this equation:

$$KHC_8H_4O_4(aq) + NaOH(aq) \rightarrow NaKC_8H_4O_4(aq) + H_2O(l)$$

Oxalic acid dihydrate reacts with NaOH in a 2:1 mole ratio:

$$H_2C_2O_4 \cdot 2\,H_2O(aq) + 2\,NaOH(aq) \rightarrow Na_2C_2O_4(aq) + 4\,H_2O(l)$$

For example, if KHP is used to standardize the NaOH solution, a precise mass of KHP (usually sufficient to prepare a 0.1000 M solution), is dissolved in water, transferred into a volumetric flask, and diluted to the required volume. A volumetric pipette is then used to transfer a precise volume to an Erlenmeyer flask into which a few drops of phenolphthalein indicator are added. The NaOH solution to be standardized is then gradually added from a burette into the acid solution. At the equivalence point, all of the KHP in the flask has been neutralized and so the next drop of NaOH solution added makes the reaction mixture basic enough to cause the indicator to turn pink. The volume of the NaOH solution required in the titration allows for the accurate determination of its concentration. Once that concentration is known, the standardized NaOH solution can then be added to an acid solution in a titration procedure.

To standardize an acidic solution, a titration against a basic primary standard such as Na_2CO_3 is performed. Appropriate indicators for this reaction would be either bromcresol green or methyl red. In a reaction with a monoprotic acid such as HCl, the carbonate anion will react in a 2:1 mole ratio:

$$Na_2CO_3(aq) + 2\,HCl(aq) \rightarrow 2\,NaCl(aq) + CO_2(g) + H_2O(l)$$

When standardizing a solution, its *approximate* concentration is often known. Because the concentration of the other solution is known, the approximate volume required of the solution being standardized in the titration can be estimated before the procedure.

Quick Check

1. Is a 4.00 g sample of NaOH likely to contain 0.100 mol of this compound? Why or why not?

_____

2. Which piece of equipment and/or procedure employed during a titration ensures the following:
   (a) Accurate and precise measurement of the volume of the solution being analyzed in the reaction flask

   _____

   (b) Accurate and precise determination of the concentration of the titrant

   _____

   (c) Accurate and precise measurement of the volume of titrant required in the titration

   _____

   (d) Correct determination of the equivalence point during the titration

   _____

Sample Problem 7.3.1 — Standardizing a Solution

A student standardizing a solution of NaOH finds that 28.15 mL of that solution is required to neutralize 25.00 mL of a 0.1072 M standard solution of KHP. Calculate the [NaOH].

What to Think About	How to Do It
1. To solve titration problems, begin with writing the balanced equation for the reaction. The mole ratio in the balanced equation is 1 mol NaOH : 1 mol KHP	$KHC_8H_4O_4 + NaOH \rightarrow NaKC_8H_4O_4 + H_2O$ $$mol\ KHP = 0.02500\ \cancel{L} \times 0.1072\ \frac{mol\ KHP}{\cancel{L}} = 0.002680\ mol$$ $$mol\ NaOH = mol\ KHP = 0.002680\ mol$$
2. The [NaOH] should be slightly less than 0.107**2** M because the volume of NaOH solution required in the titration is greater than 25.00 mL.	$$[NaOH] = \frac{0.002680\ mol\ NaOH}{0.02815\ L} = 0.09520\ M$$ (4 sig. figures) Look at the above solution. Can you identify *three steps* in the solution process?

Practice Problems 7.3.1 — Standardizing a Solution

1. If 21.56 mL of a NaOH solution is required to neutralize 25.00 mL of a 0.0521 M standard oxalic acid solution, calculate the [NaOH].

2. A 1.546 g sample of pure anhydrous sodium carbonate is diluted to 250.0 mL in a volumetric flask. A 25.00 mL aliquot of this standard solution required 23.17 mL of a nitric acid solution to be neutralized. Calculate the [HNO_3].

Common Titration Calculations

The majority of titration calculations you will be expected to perform in this course involve determining a solution concentration, solution volume, molar mass, or percent purity.

Regardless of which acid or base is involved, *the total number of moles of H+ from the acid equals the total number of moles of OH− from the base at the equivalence point*. Therefore, for any type of titration problem you are solving, it is *strongly suggested* that you begin by writing the balanced chemical equation for the titration reaction if it isn't provided.

- The first step in the calculation process normally involves using the data provided to determine the number of moles of one of the reactant species used.
- The second step uses the moles determined in the first step and the mole ratio in the balanced equation to determine the moles of the second reactant consumed.
- The third step uses the moles calculated in step 2 to determine a solution concentration, solution volume, molar mass, or percent purity.

Because a titration represents a quantitative analytical procedure, accuracy and precision are paramount. This means that you must pay particular attention to significant figures when performing titration calculations.

Calculating Solution Concentration

This represents the most common type of titration calculation you will encounter in this course. If you look again at Sample Problem 7.3.1 above for standardizing a solution, you will recognize this problem type and the application of the above steps to solve it.

Sample Problem 7.3.2 — Calculating Solution Concentration

A 25.0 mL sample of H_2SO_4 requires 46.23 mL of a standard 0.203 M NaOH solution to reach the equivalence point. Calculate the $[H_2SO_4]$.

What to Think About	**How to Do It**
1. The balanced equation shows a 2:1 mole ratio between the reacting species.	$2\,NaOH(aq) + H_2SO_4(aq) \rightarrow Na_2SO_4(aq) + 2\,H_2O(l)$ $mol\ NaOH = 0.04623\ L \times \dfrac{0.203\ mol}{L} = 0.009385\ mol$
2. Ensure that your final answer has three significant figures.	$mol\ H_2SO_4 = 0.009385\ \cancel{mol\ NaOH} \times \dfrac{1\ mol\ H_2SO_4}{2\ \cancel{mol\ NaOH}}$ $= 0.004692\ mol\ H_2SO_4$
3. As molarity × mL = millimoles, solve the question using mol and L, or mmol and mL.	$[H_2SO_4] = \dfrac{0.004692\ mol\ H_2SO_4}{0.0250\ L} = 0.188\ M$ (3 sig. figures)
4. A solution using each set of units is shown on the right.	*Alternatively:* $mmol\ NaOH = 46.23\ \cancel{mL} \times \dfrac{0.203\ mmol}{\cancel{mL}} = 9.385\ mmol$ $mmol\ H_2SO_4 = 9.385\ \cancel{mmol\ NaOH} \times \dfrac{1\ mmol\ H_2SO_4}{2\ \cancel{mmol\ NaOH}}$ $= 4.692\ mmol\ H_2SO_4$ $[H_2SO_4] = \dfrac{4.692\ mmol\ H_2SO_4}{25.0\ mL} = 0.188\ M$

Practice Problems 7.3.2 — Calculating Solution Concentration

1. The equivalence point in a titration is reached when 25.64 mL of a 0.1175 M KOH solution is added to a 50.0 mL solution of acetic acid. Calculate the concentration of the acetic acid.

Continued on next page

Practice Problems 7.3.2 (*Continued*)

2. Lactic acid, C_2H_5OCOOH, is found in sour milk, yogurt, and cottage cheese. It is also responsible for the flavor of sourdough breads. Three separate trials, each using 25.0 mL samples of lactic acid, are performed using a standardized 0.153 M NaOH solution. Consider the following table listing the volume of basic solution required to reach the equivalence point for each trial.

Titration Trial	Volume of NaOH Solution
1	33.42 mL
2	33.61 mL
3	33.59 mL

Calculate the concentration of the lactic acid.

3. Methylamine, CH_3NH_2, is found in herring brine solutions, used in the manufacture of some pesticides, and serves as a solvent for many organic compounds. A titration is performed to determine the concentration of methylamine present in a solution being prepared for a commercial pesticide. A 0.185 M HCl solution is added to 50.0 mL samples of aqueous methylamine in three separate titration trials. The data table below shows the results.

| Titration Trial | Burette Readings | |
	Initial Volume	Final Volume
1	20.14 mL	47.65 mL
2	9.55 mL	36.88 mL
3	15.84 mL	43.11 mL

Calculate the concentration of the methylamine solution.

Calculating Solution Volume

If you are asked to calculate a solution volume from titration data, you will probably be given the concentrations of both the acid and the base solutions. If you aren't given the concentrations directly, you will be given enough information to calculate them. The final step in the solution process involves converting the moles of reactant determined in the second step into a volume using the appropriate concentration value.

It is important to remember that because *the reaction goes to completion*, the volume of standard solution required in a titration is only dependent on the stoichiometry of the reaction and the moles of the species (acid or base) that it must neutralize. *It does not depend on the strength of those species.*

Review your answer to Warm Up question 3. The volume of standard NaOH solution required to neutralize 25.0 mL of 0.10 M HCl will be *the same* as that required to neutralize 25.0 mL of 0.10 M HCN.

Sample Problem 7.3.3 — Calculating Solution Volume

What volume of a standard $Sr(OH)_2$ solution with a pH of 13.500 is needed to neutralize a 25.0 mL solution of 0.423 M HCl?

What to Think About	How to Do It
1. The pH allows the concentration of the basic solution to be calculated.	$2\ HCl(aq) + Sr(OH)_2(aq) \rightarrow SrCl_2(aq) + 2\ H_2O(l)$ $mmol\ HCl\ reacting = 25.0\ mL \times \dfrac{0.423\ mmol\ HCl}{mL}$ $= 10.58\ mmol\ HCl$
2. The balanced equation shows a 2:1 mole ratio between the reacting species.	$mmol\ Sr(OH)_2 = 10.58\ mmol\ HCl \times \dfrac{1\ mmol\ Sr(OH)_2}{2\ mmol\ HCl}$ $= 5.290\ mmol\ Sr(OH)_2$
3. Express the final answer to three significant figures.	$pOH = 14.000 - 13.500 = 0.500$ $[OH^-] = 10^{-0.500} = 0.3162\ M$ $[Sr(OH)_2] = \dfrac{[OH^-]}{2} = 0.1581\ M = 0.1581\ \dfrac{mmol}{mL}$ $Volume\ Sr(OH)_2\ solution =$ $5.290\ mmol\ Sr(OH)_2 \times \dfrac{1\ mL}{0.1581\ mmol} = 33.4\ mL$ (3 sig. figures)

Practice Problems 7.3.3 — Calculating Solution Volume

1. How many milliliters of a 0.215 M KOH solution are required to neutralize 15.0 mL of a 0.173 M H_2SO_4 solution?

2. A solution of HCl is standardized and found to have a pH of 0.432. What volume of this solution must be added to 25.0 mL of a 0.285 M $Sr(OH)_2$ solution to reach the equivalence point?

3. A 5.60 L sample of NH_3 gas, measured at STP, is dissolved in enough water to produce 500.0 mL of solution. A 20.0 mL sample of this solution is titrated with a 0.368 M HNO_3 solution. What volume of standard solution is required to reach the equivalence point?

The molar mass of an unknown acid (or base) can be determined from a titration as long as we know if that acid (or base) is monoprotic or diprotic, etc. This tells us the molar ratio in the neutralization reaction that occurs. This in turn allows us to calculate the moles of the unknown compound that react during the titration. Depending on how the information is provided, we can then choose to calculate the molar mass in one of two ways, as shown in the following sample problems.

Sample Problem 7.3.4(a) — Calculating Molar Mass 1

A 0.328 g sample of an unknown monoprotic acid, HA, is dissolved in water and titrated with a standardized 0.1261 M NaOH solution. If 28.10 mL of the basic solution is required to reach the equivalence point, calculate the molar mass of the acid.

What to Think About	How to Do It
1. The mole ratio in the balanced equation is 1:1 so the mol of NaOH reacted = the mol of HA present in 0.328 g.	$NaOH(aq) + HA(aq) \rightarrow NaA(aq) + H_2O(l)$ $$mmol\ NaOH = 28.10\ mL \times \frac{0.1261\ mmol}{mL} = 3.543\ mmol$$
2. The mass of the unknown acid divided by the moles present equals the molar mass.	$$mmol\ HA = 3.543\ mmol\ NaOH \times \frac{1\ mmol\ HA}{mmol\ NaOH}$$ $$= 3.543\ mmol\ HA = 0.003543\ mol\ HA$$ $$molar\ mass\ of\ HA = \frac{0.328\ g\ HA}{0.003543\ mol\ HA} = 92.6\ g/mol$$ (3 sig. figures)

Sample Problem 7.3.4(b) — Calculating Molar Mass 2

A 2.73 g sample of an unknown diprotic acid is placed in a volumetric flask and then diluted to 500.0 mL. A 25.0 mL sample of this solution requires 30.5 mL of a 0.1112 M KOH solution to completely neutralize the acid in a titration. Calculate the molar mass of the acid.

What to Think About	How to Do It
1. Two moles of KOH are required to neutralize each mole of diprotic acid, H_2A.	$2\ KOH(aq) + H_2A(aq) \rightarrow K_2A(aq) + 2\ H_2O(l)$ $$mol\ KOH = 0.0305\ L \times \frac{0.1112\ mol}{L} = 0.003416\ mol$$
2. Calculate the concentration of the acid solution and use the volume of the original solution to determine the moles of H_2A present. This will allow you to determine the molar mass using the mass of the original acid sample.	$$mol\ H_2A = 0.003416\ mol\ KOH \times \frac{1\ mol\ H_2A}{2\ mol\ KOH} = 0.001708\ mol$$ $$[H_2A] = \frac{0.001708\ mol\ H_2A}{0.0250\ L} = 0.06832\ M$$ $$mol\ H_2A\ in\ original\ 500.0\ mL = \frac{0.06832\ mol}{L} \times 0.5000\ L$$ $$= 0.03416\ mol\ H_2A$$ $$molar\ mass\ H_2A = \frac{2.73\ g\ H_2A}{0.03416\ mol} = 79.9\ g/mol$$ (3 sig. figures)

Practice Problems 7.3.4 — Calculating Molar Mass

1. A 3.648 g sample of an unknown monoprotic acid is dissolved in enough water to produce 750.0 mL of solution. When a 25.0 mL sample of this solution is titrated to the equivalence point, 12.50 mL of a 0.1104 M NaOH solution is required. Calculate the molar mass of the acid.

2. A 0.375 g sample of an unknown diprotic acid is dissolved in water and titrated using 0.2115 M NaOH. The volumes of standard solution required to neutralize the acid in three separate trials are given below.

Titration Trial	Volume of NaOH Solution
1	37.48 mL
2	37.36 mL
3	37.34 mL

Calculate the molar mass of the acid.

3. A 2.552 g sample of a monoprotic base is diluted to 250.0 mL in a volumetric flask. A 25.0 mL sample of this solution is titrated with a standardized solution of 0.05115 M HCl. If 17.49 mL of the acid solution is required to reach the equivalence point, calculate the molar mass of the base.

Calculating Percent Purity

If a solid sample of an impure acid or base is dissolved in solution and titrated against a standard solution, the actual number of moles of the pure solute can be determined. Depending on how the information is presented, this allows percent purity to be calculated. For example, we may be told that a small mass of an impure solid is dissolved in enough water to form the solution that is titrated directly. In this case, the percent purity can be calculated by dividing the *actual mass of pure solute* present in the sample, as determined by the titration, by the *given mass of the impure sample.*

$$\text{percent purity} = \frac{\text{actual mass of pure solute (from titration)}}{\text{given mass of impure solute}} \times 100\%$$

We may also be told that a mass of impure solid is dissolved in a given volume of solution, and then a portion of that solution is withdrawn and analyzed in the titration. In this case, we can choose to calculate the percent purity by dividing the *actual solution concentration*, as determined by the titration, by the *expected concentration* in the original solution if the sample had been pure.

$$\text{percent purity} = \frac{\text{actual concentration (from titration)}}{\text{expected concentration (from original mass)}} \times 100\%$$

There are other possible approaches, but each uses a true value provided by the titration and compares it to a given value to determine percent purity.

Sample Problem 7.3.5(a) — Calculating Percent Purity 1

A 0.3470 g sample of impure $NaHSO_3$ is dissolved in water and titrated with a 0.1481 M NaOH solution. If 20.26 mL of the standard solution is required, calculate the percent purity of the $NaHSO_3$ sample.

What to Think About

1. The mole ratio in the balanced equation is 1:1.

2. The titration will allow you to calculate the actual number of moles of $NaHSO_3$ in the sample from which you can obtain percent purity.

How to Do It

$$NaOH(aq) + NaHSO_3(aq) \rightarrow Na_2SO_3(aq) + H_2O(l)$$

$$\text{mol NaOH} = 0.02026 \, \cancel{L} \times \frac{0.1481 \text{ mol}}{\cancel{L}} = 0.003000 \text{ mol}$$

$$\text{mol pure } NaHSO_3 = \text{mol NaOH} = 0.003000 \text{ mol}$$

$$\text{actual mass pure } NaHSO_3 = 0.003000 \, \cancel{\text{mol}} \times \frac{104.1 \text{ g } NaHSO_3}{\cancel{\text{mol}}}$$

$$= 0.3123 \text{ g } NaHSO_3$$

$$\% \text{ purity} = \frac{\text{actual mass pure } NaHSO_3}{\text{given mass impure } NaHSO_3} \times 100\%$$

$$= \frac{0.3123 \, \cancel{g}}{0.3470 \, \cancel{g}} \times 100\% = 90.00\% \text{ (4 sig. figures)}$$

Sample Problem 7.3.5(b) — Calculating Percent Purity 2

A 2.70 g sample of impure $Sr(OH)_2$ is diluted to 250.0 mL in a volumetric flask. A 25.0 mL portion of this solution is then neutralized in a titration using 31.39 mL of 0.131 M HCl. Calculate the percent purity of the $Sr(OH)_2$.

What to Think About

1. The balanced equation shows a 2:1 mole ratio for the reactants.

2. Compare the actual concentration of the solution to the expected concentration to determine percent purity.

3. Round the answer to three significant figures.

How to Do It

$$2 HCl(aq) + Sr(OH)_2(aq) \rightarrow SrCl_2(aq) + 2 H_2O(l)$$

$$\text{mmol HCl} = 31.39 \, \cancel{\text{mL}} \times \frac{0.131 \text{ mmol}}{\cancel{\text{mL}}} = 4.112 \text{ mmol}$$

$$\text{mmol } Sr(OH)_2 = 4.112 \, \cancel{\text{mmol HCl}} \times \frac{1 \text{ mmol } Sr(OH)_2}{2 \, \cancel{\text{mmol HCl}}}$$

$$= 2.056 \text{ mmol } Sr(OH)_2$$

$$\text{actual } [Sr(OH)_2] = \frac{2.056 \text{ mmol } Sr(OH)_2}{25.0 \text{ mL}} = 0.08224 \text{ M}$$

$$\text{expected } [Sr(OH)_2] = \frac{2.70 \text{ g } \cancel{Sr(OH)_2}}{0.2500 \text{ L}} \times \frac{1 \text{ mol } Sr(OH)_2}{126.1 \, \cancel{g}}$$

$$= 0.08565 \text{ M}$$

$$\% \text{ purity} = \frac{\text{actual } [Sr(OH)_2]}{\text{expected } [Sr(OH)_2]} \times 100\%$$

$$= \frac{0.08224 \, \cancel{M}}{0.08565 \, \cancel{M}} \times 100\% = 96.0\% \text{ (3 sig. figures)}$$

Practice Problems 7.3.5 — Calculating Percent Purity

1. Benzoic acid, C_6H_5COOH, is a white crystalline solid. It is among the most common food preservatives and is also used as an antifungal skin treatment. A 0.3265 g sample of impure benzoic acid is dissolved in enough water to form 25.0 mL of solution. In a titration, 23.76 mL of a 0.1052 M NaOH solution is required to reach the equivalence point. Calculate the percent purity of the acid.

2. A 1.309 g sample of impure $Ca(OH)_2$ is dissolved in water to produce 750.0 mL of solution. A 25.0 mL sample of this solution is titrated against a standard solution of 0.0615 M HCl. If 17.72 mL of the acid solution is required in the titration, calculate the percent purity of the $Ca(OH)_2$.

3. Nicotinic acid, C_5H_4NCOOH, (also known as niacin or vitamin B_3) is considered an essential human nutrient and is available in a variety of food sources such as chicken, salmon, eggs, carrots, and avocados. A 1.361 g sample of impure nicotinic acid is dissolved in water to form 30.00 mL of solution. The acid solution requires 20.96 mL of 0.501 M NaOH to reach the equivalence point. Calculate the percent purity of the acid.

7.3 Activity: Titration Experimental Design

Question
Can you identify the equipment and procedures associated with a typical titration and then employ them in designing a titration?

Background
As you have learned in this section, a titration is one of the most valuable analytical procedures employed by chemists. This activity is intended to review the equipment and reagents involved in a titration and then present you with the task of designing such an investigation.

Procedure
1. What is the function of each the following in a titration?
    (a) burette

    (b) volumetric pipette

    (c) Erlenmeyer flask

    (d) indicator

    (e) standard solution

    (f) acidic or basic primary standard

2. Why must every titration be repeated?

3. The concentration of a solution of acetylsalicylic acid, $C_8H_7O_2COOH$, must be determined very accurately for a clinical trial. The equipment and chemical reagents available to you to accomplish this are listed below. Using all of them, describe in point form and in order the laboratory procedures you would use.

Equipment	Reagents
<ul><li>analytical balance</li><li>100 mL beaker</li><li>2 funnels</li><li>wash bottle</li><li>250 mL volumetric flask</li><li>two 125 mL Erlenmeyer flasks</li><li>50 mL burette</li><li>two 25 mL pipettes with suction bulbs</li><li>ring stand</li><li>burette clamp</li><li>safety goggles</li><li>lab apron</li></ul>	<ul><li>pure oxalic acid dihydrate crystals</li><li>NaOH solution (approximately 0.1 M)</li><li>ASA solution (approximately 0.1 M)</li><li>phenolphthalein indicator solution</li></ul>

Titration Procedure

Results and Discussion

1. Write the balanced equation for the reaction that occurs during standardization of the basic solution and for the titration of the ASA solution.

2. (a) What salt solution exists at the equivalence point of the ASA titration?

   (b) Would you expect the pH of the solution at the equivalence point to be 7? Why or why not?

3. What concentration might be appropriate for the oxalic acid solution that you prepare?

4. Identify at least three possible sources of error and their impact on the experimental results.

7.3 Review Questions

1. A student intends to titrate two 25.0 mL acidic solutions, each with a known concentration of approximately 0.1 M. One solution is hydrochloric acid and the other solution is acetic acid. He expects to require more of a standard NaOH solution to reach the equivalence point when titrating the HCl solution because it is a strong acid with a higher $[H_3O^+]$. Do you agree or disagree with the prediction? Explain your answer.

2. During a titration, a student adds water from a wash bottle to wash down some reactant solution that has splashed up in the Erlenmeyer flask. Although this changes the volume of the solution in the flask, she is confident that the accuracy of the titration will not be affected. Do you agree or disagree? Explain your answer.

3. A student must titrate a 25.0 mL sample of acetic acid solution whose concentration is known to be approximately 0.2 M. After adding a small amount of phenolphthalein indicator to the reaction flask, the student fills a 50 mL burette with a standardized 0.0650 M solution of NaOH and prepares to begin the titration. His lab partner insists that the titration cannot succeed. Do you agree or disagree with the lab partner? Explain your answer.

4. A student requires a standard solution of NaOH for a titration with a concentration as close as possible to 0.500 M. Using a digital balance, she carefully measures 20.00 g of NaOH. She quantitatively transfers it to a 1 L volumetric flask and adds the precise amount of water. She then calculates the concentration of the resulting solution to be 0.500 M and prepares to fill a burette and begin the titration. Her lab partner insists that the concentration is inaccurate. Do you agree or disagree with the lab partner? Would you expect the calculated concentration to be too high or too low? Explain your answer.

5. A student standardizing a solution of NaOH finds that 25.24 mL of that solution is required to neutralize a solution containing 0.835 g of KHP. Calculate the [NaOH].

6. A 21.56 mL solution of NaOH is standardized and found to have a concentration of 0.125 M. What mass of oxalic acid dihydrate would be required to standardize this solution?

7. A solution of NaOH is standardized and found to have a pH of 13.440. What volume of this solution must be added to 25.0 mL of a 0.156 M $H_2C_2O_4$ solution in a titration to neutralize the acid?

8. A 4.48 L sample of HCl gas, measured at STP, is dissolved in enough water to produce 400.0 mL of solution. A 25.0 mL sample of this solution is titrated with a 0.227 M $Sr(OH)_2$ solution. What volume of standard solution is required to reach the equivalence point?

9. A 0.665 g sample of an unknown monoprotic acid, HA, is dissolved in water and titrated with a standardized 0.2055 M KOH solution. If 26.51 mL of the basic solution is required to reach the equivalence point, calculate the molar mass of the acid.

10. A 5.47 g sample of an unknown diprotic acid is placed in a volumetric flask and then diluted to 250.0 mL. A 25.0 mL sample of this solution requires 23.6 mL of a 0.2231 M $Sr(OH)_2$ solution to completely neutralize the acid in a titration. Calculate the molar mass of the acid.

Chapter 7 Applications of Acid-Base Reactions

11. Tartaric acid, $C_4H_6O_6$, is a white crystalline diprotic organic acid. It occurs naturally in many plants, such as grapes and bananas, is often added to foods to give them a sour taste, and is one of the main acids found in wine. A 7.36 g sample of impure tartaric acid is diluted to 250.0 mL in a volumetric flask. A 25.0 mL portion of this solution is transferred to an Erlenmeyer flask and titrated against a 0.223 M standardized NaOH solution. If 40.31 mL of the basic solution is required to neutralize the acid, calculate the percent purity of the tartaric acid.

12. Sorbic acid, C_5H_7COOH, is a monoprotic organic acid that was first isolated from the berries of the mountain ash tree in 1859. It is a white crystalline solid used primarily as a food preservative. A 0.570 g sample of impure sorbic acid is dissolved in water to form 25.00 mL of solution. The acid solution requires 27.34 mL of 0.178 M KOH to reach the equivalence point. Calculate the percent purity of the sorbic acid.

13. Phenylacetic acid, C_7H_7COOH, is used in some perfumes and possesses a honey-like odor in low concentrations. A 0.992 g sample of impure phenylacetic acid dissolved in solution is titrated against a 0.105 M standard $Sr(OH)_2$ solution. If 31.07 mL of the standard solution is required to reach the equivalence point, calculate the percent purity of the acid.

14. Why is a titration considered to be a "volumetric" analysis?

7.4 A Closer Look at Titrations

Warm Up

Consider each pair of reactants in the three titrations below.

	Titration 1	Titration 2	Titration 3
Solution in burette	0.100 M NaOH	0.100 M NaOH	0.100 M HCl
Solution in flask	0.100 M HCl	0.100 M CH$_3$COOH	0.100 M NH$_3$

1. Write the formula equation for each titration.

   Titration 1:

   Titration 2:

   Titration 3:

2. What salt solution exists in each reaction flask at each of the equivalence points?

   Titration 1: _____

   Titration 2: _____

   Titration 3: _____

3. Indicate whether you would expect the pH of each solution at the equivalence point to be below, equal to, or above 7, and explain your decision.

   Titration 1:

   _____

   Titration 2:

   _____

   Titration 3:

   _____

Measuring pH with Acid-Base Indicators

In section 7.3 we described titrations as a form of volumetric chemical analysis. We will now take a closer look at the procedure by monitoring the pH changes in the reaction mixture during several types of titrations. In doing so, we'll also see how the principles of hydrolysis and buffer chemistry apply to and give us a better understanding of the titration process.

Usually we measure pH using either an acid-base indicator or a pH meter. Let's begin by describing the behavior and role of an acid-base indicator in a titration. Acid-base indicators are weak (usually monoprotic) organic acids whose conjugate pairs display different and normally intense colors. Those intense colors mean that only a small amount of an indicator is needed for a titration. If the appropriate indicator has been chosen, the change from one color to another will signal when the equivalence point has been reached.

Acid-base indicators are complex organic molecules and so we normally represent their formulas as simply "HIn." A typical indicator is a weak acid as shown in the aqueous equilibrium below.

$$\text{HIn}(aq) \quad + \quad H_2O(l) \quad \rightleftharpoons \quad \text{In}^-(aq) \quad + \quad H_3O^+(aq)$$

Acidic form and color predominate when $[H_3O^+]$ is relatively high and the equilibrium favors the reactant side.

Basic form and color predominate when $[H_3O^+]$ is relatively low and the equilibrium favors the product side.

If a small amount of the indicator is placed in a solution where the hydronium concentration is relatively high, this equilibrium will favor the reactant side. Thus, the acidic form of the indicator, **HIn**, and its color will predominate. In a basic solution, where the hydronium concentration is low, the equilibrium will favor the product side and so the basic form, **In⁻**, and its color will be prominent. For example, Figure 8.4.1 shows the acidic and basic forms of bromthymol blue.

Acidic (yellow) form of bromthymol blue predominates in an acidic solution with a pH below **6.0**.

Basic (blue) form of bromthymol blue predominates in an alkaline solution with a pH above **7.6**.

Figure 7.4.1 *The acidic and basic forms of bromthymol blue*

Table A6 Acid-Base Indicators (at the back of the book) tells us that changes in indicator colors occur over a *range* of pH values rather than instantly at one pH. This is because our eyes are limited in their ability to perceive slight changes in shades of color. Normally during a titration, about *one tenth* of the initial form of an indicator must be converted to the other form (its conjugate) for us to notice a color change.

It is useful to follow the progress of a typical titration in terms of the position of the indicator equilibrium and the relative amount of each member of the conjugate pair present in the reaction flask as the titrant is added.

For example, in a flask containing an indicator in an acidic solution, the acid form of the indicator, HIn, predominates. If we now begin adding a basic solution from a burette, the OH⁻ ions reduce the $[H_3O^+]$ in the flask and the position of the $[\text{In}^-]/[\text{HIn}]$ equilibrium begins to shift towards In⁻ according to Le Châtelier's principle. As the [HIn] decreases and the [In⁻] increases, we eventually reach a point where the $[\text{In}^-]/[\text{HIn}]$ ratio = 0.10. Here, we notice *the first color change*.

As the addition of OH⁻ ions continues to reduce the $[H_3O^+]$, the ratio continues to increase until the [HIn] = [In⁻]. An equal concentration of each form of the indicator will now combine to produce an *intermediate color* in the solution. The point at which we see this intermediate color, where the indicator is *half-way through its color change*, is called the **transition point** or **end point** of the indicator. At the transition point, as [HIn] = [In⁻], then

$$K_a = \frac{[H_3O^+][\cancel{\text{In}^-}]}{[\cancel{\text{HIn}}]} \quad \text{reduces to: } K_a = [H_3O^+]$$

This tells us that the $[H_3O^+]$ at the transition point equals the value of the K_a for the indicator (sometimes called K_{In}).

If we take the negative logarithm of both sides of the above equation, we see that:
the pK_a of an indicator = the pH at its transition point

When you refer to the table of acid-base indicators (Table A6), you will notice that different indicators change colors at different pH values. Those pH values reflect the pK_a values for each indicator.

As we continue adding base, we would see the indicator's color change complete when only about *one-tenth* of the initial acid form HIn remains in the flask, that is, when $[In^-]/[HIn] = 10$. We can summarize this progression in Table 7.4.1 beginning with the first detectable color change as the basic solution is added and ending when the color change is seen to be complete.

Table 7.4.1 *Indicator Color Change During the Titration of an Acid with a Base*

Indicator Color Change First Seen	Indicator Transition Point Occurs	Indicator Color Change Complete
$\dfrac{[In^-]}{[HIn]} = \dfrac{1}{10}$	$\dfrac{[In^-]}{[HIn]} = 1$	$\dfrac{[In^-]}{[HIn]} = \dfrac{10}{1}$
so $K_a = [H_3O^+](0.1)$	so $K_a = [H_3O^+]$	so $K_a = [H_3O^+](10)$
and $pK_a = pH + - \log(0.1)$	and $pK_a = pH$	and $pK_a = pH + - \log(10)$
or $pK_a = pH + 1$	or	or $pK_a = pH - 1$
so	$\mathbf{pH = pK_a}$	so
$\mathbf{pH = pK_a - 1}$		$\mathbf{pH = pK_a + 1}$
The first color change is seen when the pH of the solution is about one pH unit below the pK_a of the indicator.	The transition point and intermediate color occur when the pH of the solution equals the pK_a of the indicator.	The color change is complete when the pH of the solution is about one pH unit above the pK_a of the indicator.

We see from the above table that the range over which an indicator's color changes is normally about two pH units extending from approximately one pH unit below to one pH unit above the indicator's pK_a. This corresponds to a 100-fold change in the $[In^-]/[HIn]$ ratio and tells us that the useful pH range for an indicator in a titration is usually given by $\mathbf{pK_a \pm 1}$.

As we will discuss later in this section, depending on the reagents used in a titration, the pH at the equivalence point can be quite different. We normally attempt to choose an indicator whose pK_a is within one unit of the pH at the equivalence point.

Had we applied the above discussion to bromthymol blue, we would have noticed the indicator's yellow color begin to change at pH = 6 and continue changing until it appears completely blue at about pH = 7.6. Halfway through that change, at an *average of the two pH values*, the transition point pH of 6.8 is reached, which equals the indicator pK_a. At the transition point, bromthymol blue displays an intermediate green color.

An indicator's transition point pH and pK_a value can be estimated by averaging the two pH values associated with the range over which the indicator changes color.

Look again at the table of acid-base indicators (Table A6) and consider the order that those indicators appear top-to-bottom. Notice that the pH values over which the color changes occur increase as we move down the table from the acidic end of the pH scale to the basic end. This means that the pK_a values of those indicators must also increase.

As an increase in pK_a corresponds to a *decrease in* K_a, this tells us that the indicator acid strength decreases as we move down the table in the same way as it does in Table A5 showing the relative strengths of Brønsted-Lowry acids and bases (see Table A5 at the back of the book).

Combining Acid-Base Indicators — A Universal Indicator

Several different indicators that each go through a different color change over a different pH range can be combined into a single indicator solution. This solution will display different colors over a wide range of pH values. A universal indicator solution can also be added to absorbent strips of paper so that when the solvents evaporate, the individual test strips can be dipped into solutions to estimate pH values.

In a universal indicator, the colors of the component indicators at each pH combine to display virtually all the colors of the visible spectrum. Commercially available universal indicators are often composed of the indicator combination shown in Table 7.4.2. The indicator colors combine over the entire range of the pH scale to produce the results shown in Table 7.4.3. (The original universal indicator recipe was patented by the Japanese chemist Yamada in 1923.)

Table 7.4.2 *Indicators That Make up a Typical Universal Indicator*

Indicator	pK_a Value	Color of Acid Form	Color of Base Form
Thymol blue*	2.0 (pK_{a1})	red	yellow
Methyl red	5.6	red	yellow
Bromthymol blue	6.8	yellow	blue
Thymol blue*	8.8 (pK_{a2})	yellow	blue
Phenolphthalein	9.1	colorless	pink

Table 7.4.3 *Indicator Colors When Combined in a Universal Indicator*

Indicator	pH < 2	pH 3–4	pH 5-6	pH 7-8	pH 9-11	pH >12
Thymol Blue*	red/orange	yellow	yellow	yellow	green/blue	blue
Methyl Red	red	red	orange/yellow	yellow	yellow	yellow
Bromthymol Blue	yellow	yellow	yellow	green/blue	blue	blue
Phenolphthalein	colorless	colorless	colorless	colorless	pink	pink
Combined color	*red/orange*	*orange/yellow*	*yellow*	*yellow/green*	*green/blue*	*purple*

* Note. Thymol blue undergoes a *color change over two different pH ranges*. What does this tell us about the chemical nature of this acid?

Sample Problem 7.4.1(a) — Estimating Indicator K_a and pK_a values

Eight acid-base indicators listed on the acid-base indicators table (Table A6) display an orange color at their transition points. Identify which of those has a $K_a = 5 \times 10^{-8}$.

What to Think About	How to Do It
1. Calculate the pK_a value from the given K_a.	$pK_a = -\log(5 \times 10^{-8}) = 7.3$
2. That pK_a represents the average of one of the pair of pH values listed for indicators on the table. Focus on the middle of the indicator table.	Phenol red undergoes its color change from yellow to red between pH 6.6 and 8.0. The intermediate color is orange.
3. Once you calculate it, immediately focus on a particular region of the table to find the appropriate indicator.	Averaging the two pH values, we obtain: $$\frac{6.6 + 8.0}{2} = 7.3$$ The indicator is phenol red.

Sample Problem 7.4.1(b) — Estimating Solution pH

Samples of a solution were tested with three different indicators. Determine the pH range of the solution given the results shown below.

Indicator	Color
thymolphthalein	colorless
bromthymol blue	blue
thymol blue	Yellow

What to Think About	How to Do It
1. Use each data entry to identify a range of possible pH values for the solution.	First data entry: pH ≤ 9.4 Second data entry: pH ≥ 7.6 Third data entry: pH ≤ 8
2. Give the final answer as a narrow pH range rather than an exact value.	The pH range of the solution is given by: $$7.6 \leq pH \leq 8.0$$

Practice Problems 7.4.1 — Acid-Base Indicators

1. The indicator bromphenol blue appears yellow below pH = 3.0 and blue above pH = 4.5. Estimate the pK_a and K_a of the indicator and determine the color it will display in a 1.8×10^{-4} M HCl solution.

2. Estimate the $[H_3O^+]$ in a solution given the following data:

Indicator	Color
Phenol red	red
Phenolphthalein	colorless

Continued on next page

Practice Problems 7.4.1 (Continued)

3. A few drops of alizarin yellow are added to 25.0 mL of a 0.0010 M NaOH solution. What color should the indicator display? Explain your answer by showing the work.

4. Like thymol blue, the indicator alizarin also undergoes a color change over two different pH ranges. Use the table below to estimate the K_{a1} and K_{a2} values for alizarin.

	Below pH 5.6	Above pH 7.3	Below pH 11.0	Above pH 12.4
Alizarin color	yellow	red	red	purple

5. The following 0.10 M salt solutions have had their labels removed: $NaHSO_4$, Na_2CO_3, NaH_2PO_4, and NH_4CH_3COO. The solutions are tested with three indicators and the following results were observed.

	Bromthymol Blue	Methyl Orange	Phenolphthalein
Solution A	blue	yellow	pink
Solution B	green	yellow	colorless
Solution C	yellow	yellow	colorless
Solution D	yellow	red	colorless

Identify each solution: A _____   B _____

C _____   D _____

Acid-Base Titration Curves

We now begin a more detailed discussion of acid-base titrations by focusing on the pH changes that occur in the reaction flask as the titrant is added from the burette. We will look at three different types of titrations and apply our knowledge of indicators in each case.

An efficient way to monitor the progress of an acid-base titration is to plot the pH of the solution being analyzed as a function of the volume of titrant added. Such a diagram is called a titration curve.

> A **titration curve** is a plot of the pH of the solution being analyzed versus the volume of titrant added.

Each of the three types of titrations we will consider has a different net ionic equation, a different titration curve with a characteristic shape and features, and a different equivalence point pH requiring selection of a suitable indicator.

We will begin by considering the titration of the strong acid HCl(*aq*) with the strong base NaOH(*aq*). The formula and net ionic equations for the titration are given below:

$$HCl(aq) + NaOH(aq) \rightarrow NaCl(aq) + H_2O(l)$$

$$H_3O^+(aq) + OH^-(aq) \rightarrow 2\,H_2O(l)$$

The titration curve for the titration of a 25.00 mL solution of 0.100 M HCl with a 0.100 M NaOH solution is shown in Figure 8.4.2. An analysis of the curve reveals several important features.

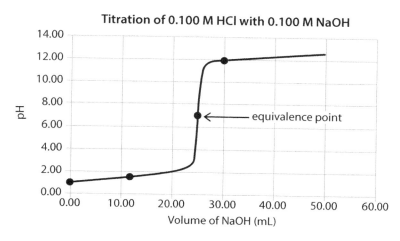

Figure 7.4.2 *Titration curve for a 25.00 mL solution of 0.100 M HCl titrated with a 0.100 M NaOH solution*

**Important Features
of a Strong Acid–
Strong Base Titration
Curve**

1. Because the acid is strong and therefore the initial [H₃O⁺] is high, *the pH starts out low.* As the titration proceeds, as long as there is *excess strong acid* in the flask, the pH will remain low and increase only very slowly as the NaOH is added.

2. The slow increase in pH continues until the moles of NaOH added almost equal the moles of H₃O⁺ initially present in the acid. Then, when the titration is within one or two drops of the equivalence point, the slope of the curve increases dramatically. The next drop of titrant neutralizes the last of the acid at the equivalence point and then introduces a tiny excess of OH⁻ ions into the flask. When this occurs, *the line becomes almost vertical and the pH rises by six to eight units almost immediately.*

3. Following the steep rise in pH at the equivalence point, the pH then increases slowly as excess OH⁻ is added.

Look at the titration curve above in Figure 7.4.2. Four points have been placed on the curve, representing key stages during the titration. Let us consider the chemical species present in the reaction flask and *calculate the pH at these four key stages.*

Stage 1: *The pH prior to the addition of any titrant*
Before any NaOH has been added, the reaction flask contains 25.00 mL of 0.100 M HCl(*aq*). As HCl is a strong acid, the [HCl] = [H₃O⁺] = 0.100 M. Therefore the pH = – log (0.100) = 1.000.
(Note the location of the *first* point on the above titration curve.)

Stage 2: *The pH approximately halfway to the equivalence point*
Once we begin adding NaOH, two changes occur in the solution in the flask that influence its pH: some of the acid has been neutralized by the added base, and the volume has increased.
Calculating the pH at this stage is similar to the process discussed in section 5.4 when a strong acid was mixed with a strong base. Recall that the calculation involves determining the diluted concentrations of H₃O⁺ and OH⁻ (designated as [H₃O⁺]$_{ST}$ and [OH⁻]$_{ST}$) before the reaction and then subtracting the lesser concentration from the greater concentration to determine the concentration of

the ion in excess. Although this method will work again in this situation, as we move forward through this and the other types of titration calculations, you will learn another approach.

This method allows us to organize and manage information efficiently when solutions are mixed and involve limiting and excess reactants. The process involves the use of an **ICF** table, which is a variation on the ICE table you are already familiar with. The "**I**" and the "**C**" still represent the "**I**nitial" and "**C**hange" in reagent concentrations, but because titration reactions go to completion, the "**E**" has been replaced with an "**F**" representing the "**F**inal" concentrations present when the reaction is complete. Let's use this method to calculate the pH of the solution present in the flask at stage 2, following the addition of 12.50 mL of the 0.100 M NaOH to the 25.00 mL of 0.100 M HCl in the flask — that is *halfway* to the equivalence point. Consider Sample Problem 7.4.2(a).

Sample Problem 7.4.2(a) — Calculating pH Halfway to the Equivalence Point

Calculate the pH of the solution produced in the reaction flask during a titration following the addition of 12.50 mL of 0.100 M NaOH to 25.00 mL of 0.100 M HCl.

What to Think About

1. Determine the diluted [HCl] and [NaOH] before the neutralization reaction. Enter these into the "Initial" row on the table as "[HCl]$_{IN}$" and "[NaOH]$_{IN}$."

2. In step 2, construct and complete an ICF table underneath the balanced equation using the [HCl]$_{IN}$ and [NaOH]$_{IN}$ determined in step 1. Notice that the *NaOH is the limiting reactant*. Omit the states (*aq*) and (*l*) in the table.

3. Use the species present in the reaction flask when the reaction is complete to determine the pH.

4. As the reactant acid and base are both strong, *neither of the ions in the product salt* can react with water to affect the pH of the solution. The product salt is therefore *neutral*.

How to Do It

$$[HCl]_{IN} = 0.100 \text{ M} \times \frac{25.00 \text{ mL}}{37.50 \text{ mL}} = 0.06667 \text{ M}$$

$$[NaOH]_{IN} = 0.100 \text{ M} \times \frac{12.50 \text{ mL}}{37.50 \text{ mL}} = 0.03333 \text{ M}$$

	HCl	+	NaOH	→	NaCl	+ H₂O
I	0.06667		0.03333		0	
C	− 0.03333		− 0.03333		+ 0.03333	
F	0.03334		≈ 0		0.03333	

Although the [OH⁻] cannot actually be zero (recall that $[H_3O^+][OH^-]$ must $= 10^{-14}$), as the excess HCl is the major species present, the [OH⁻] is insignificant.

final [HCl] = final [H₃O⁺]

pH = − log (0.03334) = 1.477 (3 sig. figures)

(Note the location of the *second* point on the curve.)

Stage 3: The pH at the equivalence point

After 25.00 mL of 0.100 M NaOH has been added to the original 25.00 mL of 0.100 M HCl, the equivalence point is reached. At this point, the total number of moles of H_3O^+ from the acid now equals the total number of moles of OH⁻ from the base. Consider Sample Problem 6.4.2(b) on the next page.

Sample Problem 7.4.2(b) — Calculating pH at the Equivalence Point

Determine the pH of the solution produced in the reaction flask when 25.00 mL of 0.100 M NaOH has been added to 25.00 mL of 0.100 M HCl.

What to Think About

1. Approach this problem in the same way as the problem above.

2. The $[HCl]_{IN}$ and $[NaOH]_{IN}$ are equal to each other and so neither will be in excess following the reaction.

3. At the equivalence point, the reaction flask will contain only water and NaCl(*aq*). As *neither ion is capable of hydrolysis, the solution in the flask will be neutral.*

How to Do It

$$[HCl]_{IN} = 0.100 \text{ M} \times \frac{25.00 \text{ mL}}{50.00 \text{ mL}} = 0.05000 \text{ M}$$

$$[NaOH]_{IN} = 0.100 \text{ M} \times \frac{25.00 \text{ mL}}{50.00 \text{ mL}} = 0.05000 \text{ M}$$

	HCl	+	NaOH	→	NaCl	+	H_2O
I	0.05000		0.05000		0		
C	− 0.05000		− 0.05000		+ 0.05000		
F	≈ 0		≈ 0		0.05000		

Neither the $[H_3O^+]$ nor the $[OH^-]$ can be zero because their product must equal 10^{-14}. However, neither is in excess so final $[H_3O^+]$ = final $[OH^-]$ = 1.00×10^{-7} M and pH = − log $(1.00 \times 10^{-7}$ M$)$ = 7.000.

(Note the location of the *third point* on the curve.)

As mentioned above, as neither ion in the product salt is capable of reacting with water, the pH of the solution at the equivalence point is 7.

> The titration of a strong monoprotic acid by a strong base will produce a solution with a pH of 7 at the equivalence point because neither of the ions present in the product salt can undergo hydrolysis to affect the pH.

As discussed, the appropriate indicator for a titration should ideally have a pK_a value that is as close as possible to the equivalence point (normally within about one pH unit). For a strong acid–strong base titration, however, the *large jump in pH* that occurs with the addition of a single drop of titrant at the equivalence point means that we have more flexibility in our choice of indicators. The table of acid-base indicators (Table A6) shows us that several indicators undergo their color change over the steep portion of the curve. Therefore, the indicators with transition points as low as pH 5 and as high as pH 9 (from methyl red to phenolphthalein) on the table are suitable for such a titration.

Stage 4: *The pH beyond the equivalence point*

After all of the acid has been neutralized, the solution now becomes increasingly basic as excess OH⁻ ions are added from the burette. We will use the ICF table below to calculate the pH of the solution in the reaction flask after 30.00 mL of the NaOH solution has been added.

Quick Check

1. Write the net ionic equation for a strong acid–strong base titration.

2. Although we have a choice of several indicators for such a titration, phenolphthalein is often chosen for practical reasons. Why?

3. Why is the pH at the equivalence point of a strong acid–strong base titration equal to 7?

A Reverse Scenario

Now let's consider the reverse scenario in which a 0.100 M NaOH solution is titrated with a 0.100 M HCl solution. The titration curve is effectively inverted compared to a strong acid titrated with a strong base, but the net ionic equation, general shape, and important features are the same. Note the inclusion of the same points at the four key stages of this titration on the curve in Figure 7.4.3.

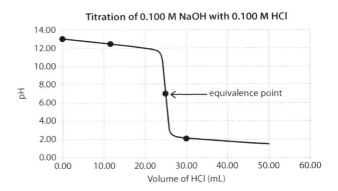

Figure 7.4.3 *Titration curve for a 0.100 M NaOH solution is titrated with a 0.100 M HCl solution*

Sample Problem 7.4.2(c) — Calculating pH beyond the Equivalence Point

Calculate the pH of the solution produced in the reaction flask when 30.00 mL of 0.100 M NaOH has been added to 25.00 mL of 0.100 M HCl.

What to Think About

1. The $[NaOH]_{IN}$ will exceed the $[HCl]_{IN}$ because the equivalence point has been passed by 5.00 mL. We therefore expect the pH to be well above 7.

2. As $[NaOH]$ will be in excess, the final $[HCl]$ will appear as zero on the table. Although the $[H_3O^+]$ cannot actually be zero, its final concentration is insignificant.

3. The subtraction yielding the final $[OH^-]$ gives an answer to two significant figures.

How to Do It

$$[HCl]_{IN} = 0.100\ M \times \frac{25.00\ mL}{55.00\ mL} = 0.04545\ M$$

$$[NaOH]_{IN} = 0.100\ M \times \frac{30.00\ mL}{55.00\ mL} = 0.05454\ M$$

	HCl	+ NaOH	→ NaCl	+ H₂O
I	0.04545	0.05454	0	
C	− 0.04545	− 0.04545	+ 0.04545	
F	≈ 0	0.00909	0.04545	

$$\text{final } [OH^-] = \text{final } [NaOH] = 0.00909\ M$$

$$pOH = -\log(0.00909) = 2.041$$

$$pH = 14.000 - 2.041 = 11.96\ (2\ \text{sig. figures})$$

(Note the location of the *fourth point* on the curve.)

Practice Problems 7.4.2 — Strong Acid–Strong Base Titration Curves

1. Consider the titration described above in the sample problems. Use an ICF table to calculate the pH of the solution in the reaction flask after 24.95 mL of 0.100 M NaOH has been added to the 25.00 mL of 0.100 M HCl. (This corresponds to about *1 drop before the equivalence point.*)

2. Use an ICF table to calculate the pH of the solution in the same flask after 25.05 mL of 0.100 M NaOH has been added to the 25.00 mL of 0.100 M HCl. (This corresponds to about *1 drop beyond the equivalence point.*)

3. Would you expect the complete neutralization of sulfuric acid by a sodium hydroxide solution in a titration to produce a neutral solution at the equivalence point? Why or why not? (Begin your answer by writing the balanced formula equation for the reaction.)

II. Weak Acid–Strong Base Titration Curves

Let's now consider the titration of the *weak acid* $CH_3COOH(aq)$ with the strong base $NaOH(aq)$. The formula and net ionic equations for the reaction are shown below:

$$CH_3COOH(aq) + NaOH(aq) \rightarrow NaCH_3COO(aq) + H_2O(l)$$

$$CH_3COOH(aq) + OH^-(aq) \rightarrow CH_3COO^-(aq) + H_2O(l)$$

Note that the acid is weak so it ionizes only to a small extent. Therefore, the predominant species reacting with the hydroxide ion from the strong base is the intact molecular acid. The diagram in Figure 7.4.4 shows the curve obtained when we titrate 25.0 mL of a 0.100 M CH_3COOH solution with 25.0 mL of a 0.100 M NaOH solution. Once again, we can identify a number of important features.

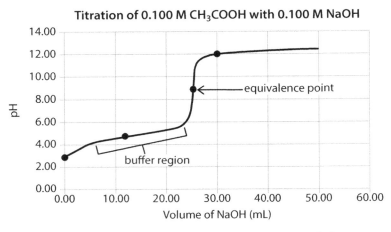

Titration of 0.100 M CH₃COOH with 0.100 M NaOH

Figure 7.4.4 *Titration curve for 25.0 mL of a 0.100 M CH₃COOH solution titrated with 25.0 mL of a 0.100 M NaOH solution*

Important Features of a Weak Acid–Strong Base Titration Curve

1. Because the acid is weak and thus ionizes only to a slight extent, the initial $[H_3O^+]$ is lower and so *the initial pH is higher* than for a strong acid.

2. There is an initial small jump in pH, but then the pH increases more slowly over a portion of the curve called the *buffer region* (labeled above) just before the steep rise to the equivalence point. However, *the pH in this region still changes more quickly than it does during a strong acid–strong base titration*. The buffer region occurs because large enough quantities of both the weak acid and its conjugate base exist in the reaction flask. This will be discussed in detail below.

3. The steep rise to the equivalence point occurs *over a smaller pH range* than when a strong acid is titrated with a strong base and *the pH at the equivalence point is greater than 7*. The solution at the equivalence point contains the anion from a weak acid (CH_3COO^-) and the cation from a strong base (Na^+). Although the cation can't react with water, the anion is a weak base and will therefore *accept protons from water, producing OH⁻ ions*. Hence the pH is greater than 7.

4. Beyond the equivalence point, the pH once again increases slowly as excess OH⁻ is added.

Note that we have again placed points on the curve at the same four key stages as we discussed in the strong acid–strong base titration. Let's once again consider the chemical species present in the reaction flask and calculate the pH at those four key stages. The calculations are different because of the minimal ionization of the weak acid and the hydrolysis reaction of its conjugate base with water.

Stage 1: *The pH prior to the addition of any titrant*
You may recognize this calculation as the first type of weak acid calculation we discussed in section 5.5, namely calculating the pH of a weak acid solution given the initial concentration and the K_a value. Recall that the minimal ionization (less than 5%) of the acid allowed us to assume that its initial and equilibrium concentrations were approximately equal. Using the same approach here, the initial concentration of 0.100 M and the K_a for acetic acid of 1.8×10^{-5} allows us to perform the calculation below.

Let $x = [H_3O^+]_{eq}$
Assume $0.100 - x \approx 0.100$

$$CH_3COOH + H_2O \rightleftharpoons CH_3COO^- + H_3O^+$$

I	0.100		0	0
C	$-x$		$+x$	$+x$
E	$0.100 - x$		x	x

$$K_a = \frac{[CH_3COO^-][H_3O^+]}{[CH_3COOH]} = \frac{x^2}{0.100} = 1.8 \times 10^{-5}$$

$$x = \sqrt{(1.8 \times 10^{-5})(0.100)} = 1.342 \times 10^{-3} \text{ M}$$

So pH $= -\log (1.342 \times 10^{-3} \text{ M}) = 2.87$ (2 sig. figures)

(Note the location of the *first point* on the titration curve in Figure 7.4.4.)

Stage 2: *The pH approximately halfway to the equivalence point*
As we begin adding NaOH from the burette, the OH^- ions react with the CH_3COOH in the flask to produce CH_3COO^- and H_2O. Therefore, from the beginning of the titration until the equivalence point is reached, the flask will contain *a mixture of a weak acid and its conjugate base*. This means that, for most of that time, the reaction mixture will qualify as a buffer solution. When you look at the titration curve, you can see that the *buffer region* represents the interval over which there are sufficient quantities of both CH_3COOH and CH_3COO^- for the solution to be a buffer.

To calculate the pH of the reaction mixture at about halfway to the equivalence point, we can use the same sequence of calculations with the ICF table as for a strong acid–strong base titration. Consider Sample Problem 7.4.3(a) below.

Sample Problem 7.4.3(a) — Calculating pH Just before Halfway to the Equivalence Point

Calculate the pH of the solution produced in the reaction flask *just prior to halfway to the equivalence point* when 12.00 mL of 0.100 M NaOH has been added to 25.00 mL of 0.100 M CH_3COOH.

What to Think About

1. Once again calculate the diluted concentrations of reactant acid and base before the reaction.

2. The final concentrations of CH_3COOH and CH_3COO^- in the solution are significant and thus constitute a buffer.

3. Therefore calculate the pH either by manipulating the K_a expression for acetic acid or, by way of extension, using the Henderson-Hasselbalch equation (see below).

How to Do It

$$[CH_3COOH]_{IN} = 0.100 \text{ M} \times \frac{25.00 \text{ mL}}{37.00 \text{ mL}} = 0.06757 \text{ M}$$

$$[NaOH]_{IN} = 0.100 \text{ M} \times \frac{12.00 \text{ mL}}{37.00 \text{ mL}} = 0.03243 \text{ M}$$

$$CH_3COOH + NaOH \rightarrow NaCH_3COO + H_2O$$

I	0.06757	0.03243	0	
C	−0.03243	−0.03243	+0.03243	
F	0.03514	≈ 0	0.03243	

$$K_a = \frac{[H_3O^+][CH_3COO^-]}{[CH_3COOH]}, \text{ so } [H_3O^+] = \frac{K_a [CH_3COOH]}{[CH_3COO^-]}$$

$$[H_3O^+] = \frac{(1.8 \times 10^{-5})(0.03514)}{(0.03243)} = 1.95 \times 10^{-5} \text{ M}$$

so pH $= -\log (1.95 \times 10^{-5}) = 4.71$ (2 sig. figures)

(Note the location of the *second point* on the curve.)

Using the Henderson-Hasselbalch Equation (Extension)

Because a buffer solution exists in the reaction flask, we could have also chosen to solve the above problem using the Henderson-Hasselbalch equation as follows:

$$pH = pK_a + \log \left[\frac{[CH_3COO^-]}{[CH_3COOH]} \right] = 4.745 + \log \left[\frac{(0.03243)}{(0.03514)} \right] = 4.745 + (-0.0348) = 4.71$$

pH of Solution = pK_a at Halfway Point

The above methods show us that just before halfway to the equivalence point in the titration, *the log of the ratio is negative* because the [base]/[acid] ratio is less than one. This means that *just before halfway to the equivalence point, the solution pH is always less than the pK_a.*

Note that *exactly halfway to the equivalence point*, half of the acid has been converted to its conjugate base, so [CH_3COOH] = [CH_3COO^-]. We therefore see that:

$$[H_3O^+] = \frac{K_a[\cancel{CH_3COOH}]}{[\cancel{CH_3COO^-}]} \qquad \text{and} \qquad pH = pK_a + \log \frac{[\cancel{CH_3COO^-}]}{[\cancel{CH_3COOH}]}$$

so $\quad [H_3O^+] = K_a = 1.8 \times 10^{-5}$ so $pH = pK_a + \log 1$

$$\mathbf{pH = pK_a = 4.74}$$

The fact that the pH of the solution halfway to the equivalence point equals the pK_a of the weak acid being titrated is a useful relationship. This allows us to determine the K_a of a weak acid by titrating it with a strong base and noting the pH of the solution exactly halfway to the equivalence point on the titration curve.

Sample Problem 7.4.3(b) — Calculating pH Just beyond Halfway to the Equivalence Point

Calculate the pH of the solution produced in the reaction flask *just beyond halfway to the equivalence point* when 13.00 mL of 0.100 M NaOH has been added to 25.00 mL of 0.100 M CH_3COOH.

What to Think About	**How to Do It**
1. Calculate the diluted concentrations and enter them into the ICF table.	$[CH_3COOH]_{IN} = 0.100 \text{ M} \times \dfrac{25.00 \cancel{mL}}{38.00 \cancel{mL}} = 0.06579 \text{ M}$
2. The solution in the reaction flask once again qualifies as a buffer.	$[NaOH]_{IN} = 0.100 \text{ M} \times \dfrac{13.00 \cancel{mL}}{38.00 \cancel{mL}} = 0.03421 \text{ M}$
3. Use the final concentrations of CH_3COOH and CH_3COO^- to calculate the pH of the solution in two ways as in the previous example.	

$$CH_3COOH + NaOH \rightarrow NaCH_3COO + H_2O$$

	CH_3COOH	$NaOH$	$NaCH_3COO$	
I	0.06579	0.03421	0	
C	− 0.03421	− 0.03421	+ 0.03421	
F	0.03158	0	0.03421	

$$K_a = \frac{[H_3O^+][CH_3COO^-]}{[CH_3COOH]} \quad \text{so} \quad [H_3O^+] = \frac{K_a[CH_3COOH]}{[CH_3COO^-]}$$

$$[H_3O^+] = \frac{(1.8 \times 10^{-5})(0.03158)}{(0.03421)} = 1.66 \times 10^{-5} \text{ M}$$

so $pH = -\log(1.66 \times 10^{-5}) = 4.78$ (2 sig. figures)

Using the Henderson-Hasselbalch Equation (Extension)

Once again, we could have chosen to solve the above problem using the Henderson-Hasselbalch equation as follows:

$$pH = pK_a + \log\left[\frac{[CH_3COO^-]}{[CH_3COOH]}\right] = 4.745 + \log\left[\frac{(0.03421)}{(0.03158)}\right] = 4.74 + (0.0347) = 4.78$$

---

pH of Solution > pK_a beyond the Equivalence Point

We can therefore see that beyond halfway to the equivalence point in the titration, *the log of the ratio is positive* because the [base]/[acid] is greater than one. This means that *beyond halfway to the equivalence point, the solution pH is always greater than the pK_a.*

During the titration of a weak acid with strong base:

- prior to halfway to the equivalence point: $[H_3O^+] > K_a$ and so $pH < pK_a$
- halfway to the equivalence point: $[H_3O^+] = K_a$ and so $pH = pK_a$
- beyond halfway and prior to the equivalence point: $[H_3O^+] < K_a$ and so $pH > pK_a$

Stage 3: *The pH at the equivalence point*

If you look again at the weak acid–strong base titration curve (Figure 8.4.4), you'll notice that the volume of 0.100 M NaOH required to neutralize 25.00 mL of 0.100 M CH_3COOH at the equivalence point is *exactly the same* as that required to neutralize the same volume of 0.100 M HCl. This reminds us that the strength of an acid has *no bearing* on the volume of base required to neutralize it in a titration.

At the equivalence point, all of the acid originally present has reacted with the added NaOH. The reaction flask therefore contains an aqueous solution of the salt produced from a weak acid and a strong base, namely $NaCH_3COO$. As noted above, although the Na^+ ion cannot react with water, the CH_3COO^- ion from a weak acid is itself a weak base and will therefore accept protons from water, producing OH^- ions. This means that the pH at the equivalence point will be above 7 due to the presence of a basic salt.

The titration of a weak acid by a strong base will produce a basic solution with a pH greater than 7 at the equivalence point because the anion present in the product salt will undergo hydrolysis to produce OH^- ions and the cation will not hydrolyze.

To correctly calculate the pH at the equivalence point, we must first consider the initial reaction that *goes to completion*. This requires the use of the IC**F** table. We must then use the IC**E** table to manage the hydrolysis reaction of the acetate anion with water, which involves an *equilibrium*. This is illustrated in Sample Problem 6.4.3(c) below.

Sample Problem 7.4.3(c) — Calculating pH at the Equivalence Point

Calculate the pH of the solution produced in the reaction flask when 25.00 mL of 0.100 M NaOH has been added to 25.00 mL of 0.100 M CH_3COOH

What to Think About	**How to Do It**
1. Once again dilute the acid and base and then enter those values into the ICF table for the reaction that goes to completion. 2. Examine the bottom line of the ICF table. It reveals that a 0.0500 M solution of $NaCH_3COO$ exists in the reaction flask at the equivalence point.	**Part 1** $[CH_3COOH]_{IN} = 0.100 \text{ M} \times \dfrac{25.00 \text{ mL}}{50.00 \text{ mL}} = 0.0500 \text{ M}$ $[NaOH]_{IN} = 0.100 \text{ M} \times \dfrac{25.00 \text{ mL}}{50.00 \text{ mL}} = 0.0500 \text{ M}$ $CH_3COOH + NaOH \rightarrow NaCH_3COO + H_2O$

	CH_3COOH	$NaOH$	$NaCH_3COO$	
I	0.0500	0.0500	0	
C	− 0.0500	− 0.0500	+ 0.0500	
F	≈ 0	≈ 0	0.0500	

Continued on next page

Sample Problem 7.4.3(c) (*Continued*)

What to Think About	How to Do It

What to Think About

3. The anion of the dissociated salt is the conjugate base of a weak acid and is thus capable of accepting protons from water in a hydrolysis reaction.

4. For the second part of the calculation, enter the 0.0500 M CH_3COO^- in the **I**nitial row of the ICE table for the hydrolysis equilibrium.

5. Calculate the pH of the solution resulting from the anionic hydrolysis of the acetate ion.

How to Do It

Part 2

Let $x = [OH^-]_{eq}$

$$CH_3COO^- + H_2O \rightleftharpoons CH_3COOH + OH^-$$

I	0.0500		0	0
C	$-x$		$+x$	$+x$
E	$0.0500 - x$		x	x

Assume $0.0500 - x \approx 0.0500$

$$K_b = \frac{[CH_3COOH][OH^-]}{[CH_3COO^-]} = \frac{K_w}{K_a} = \frac{1.0 \times 10^{-14})}{1.8 \times 10^{-5}} = 5.6 \times 10^{-10}$$

$$\frac{x^2}{0.0500} = 5.6 \times 10^{-10} \quad so \quad x = \sqrt{(0.0500)(5.6 \times 10^{-10})}$$

$$x = [OH^-] = 5.29 \times 10^{-6} M \quad so \quad pOH = -\log(5.292 \times 10^{-6})$$

$$pOH = 5.27 \quad and \ so \quad pH = 14.000 - 5.27 = 8.72$$

(2 sig. figures)

(Note the location of the *third point* on the curve.)

Choosing the Right Indicator

Because the vertical region on the titration curve around the equivalence point is shorter than for a strong acid–strong base titration, we are more limited when choosing the proper indicator. The table of acid-base indicators (Table A6) shows us that either phenolphthalein or thymol blue (based on its second transition point) would be an appropriate indicator in this case. Methyl red would not.

Stage 4: *The pH beyond the equivalence point*

After all of the acid has been neutralized, the solution again becomes increasingly basic with the addition of excess OH^- ions. Although a relatively high concentration of the weakly basic acetate ion remains in the reaction flask beyond the equivalence point, the presence of excess hydroxide ions in the flask is far more significant in determining the pH. The excess NaOH is a *strong base* and the increasing $[OH^-]$ from that base forces the weak base hydrolysis equilibrium even further to the left.

$$CH_3COO^-(aq) + H_2O(l) \rightleftharpoons CH_3COOH(aq) + \mathbf{OH^-}(aq)$$

The result is that we can safely ignore any contribution to the $[OH^-]$ in the flask by the acetate ion and thus use only the ICF table to calculate the pH. Consider Sample Problem 7.4.3(d) below.

Sample Problem 7.4.3(d) — Calculating pH beyond the Equivalence Point Calculate

the pH of the solution produced in the reaction flask when 30.00 mL of 0.100 M NaOH has been added to 25.00 mL of 0.100 M CH_3COOH.

What to Think About

1. Because the equivalence point has been passed by 5.00 mL, once again expect the pH to be well above 7.

2. As [NaOH] will be in excess, ignore the final [CH_3COO^-] when calculating pH.

3. The subtraction yielding the final [OH^-] gives an answer to three significant figures. This specifies the decimal places in the final pH.

How to Do It

$$[CH_3COOH]_{IN} = 0.100\ M \times \frac{25.00\ mL}{55.00\ mL} = 0.04545\ M$$

$$[NaOH]_{IN} = 0.100\ M \times \frac{30.00\ mL}{55.00\ mL} = 0.05454\ M$$

$$CH_3COOH + NaOH \rightarrow NaCH_3COO + H_2O$$

	CH_3COOH	NaOH	$NaCH_3COO$	
I	0.04545	0.05454	0	
C	− 0.04545	− 0.04545	+ 0.04545	
F	≈ 0	0.00909	0.04545	

$$final\ [OH^-] = final\ [NaOH] = 0.00909\ M$$
$$pOH = -log\ (0.00909) = 2.041$$
$$pH = 14.000 - 2.041 = 11.959\ (3\ sig.\ figures)$$

(Note the location of the *fourth point* on the curve.)

Comparing Titration Curves

Note that the pH at this *final stage* is the same as for the titration of 0.100 M HCl by 0.100 M NaOH, although the pH values at *the first three stages are different*.

Figure 7.4.5 compares the two titration curves. Note the position of the weak acid–strong base titration curve relative to the strong acid–strong base curve *before the equivalence point*. As the strength of the acid being titrated decreases, the portion of the titration curve before the equivalence point will shift farther and farther up so that each of the first three stages we have discussed will be associated with higher and higher pH values during the titration. Yet despite the acid's strengths being different, the volume of base required to reach equivalence remains the same!

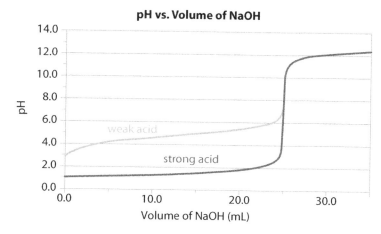

pH vs. Volume of NaOH

Figure 7.4.5 *Comparison of titration curves*

Quick Check

1. Why do we label a region of a weak acid–strong base titration curve before the equivalence point as a "buffer region"?

   _____

2. Why is the pH at the equivalence point of a weak acid–strong base titration higher than 7?

   _____

3. When titrating acetic acid with sodium hydroxide, why can we ignore any contribution to the [OH⁻] by the acetate anion beyond the equivalence point when calculating pH?

   _____

4. *On Figure 8.4.5 above*, sketch the titration curve for the titration of 25.0 mL 0.100 M hypochlorous acid, HClO, with a solution of 0.100 M NaOH, given the following information:

Initial pH of HClO Solution	pH Halfway to Equivalence Point	pH at Equivalence Point
4.27	7.54	10.12

Practice Problems 7.4.3 — Weak Acid–Strong Base Titration Curves

1. (a) Calculate the pH of the solution produced when 9.00 mL of 0.200 M NaOH has been added to 20.0 mL of 0.200 M HCOOH. Is this value less than or greater than the pK_a of HCOOH?

   (b) Calculate the pH at the equivalence point of this titration.

2. A student titrates an unknown weak monoprotic acid with a standard solution of KOH and draws a titration curve. Halfway to the equivalence point, the pH of the solution is identified to be 4.187. Identify the acid.

3. (a) A 20.0 mL sample of 0.450 M HNO_2 is titrated with a 0.500 M NaOH solution. What $[H_3O^+]$ will exist in the reaction flask exactly halfway to the equivalence point?

   (b) The equivalence point is reached when 18.00 mL of the basic solution has been added to the original nitrous acid solution. Calculate the pH at the equivalence point.

The third type of titration we will discuss can be considered the opposite of the previous type — namely, the titration of a *weak base* by a *strong* acid. Recall that the curve for a strong base titrated with a strong acid is the *same shape* as a strong acid titrated with a strong base, but is *inverted*. The same is true of the titration curve for a weak base titrated with a strong acid compared with the curve for a weak acid titrated with a strong base: *the shape is the same but inverted*.

Let's investigate the titration of a 0.100 M NH_3 solution with a 0.100 M HCl. The formula and net ionic equations for the reaction are shown below:

$$NH_3(aq) + HCl(aq) \rightarrow NH_4^+(aq) + Cl^-(aq)$$

$$NH_3(aq) + H_3O^+(aq) \rightarrow NH_4^+(aq) + H_2O(l)$$

If we compare the titration curve for the above reaction to that for a *strong base* titrated with a strong acid, we can once again identify a number of important features. Consider those two curves in Figure 7.4.6 below.

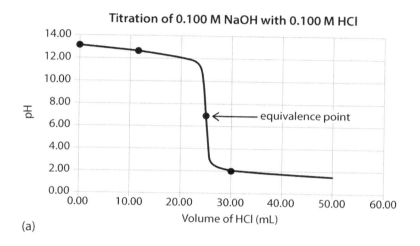

(a)

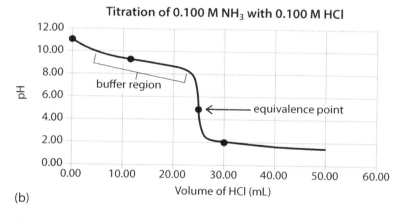

(b)

Figure 7.4.6 *Titration curves for solutions of (a) 0.100 M NaOH and (b) 0.100 M NH₃ titrated with 0.100 M HCl*

1. Because the solution we begin with is a *weak* base, we expect the initial pH to be above 7, but *lower* than if we were starting with a *strong base*.

2. There is an initial small drop in pH as the titration begins, but then the pH decreases more slowly over a *buffer region* during which significant amounts of the weak base (NH_3) and its conjugate acid (NH_4^+) are present in the flask. However, the pH in this region still changes *more quickly* than it does during a strong base–strong acid titration. The buffer region ends just before the steep drop in pH associated with the equivalence point.

3. The steep drop at the equivalence point occurs *over a smaller pH range* than when a *strong base* is titrated with a strong acid and *the pH at the equivalence point is below 7*. The solution at the equivalence point contains the anion from a strong acid (Cl^-) and the cation from a weak base (NH_4^+). Although the anion can't accept protons from water, *the cation is a weak acid and will therefore donate protons to water, producing H_3O^+ ions*. Hence the pH is below 7.

4. Beyond the equivalence point, the pH decreases slowly as excess H_3O^+ is added.

The four points have once again been placed at the same key stages of the titration. And once again, by considering the species present in the reaction flask at these stages, we can calculate the pH of the solution. The calculations are similar to the previous titration type in that they reflect, in this case, the minimal ionization of the weak base and the hydrolysis reaction of its conjugate with water.

Stage 1: *The pH before the addition of any titrant*
This calculation is the first type we discussed for weak bases in section 5.5: the pH of a weak base solution is determined given the initial concentration and the K_b value. The slight ionization of the NH_3 allows us to assume that its initial and equilibrium concentrations are approximately equal. Consider the following pH calculation:

$$K_b \text{ for } NH_3 = \frac{K_w}{K_a \text{ for } NH_4^+} = \frac{1.00 \times 10^{-14}}{5.6 \times 10^{-10}} = 1.8 \times 10^{-5}$$

Let $x = [OH^-]_{eq}$
Assume $0.100 - x \approx 0.100$

	NH_3	$+$ H_2O $\rightleftharpoons$	NH_4^+	$+$	OH^-
I	0.100		0		0
C	$-x$		$+x$		$+x$
E	$0.100 - x$		x		x

$$K_b = \frac{[NH_4^+][OH^-]}{[NH_3]} = \frac{x^2}{0.100} = 1.8 \times 10^{-5}$$

$x = \sqrt{(1.8 \times 10^{-5})(0.100)} = 1.34 \times 10^{-3} \text{ M} = [OH^-]$
so $pOH = -\log(1.34 \times 10^{-3}) = 2.872$ and
$pH = 14.000 - 2.872 = 11.13$
(Note the location of the *first point* on the curve.)

Stage 2: *The pH approximately halfway to the equivalence point*
As the titration begins and HCl is added to the flask, the H_3O^+ ions react with the NH_3 to produce NH_4^+ and H_2O. Thus, from the beginning of the titration until the equivalence point is reached, the flask will contain *a mixture of a weak base and its conjugate acid*. This means once again that, for most of that time, the reaction mixture will qualify as a buffer solution. If you look at the titration curve, you can see that the *buffer region* represents the interval over which there are significant quantities of both NH_3 and NH_4^+ in the solution.

The use of the ICF table will again allow us to efficiently organize and manage the information provided in the question.

Sample Problem 7.4.4(a) — Calculating pH before Halfway to the Equivalence Point

Calculate the pH of the solution produced during a titration following the addition of 12.00 mL of 0.100 M HCl to 25.00 mL of 0.100 M NH_3. This is almost *halfway* to the equivalence point.

What to Think About

1. Once again determine the diluted concentrations and enter those values into the ICF table.

2. Use the final concentrations at the completion of the reaction to determine the pH.

3. As we are almost halfway to the equivalence point, the $[NH_3]$ and $[NH_4^+]$ are sufficient to constitute a buffer.

4. The $[Cl^-]$ cannot react with water and so will not affect the pH of the solution.

How to Do It

$$[NH_3]_{IN} = 0.100\ M \times \frac{25.00\ mL}{37.00\ mL} = 0.06757\ M$$

$$[HCl]_{IN} = 0.100\ M \times \frac{12.00\ mL}{37.00\ mL} = 0.03243\ M$$

	NH_3 +	HCl →	NH_4^+ +	Cl^-
I	0.06757	0.03243	0	0
C	− 0.03243	− 0.03243	+ 0.03243	+ 0.03243
F	0.03514	≈ 0	0.03243	0.03243

$$K_b = \frac{[NH_4^+][OH^-]}{[NH_3]}, \quad so \quad [OH^-] = \frac{K_b\,[NH_3]}{[NH_4^+]}$$

$$[OH^-] = \frac{(1.8 \times 10^{-5})(0.03514)}{(0.03243)} = 1.95 \times 10^{-5}\ M$$

$$pOH = -\log(1.95 \times 10^{-5}) = 4.710$$

$$so\ pH = 14.000 - 4.710 = 9.29\ (2\ sig.\ figures)$$

(Note the location of the *second point* on the curve.)

Using the Henderson-Hasselbalch Equation (Extension)

Because a buffer solution exists in the reaction flask, we could have again chosen to solve the above problem using the Henderson-Hasselbalch equation. In the equation, we use the pK_a for the conjugate acid of NH_3. The pK_a for $NH_4^+ = -\log(5.6 \times 10^{-10}) = 9.252$.

$$pH = pK_a + \log\left[\frac{[NH_3]}{[NH_4^+]}\right] = 9.252 + \log\left[\frac{[0.03514]}{[0.03243]}\right] = 9.252 + (0.0349) = 9.29$$

Note that, because the [base]/[acid] ratio is greater than 1, *the log of the ratio is positive*. This means that just prior to halfway to the equivalence point, *the pH is greater than the pK_a*

---

pOH = pK_b of Weak Base at Halfway Point

Note that *exactly halfway to the equivalence point* half of the base has been converted to its conjugate acid. Therefore $[NH_3] = [NH_4^+]$. This means that:

$$[OH^-] = \frac{K_b[NH_3]}{[NH_4^+]}$$

$$so \quad [OH^-] = K_b = 1.8 \times 10^{-5}$$

$$and \quad [H_3O^+] = \frac{1.00 \times 10^{-14}}{1.8 \times 10^{-5}} = 5.6 \times 10^{-10}$$

$$[H_3O^+] = K_a\ (for\ NH_4^+)$$

$$pOH = pK_b + \log\frac{[NH_3]}{[NH_4^+]}$$

$$so \quad pOH = pK_b + \log 1$$

$$pOH = pK_b = 4.745$$

$$pH = pK_a\ (for\ NH_4^+) = 9.25$$

The fact that the pOH of the solution halfway to the equivalence point equals the pK_b of the weak base is a similar scenario to that of a *weak acid–strong base* titration. In this case, we can determine the K_b of a weak base by titrating it with a strong acid and noting the pOH of the solution

---

exactly halfway to the equivalence point on the titration curve. (Had we chosen to use the Henderson-Hasselbalch equation, we would have calculated the same pH value.)

Stage 3: *The pH at the equivalence point*
At the equivalence point, all of the base initially present in the flask has reacted with the added HCl. The flask therefore contains an aqueous solution of the salt produced from a strong acid and a weak base — in this case, NH_4Cl. We noted above that the Cl^- ion cannot react with water, but the NH_4^+ is weakly acidic and will therefore react with water to produce H_3O^+ ions. This means that the pH at the equivalence point will be below 7 due to the presence of an acidic salt.

> The titration of a weak base by a strong acid will produce an acidic solution with a pH below 7 at the equivalence point because the cation present in the product salt will undergo hydrolysis to produce H_3O^+ ions and the anion will not hydrolyze.

To calculate the pH at the equivalence point, we must once again consider the initial reaction that *goes to completion*, and then the hydrolysis reaction of the ammonium anion with water that involves an *equilibrium*. Consider Sample Problem 6.4.4(b) on the next page.

Sample Problem 7.4.4(b) — Calculating pH at the Equivalence Point

Calculate the pH of the solution produced in the reaction flask when 25.00 mL of 0.100 M HCl has been added to 25.00 mL of 0.100 M NH_3.

What to Think About

1. Dilute the acid and base and enter those values into the ICF table for the reaction that goes to completion.

2. Examine the bottom line of the ICF table. It shows that a 0.0500 M NH_4Cl solution exists in the reaction flask at the equivalence point.

3. The cation of the dissociated salt is weakly acidic and is thus capable of donating protons to water in a hydrolysis reaction.

4. For the second part of the calculation, enter the 0.05000 M NH_4^+ into the **Initial** row of the ICE table for the hydrolysis equilibrium.

5. Calculate the pH of the solution resulting from the cationic hydrolysis of the ammonium ion.

How to Do It

Part 1

$$[NH_3]_{IN} = 0.100 \text{ M} \times \frac{25.00 \text{ mL}}{50.00 \text{ mL}} = 0.0500 \text{ M}$$

$$[HCl]_{IN} = 0.100 \text{ M} \times \frac{25.00 \text{ mL}}{50.00 \text{ mL}} = 0.0500 \text{ M}$$

	NH_3	+ HCl	→ NH_4^+	+ Cl^-
I	0.0500	0.0500	0	0
C	− 0.0500	− 0.0500	+ 0.0500	+ 0.0500
F	≈ 0	≈ 0	0.0500	0.0500

Part 2

Let $x = [H_3O^+]_{eq}$

	NH_4^+	+ H_2O ⇌	NH_3	+ H_3O^+
I	0.0500		0	0
C	− x		+ x	+ x
E	0.0500 − x		x	x

Assume $0.0500 - x \approx 0.0500$

$$K_a = \frac{[NH_3][H_3O^+]}{[NH_4^+]} = 5.6 \times 10^{-10}$$

$$\frac{x^2}{0.0500} = 5.6 \times 10^{-10} \quad \text{so} \quad x = \sqrt{(0.0500)(5.6 \times 10^{-10})}$$

$x = 5.292 \times 10^{-6}$ M so pH $= -\log(5.292 \times 10^{-6}) = 5.28$

(Note the location of the *third point* on the curve.)

The relatively short vertical section of the curve near the pH at the equivalence point of 5.28 suggests that an appropriate indicator for this titration would be methyl red. The pK_a for methyl red is 5.4.

Stage 4: *The pH beyond the equivalence point*

After all of the base has been neutralized, the solution again becomes increasingly acidic with the addition of excess H_3O^+ ions. Although a relatively high concentration of the weakly acidic ammonium ion remains in the reaction flask beyond the equivalence point, its presence is insignificant in determining pH in the same way that excess acetate ions were insignificant beyond the equivalence point in the weak acid–strong base titration. In this case, the presence of excess H_3O^+ in the flask is the only significant factor in determining the pH. The excess HCl is a *strong acid* and the increasing $[H_3O^+]$ from that acid forces the weak acid hydrolysis equilibrium even further to the left.

$$NH_4^+(aq) + H_2O(l) \rightleftharpoons NH_3(aq) + \mathbf{H_3O^+}(aq)$$

The result is that we can safely ignore any contribution to the $[H_3O^+]$ in the flask by the ammonium ion and so need only use the ICF table to calculate the pH. Consider Sample Problem 8.4.4(c) below.

Sample Problem 7.4.4(c) — Calculating pH beyond the Equivalence Point

Calculate the pH of the solution produced in the reaction flask when 30.00 mL of 0.100 M HCl has been added to 25.00 mL of 0.100 M NH_3

What to Think About

1. Because the equivalence point has been passed by 5.00 mL, expect the pH to be well below 7.

2. As [HCl] will be in excess, ignore the final $[NH_4^+]$ when calculating pH. Also ignore the $[Cl^-]$.

3. The subtraction yielding the final $[H_3O^+]$ gives an answer to three significant figures. This determines the decimal places in the final pH.

How to Do It

$$[NH_3]_{IN} = 0.100 \text{ M} \times \frac{25.00 \text{ mL}}{55.00 \text{ mL}} = 0.04545 \text{ M}$$

$$[HCl]_{IN} = 0.100 \text{ M} \times \frac{30.00 \text{ mL}}{55.00 \text{ mL}} = 0.05454 \text{ M}$$

	NH_3	+	HCl	→	NH_4^+	+	Cl^-
I	0.04545		0.05454		0		0
C	− 0.04545		− 0.04545		+ 0.04545		+ 0.04545
F	≈ 0		0.00909		0.04545		0.04545

$$\text{final } [HCl] = \text{final } [H_3O^+] = 0.00909 \text{ M}$$

$$pH = -\log(0.00909) = 2.04 \text{ (2 sig. figures)}$$

(Note the location of the *fourth point* on the curve.)

Practice Problems 7.4.4 — Weak Base–Strong Acid Titration Curves

1. Calculate the pH of the solution produced during the titration described above after 13.0 mL of 0.100 M HCl has been added to 25.0 mL of 0.100 M NH_3. (This is just beyond halfway to the equivalence point). Should your answer be greater than or less than the pK_a of NH_4^+?

2. Explain how the titration curve for a weak base titrated by a strong acid can be used to determine the K_b of the weak base.

3. Calculate the pH of the solution produced in the titration described above after 40.0 mL of 0.100 M HCl has been added to 25.0 mL of 0.100 M NH_3. Does the pH value you calculate agree with the titration curve?

Quick Check

1. Why is the pH at the equivalence point of a weak base–strong acid titration lower than 7?

    _____

2. Phenolphthalein is an appropriate indicator for the first two types of titrations we discussed in this section. Why is phenolphthalein a poor indicator choice for the titration of a weak base with a strong acid?

    _____

3. When titrating aqueous ammonia with hydrochloric acid, why can we ignore any contribution to the $[H_3O^+]$ by the ammonium cation beyond the equivalence point when calculating pH?

    _____

A Titration Curve Summary Table

Strong Acid + Strong Base	Weak Acid + Strong Base	Weak Base + Strong Acid
Net Ionic Equation	**Net Ionic Equation**	**Net Ionic Equation**
Sketch of Titration Curve	**Sketch of Titration Curve**	**Sketch of Titration Curve**
Reason for Equivalence Point pH Value	**Reason for Equivalence Point pH Value**	**Reason for Equivalence Point pH Value**
Hydrolysis Reaction (if any)	**Hydrolysis Reaction (if any)**	**Hydrolysis Reaction (if any)**

Results and Discussion

1. The volume of titrant required to reach the equivalence point in each titration should be exactly the same. Explain why.

2. Explain how each of the two "weak–strong" titration curves can be used to determine one of either a K_a or a K_b value.

7.4 Review Questions

1. Consider the following for a hypothetical indicator: $K_a = \dfrac{[H_3O^+][In^-]}{[HIn]} = 1.0 \times 10^{-7}$

   So, given that $\dfrac{K_a}{[H_3O^+]} = \dfrac{[In^-]}{[HIn]}$

   Complete the following table for three different solutions given that HIn is *yellow* and In⁻ is *blue*.

Solution	[In⁻]/[HIn] Ratio in Solution	Solution Color
0.0010 M HCl		
Pure water		
0.0010 M NaOH		

2. Equal concentrations of an indicator, HIn, and one of three different acids are placed in three separate flasks and the following data was obtained for each pair of compounds:

Solution →	0.1 M HNO₃	0.1 M HA1	0.1 M HA2
0.1 M HIn color	red	yellow	red

   Use the above data to list the three acids, HA1, HA2, and HIn, in order of increasing strength and explain your reasoning.

   _____ < _____ < _____

3. You are given four 0.10 M solutions without labels and told they are HCl, NaOH, FeCl₃, and NaCN. You are also told to choose only three indicators that will positively identify each solution. Complete the table below showing your choice of indicators and their colors in each solution.

Solution →	0.10 M HCl	0.10 M NaOH	0.10 M FeCl₃	0.10 M NaCN
Indicator 1:				
Indicator 2:				
Indicator 3:				

4. Complete the table below showing the reactants in three different titrations.
   (a) State if the pH at the equivalence point of each titration will be below, equal to, or above 7.
   (b) Select an appropriate indicator from the table of acid-base indicators (Table A6) for each titration. (There may be more than one correct choice for each titration.)

	HNO_3 + KOH	NaOH + HCOOH	HBr + NH_3
pH at equivalence pt.			
Indicator			

5. Bromcresol purple undergoes its color change from yellow to purple as pH increases from 5.2 through to 6.8.
   (a) Is bromcresol purple a stronger or a weaker acid than acetic acid? Explain your answer.

   (b) Would bromcresol purple be a good indicator to indicate that acetic acid is acidic? Why or why not?

6. The following 0.10 M solutions have had their labels removed: NaCl, K_3PO_4, LiHCOO, CH_3COOH, and HIO_3. The solutions are tested with three indicators and the results in the table below were observed.

	Bromthymol Blue	**Methyl Orange**	**Thymolphthalein**
Solution A	yellow	red	colorless
Solution B	green	yellow	colorless
Solution C	blue	yellow	blue
Solution D	yellow	yellow	colorless
Solution E	blue	yellow	colorless

Identify each solution:

A _____   B_____   C_____   D_____   E_____

7. Complete the following table:

Indicator	pK_a	K_a	Color in Pure Water	Color Displayed in 0.010 M NaOH	Color Displayed in 0.010 M HCl
Phenol red					
Methyl orange					
Alizarin yellow					

8. Complete each of the following statements relating to weak–strong titrations by placing the words "lower" or "higher" in each of the blank spaces in each statement.
   (a) In a weak acid–strong base titration, the weaker the acid being titrated, the _____ (lower or higher) the initial pH of the solution will be, and the _____ (lower or higher) the pH at the equivalence point will be.

   (b) In a weak base–strong acid titration, the weaker the base being titrated, the _____ (lower or higher) the initial pH of the solution will be, and the _____ (lower or higher) the pH at the equivalence point will be.

9 The chemistry of buffers and the hydrolysis of salts must both be considered when calculating the pH at different stages during the final two types of titrations we have discussed in this section. For each type of titration below, explain why in the appropriate space in the table:

	Calculating pH Halfway to the Equivalence Point (Chemistry of Buffers)	Calculating pH at the Equivalence Point (Hydrolysis of Salts)
Titration of a weak acid by a strong base		
Titration of a weak base by a strong acid		

10. Explain why the calculation of pH at the equivalence point for each of the titration types in question 8 above requires a *two-step* process.

11. A titration is performed in which a standard 0.200 M solution of NaOH is added to a 20.0 mL sample of a 0.250 M HCOOH solution.
    (a) Determine the pH halfway to the equivalence point.

    (b) Calculate the volume of standard solution required to reach the equivalence point.

    (c) Calculate the pH at the equivalence point.

12. A student titrates a solution of a weak monoprotic acid with a standardized NaOH solution. She monitors the pH with a pH meter and draws the titration curve. The curve reveals that, halfway to the equivalence point, the pH of the reaction mixture was 3.456. Identify the weak acid.

13. A solution of the weak base ethanolamine, $HOCH_2CH_2NH_2$, is titrated with a standard HCl solution. The pH is monitored with a pH meter and the titration curve is drawn. The curve reveals that, halfway to the equivalence point, the pH of the reaction mixture was 9.50. Calculate the K_b for ethanolamine.

14. The curve below shows the titration of a 0.10 M NaOH solution with a 0.10 M HCl solution. On the *same set of axes below*:
    (a) Sketch the titration curve for a 0.20 M NaOH solution being titrated with the same acid. Choose an appropriate indicator.

    (b) Sketch the titration curve for a 0.10 M NH_3 solution being titrated with the same acid. Choose an appropriate indicator.

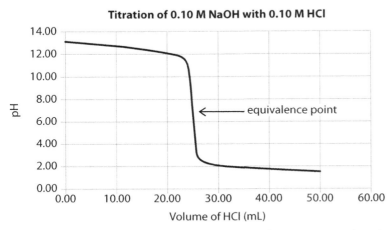

15. The curves we have discussed for the titration of both strong and weak acids have been limited to monoprotic acids. What do you think the titration curve might look like if the titration involved the titration of a weak *diprotic* acid with a strong base?

    (a) Sketch your suggested curve below:

    (b) What would you need to consider when selecting an indicator for such a titration?

8 Solubility Equilibrium

This chapter focuses on the following AP Big Idea from the College Board:

- Big Idea 6: Any bond or intermolecular attraction that can be formed can be broken. These two processes are in a dynamic competition, sensitive to initial conditions and external perturbations.

By the end of this chapter, you should be able to do the following:

- Determine the solubility of a compound in aqueous solution
- Describe a saturated solution as an equilibrium system
- Determine the concentration of ions in a solution
- Determine the relative solubility of a substance, given solubility tables
- Apply solubility rules to analyze the composition of solutions
- Formulate equilibrium constant expressions for various saturated solutions
- Perform calculations involving solubility equilibrium concepts
- Devise a method for determining the concentration of a specific ion

By the end of this chapter, you should know the meaning of these **key terms**:

- aqueous solution
- common ion
- complete ionic equation
- dissociation equation
- electrical conductivity
- formula equation
- hard water
- ionic solution
- K_{sp}
- molecular solution
- net ionic equation
- precipitate
- relative solubility
- saturated solution
- solubility equilibrium

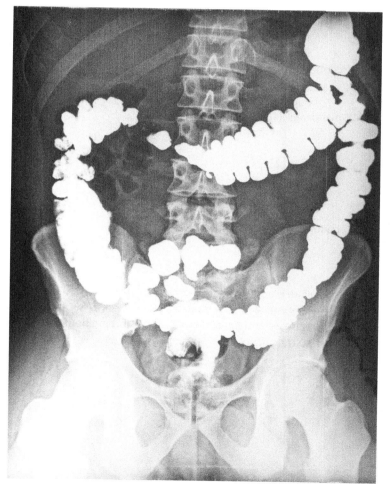

A patient must ingest a solution of barium sulfate for the large intestine (shown here) to be visible on an X-ray. The small solubility product, or K_{sp}, of $BaSO_4$ means humans can safely ingest the suspension.

8.1 The Concept of Solubility Review Questions

1. Give three examples for each of the following:
   (a) strong electrolytes

   (b) non-electrolytes

2. Compare the electrical conductivity of 1.0 M $HClO_4$ to that of 1.0 M H_3PO_4. Explain your reasoning.

3. Write dissociation equations for the following in aqueous solution. Ensure that your equations are balanced for both number of atoms and charge.

   (a) magnesium perchlorate

   (b) calcium dichromate

   (c) copper(II) acetate

   (d) manganese(II) thiocyanate

   (e) aluminum binoxalate

   (f) barium hydroxide octahydrate

4. Barium sulfate is used in medicine as a radiopaque contrast material. Patients drink a suspension of barium sulfate to coat their gastrointestinal tract. The surface of the tissue being studied is then highly visible under X-ray or CT scan. Radiologists can better see disease or trauma internally using this method. What is the molar solubility of barium sulfate if a saturated solution contains 0.0012 g dissolved in 500. mL of solution?

5. Calcium carbonate is used to treat calcium deficiencies in the body. Your body needs calcium to build and maintain healthy bones. What mass of calcium carbonate is required to produce 250. mL of solution with a calcium ion concentration of 7.1×10^{-5} M ?

6. Sodium dichromate is used in the production of chromic acid; a common etching agent. Calculate the concentration of each ion in a solution of sodium dichromate prepared by dissolving 0.50 g in 150. mL of solution.

7. Solutions of magnesium chloride and sodium chloride are mixed to make brine commonly used to keep roads from becoming slippery because of ice. The brine solution lowers the freezing point of water by up to 10°C. A brine solution is made by mixing 60. L of 5.0 M sodium chloride with 30. L of 2.4 M magnesium chloride. Calculate the concentration of each ion in this solution.

8. Describe how you would prepare 1.0 L of a saturated solution of sodium chloride.

9. Write the equation for the equilibrium present in saturated solutions of the following:
   (a) silver bromate

   (b) aluminum chromate

   (c) magnesium hydroxide

   (d) lead(II) sulfate

   (e) copper(II) phosphate

8.2 Qualitative Analysis — Identifying Unknown Ions Review Questions

1. Classify the following solutes as soluble or low solubility according to the solubility table (Table 4.2.1):

   (a) Rb_2SO_3

   (b) Al_2S_3

   (c) CuI

   (d) ammonium sulfate

   (e) chromium(III) nitrate

   (f) potassium oxalate

2. According to the solubility table, silver sulfate has a low solubility. In a saturated solution of silver sulfate, are silver and sulfate ions present in solution? Explain.

3. The solubility of silver acetate is 11.1 g/L at 25°C. According to the solubility table, would silver acetate be classified as being soluble or of low solubility?

4. Describe the difference between a formula equation, a complete ionic equation, and a net ionic equation. How are they similar? Different?

5. What is a spectator ion? Give an example of a cation and an anion that are common spectator ions in precipitate reactions.

6. Write a balanced formula equation, complete ionic equation, and net ionic equation for each of the following reactions:

   (a) $(NH_4)_2S(aq) + FeSO_4(aq) \rightarrow$

   (b) $H_2SO_3(aq) + CaCl_2(aq) \rightarrow$

   (c) copper(II) sulfate and calcium sulfide $\rightarrow$

7. Explain why it would be difficult to separate the ions Na^+ and K^+ in solution using precipitation.

8. A solution contains Cr^{3+}, Ca^{2+}, and Mg^{2+} ions. Describe a method to remove each ion individually from solution. Be sure to state the compound you would add and how you would remove the precipitate from solution. For each reaction that occurs, write a net ionic equation.

9. A solution contains PO_4^{3-}, Cl^-, and S^{2-} ions. Describe a method to remove each ion individually from solution. Be sure to state the compound you would add and how you would remove the precipitate from solution. For each reaction that occurs, write a net ionic equation.

10. Why are compounds containing nitrates used to test for anions?

11. Give two examples where re-dissolving is necessary to separate two precipitates.

12. A solution of Na_2CO_3 is added to a solution of $AgNO_3$.
    (a) Write the net ionic equation for this reaction.

    (b) Two different reagents will dissolve the precipitate formed. Write a net ionic equation for each reaction in which the precipitate dissolves.

13. (a) Define *hard water* and *scale*.

    (b) Scale can be removed by adding a solution of HCl to the water. Write a formula equation, complete ionic equation, and net ionic equation for this reaction.

    (c) Suggest a substance that could be added to water to remove both Ca^{2+} and Mg^{2+} from solution.

    (d) Explain why adding a water softener to your washing machine when doing laundry improves the cleaning job on your clothes.

8.3 The Solubility Product Constant K_{sp}

Warm Up

1. Define each of the following terms:
   (a) solubility

   _____

   (b) product (the mathematical definition)

   _____

   (c) constant

   _____

2. The solubility of lead(II) chloride is 4.4 g/L at a particular temperature.
   (a) Write a balanced dissociation equation for lead(II) chloride.

   (b) Calculate the molar solubility of lead(II) chloride at this temperature.

   (c) Calculate the concentration of each ion in a saturated solution of lead(II) chloride.

The Solubility Product Constant

Recall from chapter 5 that some chemical systems establish an equilibrium. For such systems, you learned how to write an equilibrium constant expression, K_{eq}.

In a saturated solution, an equilibrium is established between the dissolving and recrystallization of a salt. Consider a saturated solution of $PbCl_2$. We can represent this equilibrium using the following dissociation equation:

$$PbCl_2(s) \rightleftharpoons Pb^{2+}(aq) + 2\,Cl^-(aq)$$

Notice that the solid appears on the reactant side of the equation and the ions on the product side. Recalling that solids do not appear in the K_{eq} expression, for this equilibrium

$$K_{eq} = [Pb^{2+}][Cl^-]^2$$

This is a special type of equilibrium, so it is given its own equilibrium constant type: K_{sp}.

$$K_{sp} = [Pb^{2+}][Cl^-]^2 \quad \text{where } K_{sp} \text{ stands for the } \textbf{solubility product constant}$$

In the Warm Up at the beginning of this section, you defined solubility as the maximum amount of solute that can be dissolved in a particular volume of solution. You defined a product as a mathematical answer derived from multiplication. Therefore, the *solubility product* is the value obtained when the maximum concentrations of ions are multiplied together. This is different from simply the solubility. As solubility depends on temperature, so does the value of K_{sp}.

The molar solubility of a substance is the molar concentration of solute in a saturated solution.

The solubility product constant (K_{sp}) is the *product* of the ion concentrations in a saturated solution raised to the power of the coefficients in the equilibrium.

Obviously, as the solubility of a substance increases, so does the concentration of ions. It follows that the value of K_{sp} also increases.

Quick Check

1. Write an equation to represent the equilibrium present in saturated solutions of the following:
    (a) strontium carbonate

    (b) magnesium hydroxide

    (c) calcium phosphate

2. For each of the equilibria above, write the corresponding K_{sp} expression next to it.

3. Explain the difference between the solubility and the solubility product constant of strontium carbonate.

    _____

    _____

Calculating the K_{sp} From Solubility

The solubility of a substance differs from its solubility product constant, but they are related, and we can calculate one from the other. *When solving any K_{sp} type problem, it is wise to start by writing the equilibrium equation for the saturated solution and then the K_{sp} expression.*

Sample Problem 8.3.1(a) — Calculating K_{sp} from Solubility The

molar solubility of $CaSO_4$ is 8.4×10^{-3} M at a particular temperature. Calculate its K_{sp}.

What to Think About	How to Do It
1. Write an equation representing the equilibrium in a saturated solution.	$CaSO_4(s) \rightleftharpoons Ca^{2+}(aq) + SO_4^{2-}(aq)$ 8.4×10^{-3} M $\quad$ 8.4×10^{-3} M $\quad$ 8.4×10^{-3} M
2. Write the corresponding K_{sp} expression.	$K_{sp} = [Ca^{2+}][SO_4^{2-}]$
3. The solubility of $CaSO_4$ is given in mol/L. Fill in the concentrations of each ion in the equation.	
4. Substitute the concentrations of ions into the K_{sp} expression.	$K_{sp} = [8.4 \times 10^{-3}][8.4 \times 10^{-3}]$ $= 7.1 \times 10^{-5}$

Sample Problem 8.3.1(b) — Calculating K_{sp} from Solubility

The solubility of lead(II) chloride is 4.4 g/L at a particular temperature. Calculate its K_{sp}.

What to Think About	How to Do It
1. The formula is $PbCl_2$. Write an equation representing the equilibrium present in a saturated solution.	$PbCl_2(s) \rightleftharpoons Pb^{2+}(aq) + 2Cl^-(aq)$
2. Write the corresponding K_{sp} expression.	$K_{sp} = [Pb^{2+}][Cl^-]^2$
3. In order to calculate K_{sp}, the molarities of Pb^{2+} and Cl^- must be known. Calculate the concentration of each ion from the solubility given.	$[PbCl_2] = \dfrac{4.4 \cancel{g}}{1 L} \times \dfrac{1\ mol}{278.3 \cancel{g}} = 0.016$ M so $[Pb^{2+}] = 0.016$ M and $[Cl^-] = 0.032$ M
4. Substitute the concentrations of ions into the K_{sp} expression.	$K_{sp} = [0.016][0.032]^2$ $= 1.6 \times 10^{-5}$

Practice Problems 8.3.1 — Calculating K_{sp} from Solubility

1. Calculate the K_{sp} for each of the following.
    (a) $CaCO_3$ has a solubility of 6.1×10^{-5} M.

    (b) $Mn(OH)_2$ has a solubility of 3.6×10^{-5} M.

    (c) The solubility of barium chromate is 2.8×10^{-3} g/L.

    (d) The solubility of silver oxalate is 0.033 g/L.

2. A student prepares a saturated solution by dissolving 5.5×10^{-5} mol of $Mg(OH)_2$ in 500. mL of solution. Calculate the K_{sp} of $Mg(OH)_2$.

3. A student evaporated 150. mL of a saturated solution of MgC_2O_4. If 0.16 g of solute remains, calculate the K_{sp}.

Calculating Solubility From K_{sp}

Chemists can calculate the solubility of a substance from its K_{sp}. The K_{sp} values of some salts are listed in Table 8.3.1. Note that these values are for saturated solutions at 25°C.

It is very important to understand that the K_{sp} value is NOT a concentration. It is the *product* of the ion concentrations in a saturated solution raised to the power of their coefficients from the balanced dissociation equation.

Table 8.3.1 *Solubility Product Constants at 25°C*

Name	Formula	K_{sp}
Barium carbonate	$BaCO_3$	2.6×10^{-9}
Barium chromate	$BaCrO_4$	1.2×10^{-10}
Barium sulfate	$BaSO_4$	1.1×10^{-10}
Calcium carbonate	$CaCO_3$	5.0×10^{-9}
Calcium oxalate	CaC_2O_4	2.3×10^{-9}
Calcium sulfate	$CaSO_4$	7.1×10^{-5}
Copper(I) iodide	CuI	1.3×10^{-12}
Copper(II) iodate	$Cu(IO_3)_2$	6.9×10^{-8}
Copper(II) sulfide	CuS	6.0×10^{-37}
Iron(II) hydroxide	$Fe(OH)_2$	4.9×10^{-17}
Iron(II) sulfide	FeS	6.0×10^{-19}
Iron(III) hydroxide	$Fe(OH)_3$	2.6×10^{-39}
Lead(II) bromide	$PbBr_2$	6.6×10^{-6}
Lead(II) chloride	$PbCl_2$	1.2×10^{-5}
Lead(II) iodate	$Pb(IO_3)_2$	3.7×10^{-13}
Lead(II) iodide	PbI_2	8.5×10^{-9}
Lead(II) sulfate	$PbSO_4$	1.8×10^{-8}
Magnesium carbonate	$MgCO_3$	6.8×10^{-6}
Magnesium hydroxide	$Mg(OH)_2$	5.6×10^{-12}
Silver bromate	$AgBrO_3$	5.3×10^{-5}
Silver bromide	$AgBr$	5.4×10^{-13}
Silver carbonate	Ag_2CO_3	8.5×10^{-12}
Silver chloride	$AgCl$	1.8×10^{-10}
Silver chromate	Ag_2CrO_4	1.1×10^{-12}
Silver iodate	$AgIO_3$	3.2×10^{-8}
Silver iodide	AgI	8.5×10^{-17}
Strontium carbonate	$SrCO_3$	5.6×10^{-10}
Strontium fluoride	SrF_2	4.3×10^{-9}
Strontium sulfate	$SrSO_4$	3.4×10^{-7}
Zinc sulfide	ZnS	2.0×10^{-25}

Sample Problem 8.3.2(a) — Calculating Solubility from K_{sp}

Calculate the molar solubility of iron(II) hydroxide from its K_{sp}.

What to Think About	How to Do It
1. The formula is $Fe(OH)_2$. Write an equation representing the equilibrium present in a saturated solution.	$$Fe(OH)_2(s) \rightleftharpoons Fe^{2+}(aq) + 2\,OH^-(aq)$$ $$\; s \qquad\qquad s \qquad\qquad 2s$$
2. Let s be the molar solubility of $Fe(OH)_2$. The concentrations of Fe^{2+} and OH^- are then s and $2s$ respectively.	
3. Write the corresponding K_{sp} expression.	$$K_{sp} = [Fe^{2+}][OH^-]^2$$
4. Look up the K_{sp} value for $Fe(OH)_2$ and substitute in the concentrations of ions.	$$4.9 \times 10^{-17} = (s)(2s)^2$$ $$4.9 \times 10^{-17} = 4s^3$$
5. Simplify and solve.	$$s = \sqrt[3]{4.9 \times 10^{-17}/4}$$ $$= 2.3 \times 10^{-6}\,M$$

Sample Problem 8.3.2(b) — Calculating Solubility from K_{sp}

What mass is dissolved in 275 mL of saturated silver bromate?

What to Think About	How to Do It
1. The formula is $AgBrO_3$. Write an equation representing the equilibrium present in a saturated solution.	$$AgBrO_3(s) \rightleftharpoons Ag^+(aq) + BrO_3^-(aq)$$ $$\; s \qquad\qquad s \qquad\qquad s$$
2. Let s be the molar solubility of $AgBrO_3$. The concentrations of Ag^+ and BrO_3^- are then both s.	
3. Write the corresponding K_{sp} expression.	$$K_{sp} = [Ag^+][BrO_3^-]$$
4. Look up the K_{sp} value for $AgBrO_3$ and substitute in the concentrations of ions.	$$5.3 \times 10^{-5} = (s)(s)$$ $$= s^2$$
5. Solve for the molar solubility.	$$s = 7.3 \times 10^{-3}\,M$$
6. To calculate the mass, use the molar mass of $AgBrO_3$ and the given volume of solution.	$$mass = 0.275\,L \times \frac{7.3 \times 10^{-3}\,mol}{1\,L} \times \frac{235.8\,g}{1\,mol}$$ $$= 0.47\,g$$

Practice Problems 8.3.2 — Calculating Solubility from K_{sp}

1. Calculate the solubility of the following:
   (a) silver chloride in mol/L

   (b) iron (II) sulfide in g/mL

   (c) lead(II) iodate in M

   (d) strontium fluoride in g/L

2. What is the concentration of hydroxide in a saturated solution of iron(III) hydroxide? Hint: Write out the dissociation equation and K_{sp} expression first. This example is different than the ones shown.

3. What mass of calcium oxalate is dissolved in 650. mL of saturated solution?

Types of Salts

To summarize, we have introduced two types of salts: AB (such as AgCl) and AB_2 (such as $PbCl_2$) salts.

For AB salts, $K_{sp} = (\text{solubility})^2$

For AB_2 or A_2B salts, $K_{sp} = 4(\text{solubility})^3$

8.3 Review Questions

1. Write equilibrium equations and the corresponding K_{sp} expressions for each of the following solutes in saturated aqueous solution.

   (a) $Al(OH)_3$

   (b) $Cd_3(AsO_4)_2$

   (c) $BaMoO_4$

   (d) calcium sulfate

   (e) lead(II) iodate

   (f) silver carbonate

2. Consider a saturated solution of $BaSO_3$.
   (a) Write the equation that represents the equilibrium in the solution.

   (b) Explain the difference between the solubility and the solubility product constant of $BaSO_3$.

3. A saturated solution of $ZnCO_3$ was prepared by adding excess solid $ZnCO_3$ to water. The solution was analyzed and found to contain $[Zn^{2+}] = 1.1 \times 10^{-5}$ M. What is the K_{sp} for $ZnCO_3$?

4. When a student evaporated 250. mL of a saturated solution of silver phosphate, 0.0045 g of solute remained. Calculate the K_{sp} for silver phosphate.

5. Gypsum is used in drywall and plaster, and occurs naturally in alabaster. It has the formula $CaSO_4 \cdot 2 H_2O$ and its K_{sp} is 9.1×10^{-6}. What mass of gypsum is present in 500. mL of saturated solution?

6. Naturally occurring limestone contains two forms of $CaCO_3$ called calcite and aragonite. They differ in their crystal structure. High-grade calcite crystals were used in World War II for gun sights, especially in anti-aircraft weaponry. Aragonite is used in jewelry and glassmaking. Using the following K_{sp} values, calculate the solubility of each in g/L.
   (a) K_{sp} calcite $= 3.4 \times 10^{-9}$

   (b) K_{sp} aragonite $= 6.0 \times 10^{-9}$

7. Lead(II) arsenate, $Pb_3(AsO_4)_2$, was commonly used as an insecticide, especially against codling moths. Because of the toxic nature of lead compounds, it was banned in the 1980s. It has a solubility of 3.0×10^{-5} g/L. Calculate the K_{sp} for lead(II) arsenate.

8. A student compares the K_{sp} values of cadmium carbonate ($K_{sp} = 1.0 \times 10^{-12}$) and cadmium hydroxide ($K_{sp} = 7.2 \times 10^{-15}$) and concludes that the solubility of cadmium carbonate is greater than the solubility of cadmium hydroxide. Do you agree or disagree? Support your answer with appropriate calculations.

9. A titration was carried out to determine the unknown concentration of Cl^- ion in solution. The standard solution was $AgNO3$ and an indicator of K_2CrO_4 was used. The equivalence point was reached when the solution turned the red color of Ag_2CrO_4, signaling that virtually all of the Cl^- ions had been used up. Explain why a precipitate of AgCl formed before a precipitate of Ag_2CrO_4. Use data from the K_{sp} table provided in this section.

10. Silver carbonate is used as an antibacterial agent in the production of concrete. What mass of silver carbonate must be dissolved to produce 2.5 L of saturated solution?

8.4 Precipitation Formation and the Solubility Product K_{sp}

Warm Up

1. Describe how to make a saturated solution of silver chloride, given solid silver chloride and pure water. How does the concentration of Ag^+ compare to the concentration of Cl^-?

_____

_____

2. A student mixed 25 mL of 0.10 M silver nitrate with 15 mL of 0.085 M sodium chloride.
   (a) Calculate the $[Ag^+]$ and $[Cl^-]$ before a reaction occurred in the mixed solution.

   (b) How does the $[Ag^+]$ compare with the $[Cl^-]$ before the reaction? Explain why they are not equal.

   _____

   (c) Write a net ionic equation for this reaction.

Precipitates That Form When Solutions Are Mixed Together

In section 6.3, we investigated saturated solutions formed by attempting to dissolve an excess of solute in water. In such a case, the concentrations of the ions are directly related to one another. For example, if we attempt to dissolve excess AgCl in water, the $[Ag^+]$ equals the $[Cl^-]$. Similarly, if we use an excess of $PbCl_2$, the $[Cl^-]$ is double the $[Pb^{2+}]$.

In this section, we will be examining situations in which the ions forming the precipitate do not come from the same solute. Because of this, the concentrations of the ions in solution are not related to one another, but instead depend on the concentrations and the volumes of the solutions being combined. When determining ion concentrations, it is always important to *consider the source* of each ion.

Predicting Whether a Precipitate Will Form

When two solutions are mixed, we can predict whether a precipitate will form. The K_{sp} value represents the maximum product of the ion concentrations in a saturated solution. If the product of the ion concentrations present exceeds this value, the ions will not remain dissolved in solution and a precipitate will form. On the other hand, if the product of the ion concentrations is less than the value of K_{sp}, the ions remain dissolved in solution, and no precipitate forms.

The concentrations in a K_{sp} expression are the *equilibrium* concentrations of ions in a saturated solution. If an equilibrium is not present in solution, then we calculate a **trial ion product (TIP)**, also called a trial K_{sp} value or reaction quotient (Q).

If the TIP $> K_{sp}$, a precipitate forms.

If the TIP $< K_{sp}$, no precipitate forms.

If the TIP $= K_{sp}$, the solution is saturated.

Sample Problem 8.4.1 — Predicting Whether a Precipitate Will Form

Will a precipitate form when 23 mL of 0.020 M Na_2CO_3 is added to 12 mL of 0.010 M $MgCl_2$?

What to Think About

1. Determine the precipitate that will potentially form using the solubility table. Then write an equation representing the equilibrium present in a saturated solution.

2. Write the corresponding K_{sp} expression and its value.

3. When one solution is added to another, *both* are diluted. Calculate the concentration of each solution before the reaction occurs.

4. Determine the $[Mg^{2+}]$ and $[CO_3^{2-}]$ in the diluted solutions. Be sure to consider the source of the ions to determine whether these concentrations should be multiplied by a whole number.

5. Calculate the value of TIP.

6. Compare the TIP with the real K_{sp}.

How to Do It

$$Na_2CO_3 + MgCl_2 \rightarrow MgCO_3(s) + 2\,NaCl$$

$$MgCO_3(s) \rightleftharpoons Mg^{2+}(aq) + CO_3^{2-}(aq)$$

$$K_{sp} = [Mg^{2+}][CO_3^{2-}] = 6.8 \times 10^{-6}$$

$$[Na_2CO_3] = \frac{0.020 \text{ mol}}{1\,L} \times \frac{0.023\,L}{0.035\,L}$$
$$= 0.013 \text{ M}$$

$$[MgCl_2] = \frac{0.010 \text{ mol}}{1\,L} \times \frac{0.012\,L}{0.035\,L}$$
$$= 0.0034 \text{ M}$$

$$[CO_3^{2-}] = 0.013 \text{ M}$$
$$[Mg^{2+}] = 0.0034 \text{ M}$$

$$\begin{aligned} TIP &= [Mg^{2+}][CO_3^{2-}] \\ &= (0.013)(0.0034) \\ &= 4.4 \times 10^{-5} \end{aligned}$$

$TIP > K_{sp}$ so a precipitate forms.

Practice Problems 8.4.1 — Predicting Whether a Precipitate Will Form

1. Will a precipitate form when 8.5 mL of 6.3×10^{-2} M lead(II) nitrate is added to 1.0 L of 1.2×10^{-3} M sodium iodate?

2. Will a precipitate form when 1.5 mL of 4.5×10^{-3} M ammonium bromate is added to 120.5 mL of 2.5×10^{-3} M silver nitrate?

3. No precipitate forms when 24 mL of 0.17 M sodium fluoride is added to 55 mL of 0.22 M cadmium nitrate. From this information, what can you conclude about the numerical value for the K_{sp} of CdF_2? (State the K_{sp} value as a range.)

Using K_{sp} to Calculate the Concentration of Ions in Solution

These problems are very similar to the ones you analyzed earlier, except that the ions that form the precipitate are from different stock reagent sources. First, determine the concentrations of any ions present in the solution. Once another solution is added, consider the potential precipitate that might form. Then, as always, you should write an equation for the equilibrium present in a saturated solution (the dissociation of the precipitate) and then the K_{sp} expression.

Consider a solution of 0.025 M $Pb(NO_3)_2$. By writing a dissociation equation for lead(II) nitrate, we can calculate the concentration of each ion in solution:

$$Pb(NO_3)_2(aq) \rightarrow Pb^{2+}(aq) + 2\ NO_3^-(aq)$$
$$\text{0.025 M} \qquad\qquad \text{0.025 M} \qquad \text{0.050 M}$$

If a solution of NaCl is added, the precipitate that may form is $PbCl_2(s)$. If a precipitate forms, then a saturated solution of $PbCl_2$ is present and is governed by its K_{sp}.

$$PbCl_2(s) \rightleftharpoons Pb^{2+}(aq) + 2\ Cl^-(aq)$$

$$K_{sp} = [Pb^{2+}][Cl^-]^2$$

Note that the original $[Pb^{2+}]$ and $[Cl^-]$ are unrelated to each other because they came from *different* sources. The maximum concentration of Cl^- that can exist in this solution can be calculated from the K_{sp} and the concentration of Pb^{2+} provided by the $Pb(NO_3)_2$ source. From the concentration of chloride, the mass of solute required can be calculated using its molar mass.

$$1.2 \times 10^{-5} = (0.025)\ [Cl^-]^2$$
$$[Cl^-] = 0.022\ M = [NaCl]$$

Sample Problem 8.4.2(a) — Forming a Precipitate in a Solution

What mass of sodium sulfate is required to start precipitation in 500. mL of 0.030 M calcium chloride? (Assume the volume remains constant.)

What to Think About	How to Do It
1. Determine the precipitate that will form using the solubility table. Then write an equation representing the equilibrium present in a saturated solution.	$Na_2SO_4(aq) + CaCl_2(aq) \rightarrow CaSO_4(s) + 2\ NaCl(aq)$ $CaSO_4(s) \rightleftharpoons Ca^{2+}(aq) + SO_4^{2-}(aq)$
2. Write the corresponding K_{sp} expression.	$K_{sp} = [Ca^{2+}][SO_4^{2-}]$
3. The calcium ions came from the 0.030 M $CaCl_2$ solution, and the sulfate ions came from $Na_2SO_4(s)$. The chloride ions and sodium ions are spectators. Calculate the concentration of Ca^{2+} in the $CaCl_2$ solution.	$CaCl_2(aq) \rightarrow Ca^{2+}(aq) + 2\ Cl^-(aq)$ $\text{0.030 M} \qquad\quad \text{0.030 M}$
4. Substitute the value of K_{sp} (from the K_{sp} table, Table 4.3.1) and the known ion concentration to solve for the unknown $[SO_4^{2-}] = [Na_2SO_4]$.	$7.1 \times 10^{-5} = (0.030)\ [SO_4^{2-}]$ $[SO_4^{2-}] = 2.4 \times 10^{-3}\ M$
5. Calculate the mass of solid sodium sulfate required to be dissolved in 500. mL of solution from $[SO_4^{2-}]$ and the molar mass of sodium sulfate.	$\text{mass } Na_2SO_4 = 0.500\ L \times \dfrac{2.4 \times 10^{-3}\ mol}{1\ L} \times \dfrac{142.1\ g}{1\ mol}$ $\qquad\qquad = 0.17\ g$

Sample Problem 8.4.2(b) — Forming a Precipitate in Solution

What is the maximum $[SO_4^{2-}]$ that can exist in a saturated solution of $CaCO_3$?

What to Think About

1. Calculate the $[Ca^{2+}]$ in a saturated solution of $CaCO_3$.

2. The calcium ions form a precipitate with the sulfate ions. Write the equation for the equilibrium present in the saturated solution of $CaSO_4$.

3. Substitute the value of K_{sp} for $CaSO_4$ and the known $[Ca^{2+}]$ and solve for the $[SO_4^{2-}]$.

How to Do It

$$CaCO_3(s) \rightleftharpoons Ca^{2+}(aq) + CO_3^{2-}(aq)$$
$$\qquad\qquad\qquad s \qquad\qquad s$$

$$K_{sp} = [Ca^{2+}][CO_3^{2-}]$$
$$5.0 \times 10^{-9} = s^2$$
$$s = 7.1 \times 10^{-5}\,M = [Ca^{2+}]$$

$$CaSO_4(s) \rightleftharpoons Ca^{2+}(aq) + SO_4^{2-}(aq)$$

$$K_{sp} = [Ca^{2+}][SO_4^{2-}]$$
$$7.1 \times 10^{-5} = (7.1 \times 10^{-5})[SO_4^{2-}]$$
$$[SO_4^{2-}] = 1.0\,M$$

Practice Problems 8.4.2 — Forming a Precipitate In Solution

1. Calculate the maximum $[Sr^{2+}]$ that can exist in solutions of the following:
   (a) 0.045 M sodium fluoride (Remember to consider the source of the fluoride ion.)

   (b) 2.3×10^{-4} M lithium carbonate

   (c) 0.011 M sulfuric acid

2. Sodium carbonate may be added to hard water to remove the Mg^{2+} ions. What mass of sodium carbonate is required to soften 10.0 L of hard water containing 3.2×10^{-3} M Mg^{2+}? (Assume no volume change occurs.)

3. What is the maximum $[Ag^+]$ that can exist in a saturated solution of PbI_2?

The Common Ion Effect

We defined the solubility of a substance as the maximum amount of solute that will dissolve in a given volume of solvent at a specific temperature. You know that solubility depends on temperature, but it also depends on the solvent's identity. Up to now, we have only considered pure water as the solvent. The presence of other ions in the solvent also has an effect on the solubility of a solute.

The solubility of a substance depends on the presence of other ions in solution and the temperature. The K_{sp} of a substance depends on temperature only.

Consider a saturated solution of Ag_2CO_3:

$$Ag_2CO_3(s) \rightleftharpoons 2\,Ag^+(aq) + CO_3^{2-}(aq)$$

At a given temperature, the amount of Ag^+ and CO_3^{2-} in solution is governed by the K_{sp}. If the solvent already contained Ag^+ ions, the $[Ag^+]$ is increased. To maintain the value of K_{sp}, the $[CO_3^{2-}]$ must decrease. According to Le Châtelier's principle, an increase in $[Ag^+]$ causes the equilibrium to shift left. This shift causes the $[CO_3^{2-}]$ to decrease and the amount of solid Ag_2CO_3 to increase. The presence of silver ions in the solvent effectively decreases the solubility of Ag_2CO_3. This is called the *common ion effect* because the solubility of Ag_2CO_3 is decreased due to the common ion Ag^+ in the solvent. The presence of CO_3^{2-} in the solvent would cause a similar effect and resulting decrease in the solubility.

$$Ag_2CO_3(s) \rightleftharpoons 2\,Ag^+(aq) + CO_3^{2-}(aq)$$

Adding Ag^+ or CO_3^{2-} causes the equilibrium to shift left, so the solubility of Ag_2CO_3 decreases.

The solubility of a solute is decreased by the presence of a second solute in a solvent containing a common ion.

According to Le Châtelier's principle, the solubility of Ag_2CO_3 may be increased by removing the Ag^+ or CO_3^{2-} ions. This would cause the equilibrium to shift right. An example of this would be the presence of HCl in the solvent. Carbonates dissolve in acid solutions. The presence of H_3O^+ from the acid causes the $[CO_3^{2-}]$ to decrease, which in turn causes more $Ag_2CO_3(s)$ to dissolve. Additionally, the chloride ion from the acid precipitates the silver ion from the solution. The removal of the silver ion causes a further right shift, increasing the solubility of silver carbonate even further.

Quick Check

1. Consider a saturated solution of AgCl.

    (a) How can you change the K_{sp} for AgCl?

    (b) How can you change the solubility of AgCl?

2. List two substances that would decrease the solubility of $Mg(OH)_2$. Use Le Châtelier's principle to explain each.

3. List two substances that would increase the solubility of $Mg(OH)_2$. Use Le Châtelier's principle and a K_{sp} expression to explain each.

Calculating Solubility With a Common Ion Present (Extension)

The presence of a common ion in the solvent decreases the solubility of a solute. Let's compare the solubility of $Mg(OH)_2$ in water to its solubility in 0.10 M $MgCl_2$.

Sample Problem 8.4.3 — Calculating Solubility With a Common Ion Present

What is the solubility of $Mg(OH)_2$ in (a) water?   (b) 0.10 M $MgCl_2$?

What to Think About	How to Do It
(a) in water	
1. Write the equilibrium for a saturated solution of $Mg(OH)_2$.	$$Mg(OH)_2(s) \rightleftharpoons \underset{S}{Mg^{2+}(aq)} + \underset{2S}{2\,OH^-(aq)}$$
2. Write the corresponding K_{sp} expression.	$$K_{sp} = [Mg^{2+}][OH^-]^2$$
3. Look up the value for K_{sp} on the K_{sp} table and solve for the solubility.	$$5.6 \times 10^{-12} = (s)(2s)^2 = 4s^3$$ $$s = 1.1 \times 10^{-4}\ M = \text{solubility of } Mg(OH)_2$$
(b) in 0.10 M MgCl$_2$	
1. Write the equilibrium for a saturated solution of $Mg(OH)_2$.	$$Mg(OH)_2(s) \rightleftharpoons Mg^{2+}(aq) + 2\,OH^-(aq)$$
2. The equilibrium for the saturated solution is shifted on the addition of the common ion Mg^{2+} from the $MgCl_2$. Use an ICE table. In the $MgCl_2$, there is initially 0.10 M Mg^{2+}. The amount of $Mg(OH)_2$ that dissolves will increase the $[Mg^{2+}]$ and $[OH^-]$ by x and $2x$ respectively.	$Mg(OH)_2(s) \rightleftharpoons Mg^{2+}(aq) + 2\,OH^-(aq)$ I - 0.10 0 C - +x +2x E - 0.10 +x 2x
3. The amount of Mg^{2+} that dissolves from the $Mg(OH)_2$ (represented by x) is very small compared to the amount of Mg^{2+} in solution from the $MgCl_2$ (0.10 M). Assume that $[Mg^{2+}] = 0.10 + x = 0.10$.	
4. Substitute $[Mg^{2+}]$ and $[OH^-]$ at equilibrium into a K_{sp} expression.	$$K_{sp} = [Mg^{2+}][OH^-]^2$$ $$5.6 \times 10^{-12} = (0.10)(2x)^2$$
5. Solve for the solubility, x.	$$5.6 \times 10^{-11} = (2x)^2 = 4x^2$$ $$x = 3.7 \times 10^{-6}\ M$$

Practice Problems 8.4.3 — Calculating Solubility With a Common Ion Present

1. Calculate the molar solubility of silver iodate in 0.12 M sodium iodate.

2. Calculate the molar solubility of lead(II) iodide in 0.10 M KI.

3. Calculate the solubility (in g/L) of barium sulfate in 0.050 M barium nitrate.

8.4 Activity: Experimentally Determining the K_{sp} Of Copper(II) Iodate

Question
What is the approximate value of K_{sp} for copper(II) iodate?

Background
A TIP calculation can be used to determine if a precipitate will form. If TIP $> K_{sp}$, a precipitate forms. If TIP $< K_{sp}$, no precipitate forms. Five different dilutions of copper(II) nitrate and sodium iodate were prepared and mixed together. By observing which mixed solutions contained a precipitate, information about the K_{sp} can be deduced.

Procedure:
1. Five different dilutions of copper(II) nitrate and sodium iodate were prepared as shown in the data table below. The given volume of each solution was mixed together with water and the formation of a precipitate was noted. Answer the questions below.

	Mixture 1	Mixture 2	Mixture 3	Mixture 4	Mixture 5
Volume 0.010 M $Cu(NO_3)_2$ (mL)	10.0	8.0	6.0	4.0	2.0
Volume 0.020 M $NaIO_3$ (mL)	10.0	8.0	6.0	4.0	2.0
Volume water added (mL)	0.0	4.0	8.0	12.0	16.0
Observation	precipitate	precipitate	precipitate	no precipitate	no precipitate

Results and Discussion
1. Write balanced formula, complete ionic, and net ionic equations for this reaction.

2. Calculate the $[Cu^{2+}]$ in each of the mixtures.

3. Calculate the $[IO_3^-]$ in each of the mixtures.

4. Write the equation for the equilibrium involving the precipitate, and the K_{sp} expression.

5. Calculate a TIP value for each mixture.

6. State the K_{sp} as a range of values from this data.

7. Compare your range to the stated K_{sp} value on the K_{sp} table.

8.4 Review Questions

1. The following solutions were mixed together. Write the equilibrium equation for the precipitate that forms and its K_{sp} expression.
   (a) $FeCl_2$ and Na_2S

   (b) $Sr(OH)_2$ and $MgBr_2$

   (c) silver nitrate and ammonium chromate

2. A student mixed equal volumes of 0.2 M solutions of sulfuric acid and calcium chloride together.
   (a) What precipitate forms?

   (b) Write an equation for the equilibrium present and the K_{sp} expression.

   (c) In the resulting solution, does $[SO_4^{2-}] = [Ca^{2+}]$? Explain.

3. What is the maximum $[Pb^{2+}]$ that can exist in 0.015 M $CuSO_4$?

4. Kidney stones are crystals of calcium oxalate that form in the kidney, ureter, or bladder. Small kidney stones are passed out of the body easily, but larger kidney stones may block the ureter causing severe pain. If the $[Ca^{2+}]$ in blood plasma is 5×10^{-3} M, what $[C_2O_4^{2-}]$ must be present to form a kidney stone?

5. What is the maximum $[CO_3^{2-}]$ that can exist in a saturated solution of AgBr?

6. A 100.0 mL sample of seawater was tested by adding one drop (0.2 mL) of 0.20 M silver nitrate. What mass of NaCl is present in the seawater to form a precipitate?

---

7. Does a precipitate form when 2.5 mL of 0.055 M $Sr(NO_3)_2$ is added to 1.5 L of 0.011 M $ZnSO_4$? Justify your answer with calculations.

8. Does a precipitate form when 0.068 g of lead(II) nitrate is added to 2.0 L of 0.080 M NaCl? Justify your answer with calculations. (Assume no volume change.)

9. In section 4.2, you learned that the addition of Ag^+ to a solution containing Cl^- and I^- will cause precipitates of both AgCl and AgI to form. Because AgCl and AgI have quite different K_{sp} values, you can use this information to separate Cl^- from I^- in solution by carefully manipulating the $[Ag^+]$ so that only one of Cl^- or I^- precipitates at a time. Consider a solution containing 0.020 M Cl^- and 0.020 M I^-. Solid silver nitrate is slowly added without changing the overall volume of solution.

    (a) Write the equilibrium equation for each precipitate that forms.

    (b) Beside each equilibrium equation, write the corresponding K_{sp} expression and value from your K_{sp} table.

    (c) Based on the K_{sp} values, which precipitate will form first?

    (d) Calculate the $[Ag^+]$ required just to start precipitation of the first precipitate.

    (e) Calculate the $[Ag^+]$ required just to start precipitation of the second precipitate.

    (f) State the range of $[Ag^+]$ required to precipitate I^- but not Cl^-.

    (g) What $[I^-]$ remains in solution just before the formation of AgCl?

    (h) What percentage of I^- is precipitated out before the AgCl starts to precipitate?

10. Washing soda, $Na_2CO_3 \cdot 10\ H_2O$ is used to treat hard water containing Ca^{2+} and Mg^{2+}. A 1.0 L sample contained 12 mg of Mg^{2+}. What mass of washing soda is required to precipitate out the Mg^{2+}?

11. List two substances that, when added to water, that would decrease the solubility of lead(II) iodate. Explain each.

12. Explain why $BaSO_4$ is less soluble in a solution of Na_2SO_4 than in water.

13. Is iron(III) hydroxide more or less soluble in water than in 0.1 M HCl? Explain.

Extension

14. An aqueous suspension of $BaSO_4$ is used as a contrast agent to improve the quality of intestinal X-rays. The patient drinks a suspension of $BaSO_4$. However, Ba^{2+} is toxic, so the $BaSO_4$ is dissolved in a solution of 0.10 M Na_2SO_4.
    (a) Calculate the maximum mass of $BaSO_4$ that can be dissolved in 200. mL of water. (Assume no volume change.)

    (b) Calculate the maximum mass of $BaSO_4$ that can be dissolved in 200. mL of 0.10 M Na_2SO_4 without forming a precipitate.